SURVEY OF BIOLOGICAL PROGRESS

VOLUME I

SURVEY OF
BIOLOGICAL PROGRESS

VOLUME I

GEORGE S. AVERY, JR.
Editor-in-Chief

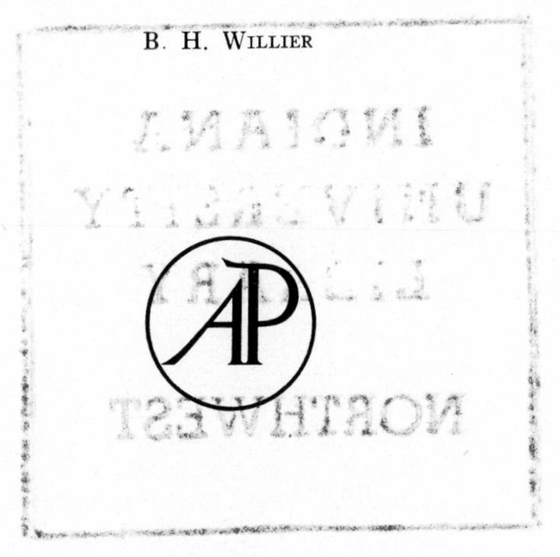

1949
ACADEMIC PRESS INC., PUBLISHERS
NEW YORK, N. Y.

125 EAST 23rd STREET
NEW YORK 10, N. Y.

PRINTED IN THE UNITED STATES OF AMERICA

PREFACE

It is a pleasure to present the first volume of what we hope will be an annual SURVEY OF BIOLOGICAL PROGRESS. The Survey is intended to serve the biologist who wishes to be well informed in fields marginal to or beyond his own special sphere of interests—fields he would have neither the time nor opportunity to follow systematically in the original literature. By thus providing a medium for integrated presentation of facts and thoughts from all fields of biology, the Survey aims to offset in a certain measure the isolating effect of rapidly increasing specialization.

All concerned with the editorial and advisory problems of this first volume would like to publicly record their deep appreciation of the thoughtful co-operation of authors in making it possible.

GEORGE S. AVERY, JR.
Brooklyn Botanic Garden
New York, N. Y.

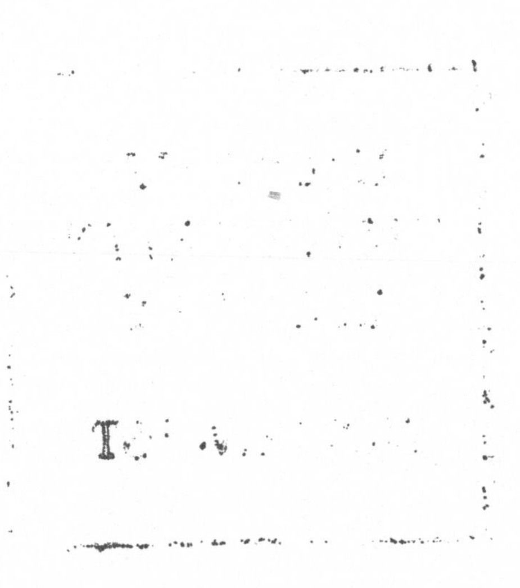

CONTENTS

CONTENTS

Newer Methods in the Rapid Development of Disease-Resistant Vegetables

By W. A. Frazier, *Hawaii Agricultural Experiment Station, University of Hawaii, Honolulu, Hawaii*

Influence of Environmental Factors on the Vitamin Content of Food Plants

By Karl C. Hamner, *U. S. Plant, Soil, and Nutrition Laboratory, U. S. Department of Agriculture, Agricultural Research Administration, Tower Road, Ithaca, New York*

Ecological Studies on Populations

By G. E. Hutchinson, and E. S. Deevey, Jr., *Osborn Zoological Laboratory, Yale University, New Haven, Connecticut*

Teaching Biology Today

BY HARRIET B. CREIGHTON

Department of Botany, Wellesley College, Wellesley, Massachusetts

So much has been written during and since World War II on education in general, and on science education in particular, that any attempt to survey the status of biology teaching at the present time is a superhuman task. Partly, this is because of the impact of research and technological advances on our thinking and on world problems, and partly, because as a nation we are seriously contemplating the training not only of scientific personnel but of educated citizens. The teaching of the biological sciences, along with the others, has been brought under scrutiny because of biology's relationship to the human problems of disease and nutrition, to problems of food production, and to problems of conservation of the world's natural resources. The urgent need for trained biologists and the no less pressing need for citizens with a comprehension not only of biology but of science and its meaning in the world has made the teachers of the life sciences keenly aware of the magnitude and significance of their task today.

Some limitations must be set for the present article if it is to avoid the pitfall of covering so much so thin that it actually covers nothing. First, then, it will be concerned primarily with college and university biology teaching. Second, it will deal more with the thoughts that are behind the teaching than with the detailed, day-by-day methodology. And third, it will not be in any sense an exhaustive review of what has been written on the subject, but rather a selection of ideas from papers that the author has felt would be readily available for reference and would help the reader to understand trends that seem to be developing today. In addition, an attempt will be made to review some of the problems that confront the teacher of the life sciences at the college level and to note certain constructive thoughts that have been set forth recently.

There are many ways to organize a discussion of the current approaches to the teaching of biology. The way chosen is to devote attention to the following questions: who is being taught, and what is being taught and why? This leaves for someone else the closely related questions: how is biology being taught and how well is it being taught? The basic question, "Who is doing the teaching?" insinuates itself into all of our thinking, for upon the answer to it depends to such a great extent the achievement of education. It is of utmost importance that the teacher be a liberally educated person, well grounded in the disciplines of biological science, yet continuously cognizant of the significance of biology's facts and theories for the world's affairs. He must have catholicity of interests coupled with humility in discussing matters beyond his area of competence. He must be aware of the limitations of biological probings into age-old philosophical, sociological and religious questions, as well as knowing the contributions which biological investigations and thought have made and can make to man's understanding of himself and his surroundings. Most important of all, he must be a scientist, master not only of his facts but of his thinking.

As a starting point, let us consider the large categories of students who take an introductory course in the life sciences, categories that are artificial and, therefore, conform only generally to the real situation. At present, there seem to be two, fairly distinct groups. The students in one group plan to use their knowledge of biology professionally, in teaching, in medicine, in agriculture or in research in any of the fields of biology. These students can be designated as "pre-professional," and the courses designed for them "pre-professional" courses. Students in the second group have primary interests in other aspects of our world, but wish to know, or have been told that they should know, something about biology. These students can be called "general" students and the courses for them "general" courses. The setting up of general courses distinct from pre-professional courses is not new, but at present the number of institutions that offer general courses seems to be on the increase. It is very difficult, however, to judge from catalogue descriptions or even from course outlines the point of view of those who present the material. A good characterization of general education courses that would include general biology courses is to be found in the Report of the President's Commission on Higher Education, Vol. I. Also, recently, a volume entitled "Science in General Education" has been published by the Dean of the College of Liberal Arts of the State University of Iowa, from which can be gained the most comprehensive review of this whole educational development.

In some institutions the general course in biology has been an addition to the curriculum, often open only to students who do not plan to major in a biological science. In other colleges, the existing introductory course has become the general course and the pre-professional work has been put into a separate course or into advanced courses. The number of kinds of pre-professional introductory courses has increased also in late years often as a result of the growth of strong departments representing branches of biology, such as bacteriology and physiology. The pros and cons of this trend will not be discussed in the present review.

The development of the idea of giving general courses distinct from pre-professional courses has been gradual. Many institutions have not made a separation for pedagogical reasons, whereas, other institutions have not for financial or administrative reasons. The rash of new curricula, however, with "modern" courses, sometimes preceded and sometimes followed by "up-to-date" textbooks is a phenomenon, almost a disease of the present time. Pressure has been strong to rethink what the college students of today should be taught. Biology teachers must continue to give attention to the selection of the content of a biology course. They are the only people qualified to decide which concepts, which principles, which facts and which techniques can be cogently presented in one year to the college students of today. Teachers are painfully aware that to make room for new topics and to insure that any large proportion of the ideas presented are really received by the students, some topics must be either eliminated or markedly curtailed. Many teachers have concluded that it is no longer possible to present a single introductory course for all students. One strong reason for this is that 40 or 50 or even 20 or 30 years ago, a large proportion of all that was known could be presented in 1 year. A student could come nearer then than now to grasping what the teacher knew. Thus, it was more reasonable, in the past, to offer one course for all students, the casual partaker of a bit of biology and the beginner in training for a career. Tragically, too many introductory courses of today still follow blindly the pattern of the past, attempting to survey the whole field of modern biology. Another reason for offering two introductory courses is based on the recognition that all college students are not equal in interest, nor in previous training, nor in manipulative and thinking ability. In the past this was not so evident when a smaller proportion of high school graduates attended college, and when high school curricula were more nearly alike. Today, we recognize that pre-college training is diverse and that college students have a wider range of capabilities. All this leads many teachers to feel the need for selection of material for two main groups of students, the general and the pre-professional. Usually, the general course will have in it students with the most diverse backgrounds, interests and abilities. The pre-professional introductory course will have a far from uniform group of students, but, at least, there will be some community of interests.

Even among the general biology courses that have been offered there have been two distinct types, both of which can be called general only in the sense that they are planned for non-specialists. One type is a "survey" course, in the spotlight a few years ago but now largely abandoned, in name at least. The other type has no nickname, but is selective in its coverage. The teachers of this kind of general course do not attempt to cover the whole field lightly, but rather to select a few topics and do them well. The bases for the selection vary with the planners of the course. Some suggestion of them will be given in a later section as we consider some of the aims of biology courses. It should be pointed out here, however, that in planning any general course attention is held on the fact that the great majority of students are not going to be scientists, let alone biological scientists. Because of this, the program of these courses has to be, in part, negative—not to teach too much biological detail. This aim, in theory, is more than counter-balanced by the aim of making the meaning of facts understandable and highlighting what are called the "principles" of biology. Teachers of these courses are often on the defensive and probably will continue to be for some time, attacked now by the directors of graduate work in universities for not having thoroughly grounded their students in facts and techniques, and now by their colleagues for failure to accomplish the miraculous and lead all students to life-long understanding of biological science, its methods, its implications, its concepts, and its principles. Nevertheless, there appear to be a growing number of thoughtful teachers who are attempting to organize introductory courses in the life sciences that are "general" in a very real sense, although their content is rigorously selected.

Pre-professional courses for the student who is going to use biological facts and ideas in his life work, have had to begin to teach him what his predecessors have discovered. So great is the body of information and technique that often these pre-professional courses have not been in any sense introductory to the biology, but have started to prepare a student for medicine, or bacteriology, or agriculture, or deplorably enough, for specialties within large fields, such as human physiology, entomology, genetics, or plant physiology. These limited courses are definitely not for the non-biologist who has time for only one course. There is a grave doubt as to the extent to which they are really fit for the student specializing in biology. Clearly in their extreme forms they do not properly prepare him for comprehension of findings made in fields other than his own, nor later for application of these findings to the solution of his own research problems. In these times when research in so many different fields is contributing so much to biological endeavor, the selection of biological material for presentation to the beginning biologist must be clairvoyantly judicious. Biological principles and general concepts and methods of thinking must be emphasized for these pre-professional students just as for the general students. Pre-professional courses, however, must try to help the student amass many observations and facts so that he can share some small part of the experience of pioneer biologists in discovering significance. He must begin to learn the methods of thought and of manipulation in biology. How frequently this goal is attained and at how early a stage in the development of an individual is one of the great unknowns of education. To what extent selection of subject matter presented has anything to do with the development of a student's ability to use biological facts is also not known. One thing is certain that in the pre-professional course as compared with the general course the student must be presented not only with more detailed information, but also with more of the techniques of observing, experimenting, and reasoning.

More must be said of the general compared with the pre-professional course, but at some point we must consider another facet of the problem. This is the question of whether the life sciences should be presented as a whole, what is called, biology, or in part, that is, botany, or zoology, or with the focus not on the plant or animal kingdom but on man in relation to animals and plants. Some teachers take the point of view that since one of the basic biological concepts is that all organisms have a fundamental likeness, the life sciences should not be divided into plant and animal science. Biology is a science, they maintain, not a summation of botany and zoology. One point of view, then, is that at the outset of college instruction biological topics should be presented—such as basic physiological processes, heredity, responses to changes in the environment, health, growth and development. Contrary-minded argue that the presentation of botany or zoology to exemplify biological concepts and principles is just as effective or more effective in the end. For example, by starting with consideration of plants, only, or animals, only, they maintain that it is possible to convey an idea of the similarity of all living things, In this approach they feel they can follow the pattern by which our knowledge and understanding have been acquired because, historically, detached bits of information about plants or about animals have been integrated by a few synthesizing minds. The program is to go from the study of plants or animals to the general truths of the life sciences, using either a historical approach or some logical orientation of facts. Proponents of this view argue that students cannot comprehend any large part of the accumulated information about the organic world, integrate its welter of detailed differences in their minds and understand the underlying likenesses of living things. The over-all picture must be built up, they contend, supported by a selection of material that is pertinent, material that is limited enough in extent that it can be studied in detail.

There is a third group of people teaching the biological sciences who feel that the important point for general or for pre-professional students is to understand man in relation to the biologic world. According to their view, the aspects of plant and animal life that should be studied are primarily those that affect man. Sometimes in these courses, it should be noted, the threads of connection between the biological facts presented and man are very tenuous. Frequently the relationship of a lot of information about plants and other animals to man and his problems is not made clear to the students. In the past few years, there has been a great deal of talk about "man-centered" courses, mainly, it seems, because of the realization by many non-biologists that their own undergraduate course in the life sciences did not provide them with an understanding of man's place and problems in the world. The implied or stated criticism of the traditional courses is being considered very seriously by many people who are planning general courses whether they reorganize their courses or not. In fact, at present, one of the principle aims of all types of courses is to make biological science and its role in our society more understandable to the average person.

The arguments pro and con biology courses versus botany or zoology or man-centered courses can and probably will go on and on. All too frequently they end with the protagonists becoming more convinced of the rightness of their side. In practice, when the decision as to the type of course to be offered is made by a faculty or by a department, secondary factors frequently influence the settlement. The approach may have to be chosen with regard to the competence of the teachers to handle the material, for account must be taken of the knowledge and methods of thought that the teachers have. It is entirely possible that the instructor whose training and inclination has made him more competent to use examples from the animal kingdom will do a better job if he does not have to make excursions into the world of microorganisms or of plants. His general understanding of the variety of living forms may be sufficient for him to make clear to his students the broader applicability of concepts he has derived from teaching a limited number of living forms. Many people feel that until there are more teachers trained in biology, it may be desirable to stick to the specialized disciplines as a point of departure for presenting general concepts and principles. This does not mean that biologists are content with well-trodden approaches, but rather that they recognize that they must achieve their ends with the most effective use of the staff.

Returning from the brief discussion of administrative difficulties that influence the decision as to whether biology, botany, or zoology courses shall be given, we find similar problems appearing in the discussion of courses for general as compared with pre-professional students. There is the real problem of finding competent teachers for the kind of general course that is desired. To a great extent the success of a general course depends on its being taught by a "generally" educated person, a scientist well grounded in the whole field of biology who can teach a wide variety of students. Also, there is the problem of planning advanced courses in the life sciences that can accommodate not only the pre-professionally trained students but also those from the general course, who find their interest in biology whetted and who want to take advanced courses. Unless these students are penalized for not having known that they would be interested in further work in biological science by not allowing them to follow their newly found interest, they must be taken into advanced pre-professional courses even though these courses may have to be reorganized to accommodate them. Both of these practical problems complicate the decision as to whether a general course can be given. All biologists, whether they teach an introductory course or not, have a stake in the decision today.

So far attention has been devoted to some of the problems that arise from the questions of "who is being taught" biology in college today and "what is being taught, and why." There are many other aspects of this latter question that must be considered. One is "what are we trying to teach," that is, what are our goals? In discussing aims it is reasonably accurate to say that a general course and a pre-professional course will have in common many general aims. In the two kinds of courses the emphasis may be different and the degree of detail into which the student is taken will be different. Also, whether the course is to be one in botany or one in zoology or one in biology, it is generally true that the main aims will be the same..

One of the most frequently mentioned aims of a biology course is to present to the student the "fundamental principles" of biological science. This has long been recognized by textbook authors and is almost invariably mentioned in their prefaces as something that will be accomplished by the text. To the consternation of students (some of whom later become teachers) it is well nigh impossible to find clear statements of these principles in the text. Evidently, biologists have not succeeded in making them understandable, because faculty curriculum committees usually made up of people who have been exposed to biology in their college days, are insistent that in the "improved" courses they urge, the principles of biology must be emphasized. In what both students and faculty say two suggestions are implicit. First, principles should be labeled principles and discussed as such, and second, the meaning and the implication of these principles should be made more clear.

The fundamental principles or laws of biology are the statements of general truths about organisms, just as the principles of physics and chemistry are general statements about the nature and behavior of energy and matter. The collection of all the biological principles would give us the epitome of biology. A listing of them should include the laws of physics and chemistry which apply to organisms, and certainly in a biology course there should be discussion of and laboratory work with these pertinent principles. In addition, it should be made clear that some biological laws are statements that characterize organisms as individuals, others, as races, others, as societies. Still different principles are those that state truths about the relationship between different kinds of plants and between different kinds of animals, and between certain plants and animals.

Since there is such general insistence in curriculum discussions that biological principles be taught, one would expect to be able to find many concise expositions of them in texts. Such is not the case, as a perusal of introductory texts will make immediately evident. It seems strange that they are so buried in texts, even in those using "Principles of . . . ." as their titles. In fact, nowadays the beginning student would expect to find principles set up in bold-face type, the way new terms are set out in many texts to make them inescapable. Even in the summaries at the ends of chapters, statements of principles are hard to find. In the much discussed Harvard Report there is not even an example of a principle given in the paragraphs proposing "A Course in the Principles of Biological Science."

To make explicit the nature of the aim to present biological principles in an introductory course, certain principles will be set down here, in particular, those that concern organisms as structural and functional units. These statements have been gathered together from a number of sources and are organized not in any formal manner, but rather for pedagogical usefulness. Diverse forms of these statements are encountered in biological literature and the following formulation is meant to be only illustrative of what the term biological principle connotes.

All organisms come from pre-existing organisms, meaning that there is no evidence of spontaneous origin of new living entities. Protoplasmic units come only from like protoplasm; all protoplasm reproduces its kind. Texts devote much space to reproduction and the panorama of detail of the process in plants and animals. Frequently texts make reference to the discarding of the once held Theory of Spontaneous Generation, but usually only in connection with the study of microorganisms. Authors of texts generally indicate that all cells arise only from cells, but rarely is the idea put across that one of the fundamental principles of biology is that living things come only from living things.

All organisms grow, that is, they make more of themselves out of materials of the environment. This generalization is usually pointed out to students during the study of the characteristics of protoplasm and again, sometimes, in the studies of nutrition. Unfortunately, in many introductory courses emphasis on physiology is not made strong by experiments and laboratory observations. This means frequently that the student does not sense the real meaning of the building up by an organism of distinctive body materials from the miscellaneous assortment of nutrients available. He learns the necessary minerals, the role of carbohydrates, proteins, vitamins, etc., the importance of translocation of these materials, the intricacies of food-getting mechanisms and many other things. He puts this knowledge into mental pockets from which it can be withdrawn for many uses, but he loses sight, if he ever gains it, of the fact that capacity for growth is a fundamental characteristic of all organisms, no matter what their kind, size, or degree of complexity.

All organisms develop a characteristic form, that is, concomitant with growth or not, organisms develop into a predictable size and shape. Most kinds of organisms can be distinguished from other kinds on the basis of their appearance, without recourse to a study of physiological differences. The study of morphogenesis is of long standing. Texts present some of our knowledge, usually without clearly pointing out that the details are to give students examples of a general truth about living things. For the beginning student, blastomeres, hormones, axial gradients, colonial forms, genetic control of the development of the leaf or larval shapes are items to be learned and forgotten unless their greater significance is driven home.

All organisms have a characteristic life history. The phrase "life history" generally brings out groans from students who have learned them with painful thoroughness. Students store away enough of such facts from the study of plant and animal life histories to make this principle easily understood, but it is rare that biologists, in texts at least, have emphasized the generalization and pointed out how it affects our thinking.

All organisms inherit certain potentialities from their progenitors and transmit certain potentialities to their descendants. Genetics has been a favorite topic in introductory courses for years, partly for its intrinsic values, partly because it is obviously important to man in a practical way, and partly because its precision makes it delightful to teach. The laws of inheritance set forth by Mendel have been included in biology texts for some years, and students are usually given exercises in arithmetic by working on simple problems. Authors have included a few of the modifications of Mendel's generalizations, but most of modern genetics has not yet been added to our teaching. The most serious omission is that the impact of knowledge of genetics upon biological and human thought has not been stressed. The discussion of nearly every topic needs to have included in it the role that heredity plays. Also, the application of modern knowledge of inheritance to the problems of plant and animal breeding should be discussed when the contribution of biology to world problems is considered.

All organisms have the possibility of sudden change in their hereditary potentialities. Concurrent with the discussion of heredity and with that of morphogenesis there cannot help but come mention of the aberrancies that are observed. Distinction betweeen those that are inherited and those that are not must be made. Only rarely in biology texts, however, is a discussion of mutation found and even then its general significance is not usually made plain. In the study of genetics students learn mutant genes by name but only rarely is mutation as a fundamental phenomenon discussed. With all the recent work on experimentally induced mutations in molds and bacteria added to the previous mass of data from other types of organisms, this principle is one of the easiest ones to make clear. On it is based much of modern thinking about evolution and about plant and animal classification and distribution. In most biology courses a great deal of time and effort is devoted to presenting evidence for the occurrence of evolution. The historically interesting theories are often battled over as if today's students lived in Darwin's and Huxley's time. The principle of change is lost for many students, and the present status of thought on evolution with its implications for modern man are never glimpsed.

All organisms are sensitive to changes in their environment. Irritability, tropic and nastic movements, stimulus and response—all these topics are the subjects of chapters or at least chapter subheads in texts and yet, because they are presented as ideas concerned with protoplasm or with the behavior of particular types of animals or plants, their general significance is not always made apparent, nor is the fact that they are all manifestations of a fundamental principle.

Enough has been said, perhaps, to indicate the kind of generalized statement that helps a student to see that there are principles in biology and that what he is learning is not a mass of unrelated items or items related only to some one idea, such as evolution. Certain of the principles listed may not be considered principles by some biologists. Other biologists would stress other principles. It is hoped, however, that what has been said, at least, will have made clear the kind of considerations that are in the minds of many biologists who are giving or planning to give biology courses for general students. The topics of their course outlines and the heading of their texts show that they include much that has been in previous courses, but the information is woven together in a way that should make biological principles more readily understandable.

Presentation of fundamental principles is only one of the aims of an introductory course. Biologists in the prefaces to texts and in other statements usually include the aim of presenting some of the important "concepts" of biology. What these concepts are is difficult to ascertain from reading most books. Students will always get some mental picture and it is important that they be guided. One of the difficult tasks of a teacher is to select facts that make it possible for students to construct in their own minds a facsimile of the concept that more experienced and better informed biologists have evolved. The concepts that biologists hold are very numerous and range widely in complexity and scope. A few examples will be listed to indicate that kind of mental picture that it would seem important for the general student or for the pre-professional student to acquire.

An organism is a functioning whole, not as a summation of its various parts.

Organisms are fundamentally alike in their basic requirements for living.

Living things can be distinguished from non-living not because they possess some one thing, life, but because they are able to carry on certain physiological processes in accord with the known laws of chemistry.

Patterns of growth and development under normal environmental conditions are determined by hereditary units, the genes.

The occurrence and the rate of many biological activities are controlled by hormones.

This small sample of concepts, omitting whole fields of biological thought, merely indicates the kind of thing that is meant when biological concepts are mentioned. Teachers must make a conscious selection of the most important concepts to present to introductory students remembering that students will develop concepts whether they are presented or not. Frequently, a teacher never discovers the strange, erroneous notions that a student takes from his course. There does not seem to be any core of concepts, the teaching of which biologists agree is essential. There is a similarity of topics discussed in texts, but that does not insure similarity in thinking about organisms. Clear statements of significant concepts would help general students and pre-professional students to comprehend modern biology and to see how it contributes to thinking in other areas of human interest.

Presentation of biological principles and of biological concepts are not the only aims of biology courses. Training of minds is accorded high priority. Keen and correct observation, precise and accurate measurement and recording of information are arts and skills especially developed in laboratory exercise. The ability to reason unfalteringly and the development of a great enough imagination to find a solution in harmony with the known facts, can be the products of work in the sciences. In a pre-professional course, mental training admittedly is of paramount importance. Where it stands in order of importance as an objective in a course for general students is a moot point, but judging from the laboratory outlines of several such courses, it is high on the list. But training of minds is slow and time must be devoted to it. Humans will do almost anything to evade thinking. Unless the teacher persistently requires reasoning, careful observation and rigorous experimental work, and then allows time enough for practice, a science course can be a travesty on science.

There are several other goals that most biology teachers hope to attain. One is to convince students of how necessary it is to good citizenship for people to know enough about biology to understand its applications to everyday affairs. Most teachers have found out that in the presentation of factual material in biology courses it cannot be assumed that students will see the bearing of these facts on their lives, or on community or world problems. Digressions must be made by the instructor to point out the uses that industry, agriculture, and medicine have made of biological information. The fact is that many college students are unfamiliar with agriculture or with many types of manufacturing or with medicine and cannot see the connections with the materials they are studying. In this age of technological complexity men and women, general students and pre-professional alike, must learn of the practical contributions of biological science to our culture. Only an informed citizen can make wise decisions on local or national policy.

Beyond these rather frequently discussed goals, there are some others, the attainment of which is desirable. These aims involve the inculcation of attitudes. Too often teachers do not attempt the task. Their achievement depends to a greater extent upon the inner convictions of the teacher and is the result of a subtle transmission from teacher to student of a spirit, a point of view, a quality of mind.

Critical-mindedness is one of these qualities. Some students are further along the road to developing it than others, but all can receive inspiration and acquire techniques from watching a critical mind at work. The questioning of statements, the testing of facts, the weighing of evidence and the objective judging of conclusions, these are qualities of mind our world so badly needs. Emphasis must be put upon them in all kinds of courses, but most assuredly in biology courses the opportunity must not be missed.

The second of these more subtle objectives is the transmission to student of the excitement, the thrill of adventure, in biological science. Young people are not always eager to reach out into unfamiliar mental territories. Sometimes, for many reasons, their curiosity has been all but killed by the time they reach college. But in college, particularly when the student has broken away from home ties, there is a great opportunity for teachers to help to open again the gateways to a new world. Surely a biology course should engender in students an enthusiasm for the discovery of new facts, new correlations, new syntheses.

Another aim of the many that might be briefly discussed is the aim of helping to orient the student in the realm of religion. Because of the diversity of backgrounds of the students and because of the manifold difficulties for the teacher, the whole matter of the relationship of science, particularly biology, to religion is frequently avoided. The biologist should not leave this whole important area of human consciousness to the philosophers or to the teachers of religion, or to undirected student discussions. The facts of science that have shattered many of man's time-honored beliefs offer the basis for conviction and a foundation for faith. Biologists, especially those teaching courses for general students, have an obligation to help build the foundations on which can be grounded faith that will give power to dispel some of man's confusion in our complex world. The good teacher will avoid dogmatic presentation of his own ideas, but will carefully and dispassionately present different points of view, and help students toward satisfactory solutions of their own religious problems.

There is another type of consideration that enters into the choice of what to teach in any introductory course in the life sciences. It is recognition of need for introducing students to at least some of the classic experiments or descriptive landmarks of the science as a means to the end of understanding how man has learned about his world and himself. To give students this "feel" for science two methods seem possible. One is to have students participate in actual research with the instructors. To whatever extent it can be done this is highly desirable, if the problem is significant and the researcher is a real scientist. The other, more practicable, method is to tell the story of the development of modern views on certain topics, such things as the germ theory of disease, or the process of respiration, or the concept of the gene. From either type of tutelage students should learn several lessons. For one thing, they should see that contradictory facts never overthrow an accepted theory. It is only discarded when someone devises a better theory. For a second thing, they should realize that progress in science is slow and beset with difficulties. The establishment of a fact as a fact is not accomplished overnight. They would see the pitfalls of experimentation and the idea of a controlled experiment would be driven home with all the force and skill available. Furthermore, it should become clear that biological science and all science is a cooperative venture, involving many people, in many countries and often at widely separated times. The influence that the ideology and the culture of a particular time or place may have upon scientific research should be made evident. The dependence of one discovery upon the prior occurrence of another would show up. The end result for the student should be a better understanding of what scientific work is and what can be expected from it.

In all the preceding paragraphs reviewing current thought on what should be taught in an introductory biological science course, the concern has been with the general aims, the goals of the teaching. Obviously, the biological facts that are taught are selected to make possible the achievement of the aims. The best possible material should be used to present in an understandable form the most important principles of biology; to make clear certain biological concepts; to set forth what biology is today and what it is not, both as to methods and to findings; to inculcate in the student an understanding of, in fact a desire for critical mindedness, for accuracy of observation and honesty and clarity of reasoning; to imbue him with the spirit of science as an adventure into the undiscovered; to guide him to ways of philosophical and religious thought; and finally to do all that it is possible to do to help students to understand the world, and man's place in it. This, briefly, is the task of biology teaching today.

The Genes and Gene Action

BY BENTLEY GLASS

The Johns Hopkins University, Baltimore, Maryland

SYNOPSIS

The science of genetics is the child of the twentieth century. In spite of the astounding prevision of Mendelian heredity by Maupertuis in the middle of the 18th century, and the real achievements of Kölreuter, Gärtner, Knight, and other hybridizers of that century and the next, no one before Mendel clearly analyzed the mechanism of heredity. And it was therefore only in 1900, when Mendel's work was rediscovered and confirmed, that the validity and generality of the Mendelian mechanism of heredity was fully established.

The first decade of the present century saw Sutton's formulation of the Chromosome Theory and Morgan's lucky choice of the fruit-fly *Drosophila melanogaster* for breeding experiments. Then, in breath-taking succession hardly checked by the First World War, came those momentous discoveries of the linear order of linked genes, of the existence of multiple alleles, and of chromosome non-disjunction. The parallel cytological and genetic studies of the latter established the validity of the Chromosome Theory. The analysis of crossing over enabled investigators to map for each chromosome the loci of the invisible genes within it, according to their serial order and relative distances apart (as measured by their frequencies of recombination). The study of multiple alleles, deficiencies, and duplications made possible a deeper insight into the nature of the gene and its action, through a comparison of different states and different dosages. These superlative achievements of the corps of students Morgan gathered about him and trained were accompanied by confirmatory studies of the genetics of many other organisms, especially of maize. Nor should one overlook the development in these same years of the theory of multiple factors, which brought into harmony with Mendelian genetics the inheritance of quantitative traits, such as size and weight, fertility and longevity.

In 1927, Muller discovered that x-rays enormously increase the frequency with which genes mutate—and a new era of genetic investigations began, the era of experimentally induced changes in heredity. The discovery that high energy radiation also breaks chromosomes, and that the broken ends may thereupon unite in new arrangements, so as to produce translocations, inversions, deficiencies, and duplications, brought the cytologist more than ever into league with the geneticist in analyzing and interpreting chromosome phenomena. Thus, 20 years ago, cytogenetics, lusty offspring of the union of cytology and genetics, was emerging from infancy and beginning to manifest the full vigor of a youthful science. In the nineteen-thirties, the giant banded chromosomes of the salivary glands of dipterans, the meiotic prophase chromosomes of maize, and the chromosomes of the pollen grain mitoses in the spiderwort provided illimitable scope for the maturation of the new science.

The nature of gene action remained obscure. Goldschmidt had developed the theory that all genes act quantitatively, by controlling the rates of specific developmental processes; and Goldschmidt, Wright, and others had focussed attention on the relation which must exist between the genes, which control specific morphogenetic traits, and the enzymes, which control specific metabolic processes. But facts to substantiate these views were scanty until the methods of experimental embryology were applied to the study of gene-controlled reactions. Ten years ago it was already evident that the offspring of this new scientific union, between genetics and experimental embryology, would equal in vigor its half-sib, cytogenetics; and the advances of the past decade in physiological genetics have not belied that promise. In particular, the work of Ephrussi and Beadle demonstrated the possibilities of analysis along the new lines. By transplanting larval tissues of *Drosophila* from donors of one genotype into hosts of a different genotype, they discovered the existence of two diffusible hormones that govern two successive steps in the formation of eye pigment; and this led further to their eventual isolation and chemical identification. Such success was, however, qualified by the evidence that relatively few developmental processes involve gene participation by way of diffusible substances. Beadle, collaborating with Tatum, was therefore inspired to seek for a wholesale method of detecting gene mutations by their biochemical effects. A suitable organism, the mold *Neurospora,* was chosen, and its spores were irradiated to produce mutations. The treated spores were then grown on a "complete" medium that contained, in addition to the substances in the minimal synthetic medium on which the original wild-type mold would grow, a supply of the more complex substances contained in yeast extract and hydrolyzed casein. After the treated strains had been established on this medium, they were tested on the minimal medium in order to isolate those strains in which there had occurred a mutation that interfered with the synthesis of some one of any of those substances present in the complete medium but lacking in the minimal medium. Further tests could then be made to determine the particular substance whose synthesis the gene mutation had blocked. Many biochemical mutations were found, blocking the synthesis of individual amino acids or vitamins, etc.; and each such mutation was also found to block the synthesis at one particular step, and one only. From this body of evidence arose the one gene—one enzyme theory, which postulates that in general genes control metabolic syntheses by individually determining the presence or absence of specific enzymes, each of which in turn controls directly a single step in the chemical system of the cell.

Today genetics seems just as ready as ever to fulfill the implications of its name, to enter into union with other fields of scientific endeavor, to impregnate old fields with new ideas, and so to increase its scientific progeny. At the present date, in fact, several liaisons appear to be progressing simultaneously, a phenomenon which ought to be sufficient answer to any who may claim—as some do—that genetics is a doddering, elderly science, already completely worked out. In one new alliance, the experimental study of evolutionary processes has been profoundly stimulated, analyses of the genetic nature of population differences, of the effects of selection, and of isolation mechanisms having added greatly to our understanding of evolution in recent years. These problems are to be discussed elsewhere in this series. In other unions, genetics is today penetrating the fields of biochemistry and microbiology and inseminating them with fruitful new techniques and concepts. The vigorous young progeny are those to be considered here.

The great problems of genetics in the present day may be framed in the three following questions:

(1) What is the nature of the gene?

(2) What is the mode of gene action?

(3) What is the relation of the genes to the chemical composition, structure and behavior of the chromosomes?

As to the first of these, light has been gained in recent times chiefly from the study of changes occurring in the genes themselves, i.e., from the phenomenon of gene mutation. Inasmuch as microorganisms, and especially the bacteria and viruses, exhibit morphological organization of extreme simplicity combined with biochemical organization virtually as elaborate as that of any organisms, the mechanism of heredity in these organisms is of crucial significance. Until recently, however, it seemed an insoluble riddle. Were the frequently observed variants due to gene mutations? or to environmentally induced modifications? or to special types of "transformation"? In the absence of sexual reproduction, genetic analysis remained impossible, and one could only guess, in accordance with one's predisposition, at the answer. Then, 5 years ago, a new type of analysis was developed, one which enables the investigator to distinguish with some certainty between mutations, on the one hand, and environmentally induced modifications, on the other. As a result, it is now quite apparent that most hereditary variants appearing in cultures of bacteria and viruses are due to gene mutations (see Section I, 1). Moreover, the methods worked out for the study of biochemical mutations in *Neurospora*, applied with further refinements to bacteria and viruses, have in the past year led to the unexpected disclosure of the existence of sex, in its essential aspect of genetic recombination, in both of these groups of organisms (see Section I, 2 and 3). Together with the revelation of the true bacterial nucleus, made evident by cytological advances in this same recent period (see Section I, 4), these discoveries are epochal for biology as a whole.

X-rays and other sources of penetrating radiation provide a convenient tool for the induction of gene mutations, but they scarcely indicate what sort of chemical change is involved, or reveal the chemical nature of the genes themselves. Many a worker in genetics had hoped to discover a better method of analysis by finding some chemical substance which would cause genes to mutate—but all efforts remained fruitless; the results, at best, were dubious. This situation was completely altered by the recent discovery of real, highly effective chemical mutagens (see Section II, 1). The road to the production of specific mutations by specific chemical agents now appears open.

Meanwhile, the further analysis of the mutagenic effects of physical agents, singly and in combination, has not lagged (see Section II, 2). The study of "position effects," whereby the action of a gene is modified because of a change in its position in the chromosome, seems now to throw less light on the nature of the gene itself than upon gene action (see Section II, 3). On the other hand, the study of multiple alleles promises to yield new secrets about the structure of the gene in the near future (see Section II, 4). This is particularly true of those genes concerned with the production of antigens, which share with genes and enzymes that unique degree of specificity so characteristic of the living system.

Gene action and the relations of genes to the chemical composition, structure, and behavior of chromosomes are discussed but briefly here (see Sections III, IV)—for they have been reviewed extensively and frequently in recent months. In these fields, too, the rapid advance of knowledge brings, almost weekly, further evidence that draws genes, enzymes, plasmagenes, and antigens into closer relationship to one another and to the chemistry of the ribose and desoxyribose nucleoproteins.

I. The Genetics of Microorganisms

1. *Mutation in Bacteria and Viruses*

During the war years an enormous amount of research was devoted to the study of variation, spontaneous or induced, in microorganisms; much of this work is still in course of publication. In sexual microorganisms, such as yeast or *Neurospora,* the physical basis of heredity has long been recognized as genic and chromosomal, like that in higher plants and animals. For asexual fungi, bacteria, and viruses, one can reason as to this only by analogy. The hereditary variations of bacteria, for example, like the gene mutations which occur in higher organisms, are permanent, occur spontaneously and at definite rates, are independent of other mutations in the same organisms, are reversible, can be induced by the same agents, and produce analogous physiological and biochemical effects (see Luria, 1946). For example, the classic experiments of Beadle and Tatum, dating from 1941, demonstrated that the genes of *Neurospora,* which had previously yielded numerous morphological mutants, may also be induced by x-rays to mutate so as to produce physiological mutants, detectable only by their loss of the capacity to synthesize some particular amino acid, vitamin, or other essential metabolite. Experiments performed shortly thereafter to determine whether such variants could also be induced in bacteria gave positive results (Gray and Tatum, 1944; Roepke, Libby and Small, 1944).

Another essential step toward the genetic analysis of mutation in microorganisms was taken when Luria and Delbrück (1943; Delbrück, 1945) outlined a valid method for distinguishing between those resistant variants that arise, on the one hand, by hereditary immunity acquired through exposure to a specific agent, and those, on the other hand, that arise by mutation occurring irrespective of exposure to the agent. This initial work showed that the alteration of bacteria (*Escherichia coli*) from a virus-sensitive condition to one of virus resistance is attributable to mutation and not to hereditary immunity acquired as a specific response following exposure to the virus. For if the latter theory were correct, and such hereditary changes are specific adaptive responses to specific agents, then the numbers of detected mutants per culture ought to fall into a Poisson distribution. But if mutation occurs irrespective of the treatment, the distribution of the mutants should reveal great irregularities—an enormous variance, in other words. And the latter is what Luria and Delbrück found, as has every worker who has applied a like analysis since that time. Mutations of strains of *Staphylococcus aureus* to resistance to penicillin (Demerec, 1945) or to sulfonamides (Oakberg and Luria, 1947), of strain B of *E. coli* to resistance to bacteriophage (Demerec and Fano, 1945) or to ultraviolet radiation or x-rays (Witkin, 1946, 1947), and of strains of *Clostridium septicum* dependent upon uracil to uracil-independence (Ryan, Schneider and Ballentine, 1946)—all show the expected, much greater variance of samples from independent cultures than of those taken from within single cultures.

The mutant strain *B/r* of *E. coli,* isolated and studied by Witkin (1946, 1947) is particularly interesting. Not only does it manifest resistance to both x-rays and ultraviolet radiation and to both lethal and division-inhibiting actions of each of these agents, but it also possesses considerable resistance to both lethal and division-inhibiting effects of penicillin and sulfathiazole. Other independent radiation-resistant mutant strains revealed the independence of these effects; for some of these strains proved to be resistant to both antibiotic substances, some to one or the other only, and still others to neither. The question of interest is: do these mutant strains carry coincident mutations, or are the several effects produced by various modifications (i.e., "alleles") of the same "gene." It is tempting, if premature, to think of these bacterial mutants in terms of the known genetics of higher organisms, in which coincident mutation is very rare, but in which series of multiple alleles may exhibit a diversity of effects in virtually all possible combinations.

Some light is thrown on this question by the determination of mutation rates. Witkin, for example, has calculated that the rate of spontaneous mutation of strain B to radiation-resistance is 10^{-5} mutations per bacterium per generation, and to phage-resistance it is 1 or 2×10^{-8}. *S. aureus,* according to Oakberg and Luria (1947), has a rate of mutation to sulfonamide resistance that is considerably lower than these rates, namely, between 2×10^{-9} and 4×10^{-10} per bacterium per generation. It is therefore clear that the random coincidence of three independent mutations in bacteria could scarcely occur at a rate of more than 10^{-15}. Yet actually the mutant type that acquired resistance to radiation, penicillin, and sulfathiazole simultaneously was the commonest type of mutant Witkin obtained.

Permanence, spontaneous origin, definite rate, independence of one another, and reversibility also characterize the mutations of bacterial viruses (bacteriophages) as to their antigenic specificity, host specificity, and type of plaque (i.e., appearance of the lysed area produced when a virus is cultured on susceptible host bacteria on an agar plate) (Hershey, 1946b). Luria (1945a, b) was the first to study such mutations quantitatively, and Hershey (1946a) measured one mutation rate and found it to be about once in 1.5 to 3.5×10^{-9} duplications of the virus. The rate of the *r* mutation, which produces rapid lysis and a large, distinctive plaque, has been measured in both directions, and is $r^{+}\longrightarrow r = 10^{-3}$; $r\longrightarrow r^{+} = 10^{-8}$ (Hershey, 1946a, b). The *r* mutations mutate independently of mutations to clear plaques or to new host specificities.

From these experiments the conclusion is to be drawn that in viruses, as in bacteria, there are distinct genetic, mutational units, which correspond to the mutational units ("genes") of higher organisms. That the correspondence goes even beyond this, the sequel will show.

2. *"Gene Transfer" Between Viruses*

In 1946, Delbrück and Bailey found a very remarkable phenomenon. When a mixture of two unrelated viruses infects a single host bacterium, only one of them multiplies and the other is lost. On the other hand, when a mixture of wild-type and *r*-type particles of any two of the related viruses T2, T4 or T6 is inoculated, the principle of mutual exclusion breaks down, and new types are produced that represent recombinations of the host specificity (T2, T4, T6) with the *r*-type. This was interpreted at the time as being due to "induced mutations," but the alternative of genetic transfer, or exchange, was clear. Hershey (1946b) confirmed the existence of this phenomenon by finding recombinations of three loci, two governing host specificity and the third governing rapid lysis. Whenever bacteria were treated with a mixture of viruses of two strains (h^+h^+r and $h^bh^cr^+$), in addition to the two initial strains, other combinations of the hereditary factors were recovered. In fact, of the six possible recombinations, no less than five were obtained, certain of them with a high frequency; and special reasons could be suggested why the sixth possible recombination failed to appear. This discovery clearly indicated that genetic factors might be independently transmitted, or transferred, from one virus to another.

In the past year, Luria (1947b) has demonstrated beyond a doubt that actual transfer of some kind is involved in a similar phenomenon. Ultraviolet radiation will inactivate particles of bacteriophage, a single quantum being the effective "hit." In studying this effect, Luria found that when he mixed inactivated virus particles and normal particles of the same or a related strain, the inactive particles could be reactivated. If the ultraviolet rays had induced what one might call "lethal mutations" in the treated virus particles, a transfer of normal "genes" from an unaffected virus to the affected one appeared to be possible. This hypothesis was supported by finding, first, that the reactivation can only take place if the host bacteria are capable of adsorbing both kinds of phage particles; and second, that the reactivation could be secured with phage purified of extraneous material by centrifugation. Moreover, if reactivation can only occur inside of bacterial cells that have absorbed at least two virus particles, it should vary with the proportion of multiple-infected bacteria, in mixtures made up in various proportions of bacteria and irradiated phage. This expectation Luria also confirmed.

Reactivation should also depend on the dose of the radiation, for presumably reactivation can only take place if the same locus has not received a lethal hit in all the virus particles that infect a given cell. This reasoning could be formulated mathematically and tested experimentally by studying the actual dependence of the probability of reactivation on the dose of the radiation. A large number of experiments yielded results that agreed with the expectations, and enabled Luria to calculate the approximate minimum number of independent genetic units subject to inactivation by ultraviolet and to transfer from one particle to another. These interesting values, which checked very well with estimates based on an independent method of calculation, are: 45 to 50 for phages T2 and T6, 30 to 35 for T4, around 15 for T5. The number of loci varies in this series directly with resistance to ultraviolet, and also, apparently, with absolute size, for the small viruses T1 and T7, which manifested no reactivation in these experiments, must have by calculation fewer than 8 or 10 loci.

The analogy of this process of phage reactivation with the known processes bringing about genetic recombination in sexual organisms is a striking one. But the experiments just described yielded no evidence of linkage in the transfer of "genes" from one virus particle to another. For if the units were transferred in groups rather than independently, there would be less reactivation at high doses than calculated, as the probability of two or more lethals within a single linkage group increased. Without linkage, crossing over is not to be expected, of course, but there remains the possibility that the transfer of genetic units is reciprocal, i.e., an exchange. Luria has tested this by mixing a heavily irradiated phage with an unirradiated one in proportions of virus to bacterium such that most host cells would adsorb a single active and one or more inactive particles. If a genetic exchange were to take place prior to any reproduction of the virus particles, then in most cases two inactive particles should result, and as a consequence the bacterium might survive. This never happened—but of course that result only excludes the less likely probability analogous to two-strand crossing over in higher organisms, which also does not occur. It remains possible that genetic exchange takes place, but at a time when virus particles are reproducing. In such a case, as in crossing over between two of four strands, the original genetic combinations are not replaced by the recombinations, but survive along with them. The survival of the original active phage would then kill the bacterium. Luria's experiment was not planned to test this possibility.

3. *Gene Recombination and Linkage in Bacteria*

In 1946 (a, b) Lederberg and Tatum briefly reported obtaining some novel genotypes in mixed cultures of biochemical mutant strains of the bacterium *E. coli*. The full report of this work (Tatum and Lederberg, 1947; Lederberg, 1947) establishes the existence in this bacterium of all the essential features of genetic recombination in sexual organisms. Lederberg and Tatum have made use of biochemical mutant strains which are unable to synthesize certain essential substances and which consequently can grow only on media to which those substances have been added as nutrients. For example, one strain used was unable to synthesize biotin (B^-) and methionine (M^-), and another, proline (P^-) and threonine (T^-). Strains deficient in a single synthetic ability revert to normal by mutation at a frequency of ca. 10^{-7}; but the use of doubly deficient, or multiple-mutant, strains reduces reversion to normal to negligible proportions. However, when two such double mutants as the above are grown in mixtures in minimal medium (i.e., lacking the said nutrients), there appear appreciable numbers of genetic recombinations which can synthesize all the enumerated substances and consequently survive. The authors have called these "prototrophs."

Lederberg has also made use of strains which differ as to the ability or inability to ferment lactose (Lac^+/Lac^-), and in resistance or susceptibility to a specific bacterial virus (V_1^r/V_1^s). It was found that when V_1^r was coupled with B^-M^- (or the like) and V_1^s with P^-T^- (or the like), the surviving prototrophs isolated from mixtures plated on minimal media were predominantly virus-resistant (205:37 or 85%). But when coupled in the converse fashion, the prototrophs proved to be predominantly susceptible to virus (259:88 or 75%). This suggestive result was followed by growing the cross $B^-M^-T^+L^+B_1^+ \times B^+M^+T^-L^-B_1^-$ (*L*, leucine; B_1, thiamine) on minimal medium supplemented with a single one of the nutrients. It was thus possible to isolate single mutant deficient types as well as the prototrophs. From the analyses of these single mutant deficient types it was demonstrated that *B* and *M* are linked, that *T* and *L* are linked, and that B_1 is linked to *B* and *M* but probably not so closely as they are to one another. The next procedure was to study the segregation of both *Lac* and V_1 into the prototroph and thiamine-deficient (single mutant) types. The results showed linkage between *Lac* and *BM* and between V_1 and *TL*. But *Lac* and B_1 segregated independently, although the latter had already been shown to be linked with *BM*. Consequently, if we assume a linear seriation of the genes, their order must be: B_1—*BM*—*Lac*; and since *Lac* and V_1 also show linkage, the linkage map may be extended to include V_1—*TL*. With the recombination values the full map (including another gene, V_6, located in separate experiments) is:

B_1		[*MB*]		V_6		*Lac*		V_1		[*TL*]
	9		17		5		38		20	

The fact that the first seven genes definitely located, and eight others tentatively located, all belong to the same linkage group is quite enough to make it appear highly probable that in *E. coli* only one linkage group exists. Presumably a zygote must be formed, if the chromosomes of different strains are to cross over and yield recombinations. And if that is so, one might expect to find a complementary crossover type with each segregant. Or if four-strand crossing over prevails, as in most sexual organisms, there should be supplementary segregants from the same zygote too—either parental types or additional types of crossovers. So far, Lederberg has not been able to detect any of these.

One might suppose that the recombinations in *E. coli* are produced in a way like that proposed for the famous "transformations" of pneumococci (see McCarty, Taylor and Avery, 1946), by means of transforming substances able to diffuse through the medium. The mathematical relations between the recombinations make this scarcely plausible, but in addition an ingenious experiment has been performed which may be regarded as altogether disposing of the possibility. This experiment consisted of testing the effects of triple mixtures. For if diffusible transforming substances are at work, recombinations of genes from all three strains should be found in a single prototroph. But if the mechanism is that of zygote formation followed by meiosis with crossing over, only two parental types should ever contribute to any one recombination. And this was found to be the case in an examination of 628 recombinant prototrophs.

The simplest theory to fit all the facts remains that of orthodox genetics. Otherwise it is difficult to explain, for example, why the frequency of exchanges between *BM* and *Lac* depends upon coincident interchanges between *BM* and V_1—as is clearly the case, since when *Lac* segregates from *BM*, V_1 nearly always segregates from *BM* too; but when *Lac* and *BM* retain their original combination, the recombination of V_1 with *BM* is low. This relationship is intelligible if the factors form a linear series and if, as in crossing over in sexual organisms, interchanges between proximal factors lead, in the absence of multiple crossing over, to exchanges between distal factors as well. The rarity of multiple recombinations is also in agreement with the theory. In short, the logic of the analysis is precisely that applied by Sturtevant in 1913 to establish the linear seriation of genes in *Drosophila melanogaster* and to construct the first chromosome maps for that organism. "It is . . . our view," says Lederberg, "that since we have been able to demonstrate no appreciable point of difference between the features of gene exchange in this strain of *E. coli* and in the classical materials of Mendelian experimentation, the most economical conclusion is that the mechanisms involved are also similar." These results greatly strengthen the force of the original speculation made by Muller (1947) that the pneumococcus transformation is the result of "still viable bacterial chromosomes or parts of chromosomes floating free in the medium . . . these have penetrated the capsuleless bacteria and in part at least, taken root there, perhaps after having undergone a kind of crossing over with the chromosomes of the host."

The recombination rate is of course very low. As Lederberg suggests, the great bulk of the cells in a mixed culture may be likened to the vegetative or somatic cells of multicellular organisms. It must also be noted that efforts to detect recombination in two other strains of *E. coli* have so far been unsuccessful. Nonetheless, the significance of this discovery is of overwhelming importance from many points of view, not the least the evolutionary one. It was long ago recognized, and has recently been re-emphasized by Muller (1947b), that the essential significance of sexual processes resides in their provision of genetic recombination, so that favorable mutations in different lines of descent may be brought together in a variety of combinations, without the delay and danger of loss that would be necessitated by the accumulation of successive mutations in a single line of descent. For, as the failure on the part of doubly deficient biochemical mutants in bacteria to produce prototrophs has shown, the chance of getting a combination of even two favorable gene changes solely by mutation is negligible, even in the enormous populations of bacteria. It has been a great mystery how bacteria could ever have played the role they have in the pageant of evolution, and how they could have evolved as they presumably have, without the least assistance from the genetic recombination provided by sex. That mystery has now been penetrated. Even in bacteria and viruses, as Lederberg and Luria have shown, genetic recombination, in an almost orthodox fashion, is to be found.

4. *Bacterial Cytology*

Sooner or later, we may hope, the genetic findings just described will reveal a counterpart in microscopically visible phenomena. Already there are indications of this. Dienes (1946) has described complex reproductive processes in *Streptobacillus moniliformis* and other Gram-negative bacteria. Large bodies may be formed within which bacteria are reproduced. In most bacteria these are found only occasionally, but in *B. proteus* they form regularly whenever spreading cultures of certain strains come in contact. No fusion of cells has been observed, but in the light of Lederberg's work, it may occur.

The identification of the bacterial nucleus has gone apace in the last few years. A review of the earlier work on the bacterial nucleus has been made by Robinow (1945), whose own studies, using HCl hydrolysis and Giemsa staining, have constituted a brilliant and fundamental advance in bacterial cytology. Knaysi and Baker (1947) have used the electron microscope to demonstrate a discrete nucleus in *Bacillus mycoides* grown in a nitrogen-free medium. Particularly interesting is the technique of Tulasne and Vendrely (1947). These workers started out from the observation that HCl with Giemsa stain is effective in staining the bacterial nucleus because it removes ribose nucleic acid prior to removing desoxyribose nucleic acid. They therefore undertook to purify a ribonuclease, and upon obtaining it were successful in securing unique photographs of the nuclei of bacteria such as *E. coli, Corynebacterium,* and *Gonococcus.* The purified ribonuclease clearly demonstrated that ribose nucleic acid is localized in the cytoplasm of the organisms, and upon the removal of the ribose nucleic acid a chromophilic nuclear body (Feulgen positive) was clearly revealed. In *E. coli* some cells possess a single central nucleus, whereas others, presumably in a more advanced phase of the life cycle, have regularly spaced dual or multiple nuclei in chains. Zygote formation, such as Lederberg's studies demand, would probably require a fusion of cells with single nuclei, inasmuch as the data clearly indicate essential haploidy in the complete manifestation of all genes in parent strains and recombinations alike. On the other hand, the occurrence of multinucleate cells may help to explain other bacterial phenomena.

II. Mutation and the Nature of the Gene

1. *The Chemical Induction of Mutations*

For many years efforts to induce mutations by means of chemical agents failed altogether or achieved only dubious results that could not be confirmed. Yet workers in the field of mutation have persisted in these efforts, for it hardly seemed possible, from a theoretical viewpoint, that the genes, assuredly chemical in nature, could fail to be permanently modified by reaction with appropriate substances. The real problems were, first, to find the right agents, and next, to assure their penetration into the nuclei of germ cells. The long search was ultimately rewarded. After first reporting, in 1944, that mustard oil (allyl isothiocyanate) will induce mutations in *Drosophila,* Auerbach and Robson revealed, in 1946, that work done in 1941 under the cloak of wartime secrecy had first established the fact that a far more potent mutagenic activity is possessed by mustard gas $(ClCH_2.CH_2)_2S$. Up to 24% of recessive sex-linked lethals were produced by mustard gas in the spermatozoa of *D. melanogaster,* as compared with 0.2% in the controls; and visible, as well as chromosomal, mutations were also found (Auerbach and Robson, 1947a; Auerbach, Robson and Carr, 1947). The considerable reduction in hatchability of eggs laid either by treated females, or by untreated females mated with treated males, was found to be proportional to the dosage of the treatment, and indicated that dominant lethals are also produced. The production of mutations with visible effects was somewhat less than one-tenth of the frequency of sex-linked recessive lethals, a ratio like that found among mutations induced by x-rays. There was no indication that specific mutations, in some way related to the nature of the chemical treatment, were being induced; on the contrary, as for x-ray induced mutations, those which occurred appeared to be a random sample of the potential mutations of the species. One possible exception to this rule, a new type of sex-linked mutant that occurred four times in all, arose in each instance in the same treated Florida-4 stock, so that the alternative explanation of a specially mutable gene in this stock, rather than that of a specific induction of the mutation, must be considered.

Chromosome rearrangements were also produced by the treatment with mustard gas, both translocations and deletions of large segments being found in appropriate tests. Here, however, a significant difference was found to distinguish the effects of mustard gas and those of x-rays. A dose of 3,000 *r* units of x-rays produces about 9% of sex-linked lethals, and about 6% of translocations between chromosomes 2 and 3. But a dose of mustard gas that produces an equivalent proportion of sex-linked lethals was found to yield only 0.5% of such translocations. The same relation holds for the production of the large deletions, hardly half the number that would be expected from a dose of x-rays of equivalent lethal production appearing. Yet an analysis of the giant salivary gland chromosomes of the offspring of treated individuals showed that the relative frequency of minute rearrangements (deficiencies, in particular) is not below the normal 20% in a sample of sex-linked lethals (Slizynski, 1947). In all these respects, the action of mustard gas parallels that of ultraviolet radiation and differs from the effects of ionizing radiations. One of the most promising attacks on the nature of mutation lies in the elucidation of the causes for the differences in relative frequency of the various types of mutations appearing after the action of different agents.

The action of mustard gas as a mutagenic agent is even more remarkable in certain other respects. The time when the mutation is expressed is frequently delayed, so that the mutant individual produced by a treated sperm is not a mutant in entirety but a mutant only in part of its body, that is, a mosaic. X-rays also produce mosaics, but usually few (less than 15%). After mustard gas treatment, mosaics may amount to 50% of all mutant individuals (Auerbach, 1946). The mosaicism may include parts of the gonads as well as parts of the somatic tissues, and daughters of gonadic mosaics may be gonadic mosaics in their turn (Auerbach, 1947b). In some way the mustard gas appears to produce an unstable condition at some particular locus in a chromosome, so that it continues to mutate in identical fashion over several generations and with a high frequency.

Does this delayed effect mean that the action of the mustard gas is only exerted *indirectly* upon the chromosome and its genes, by way of some altered, directly affected component of the cystoplasm? It would seem not. Auerbach and Robson (1947a) tested the result of introducing untreated chromosomes (from the male) into the treated cytoplasm of eggs, and they found no significant induction of mutations in such paternal chromosomes. The delayed effect seems, therefore, to be exerted directly upon the chromosome, rendering it unstable at a particular locus. The existence of any indirect mutagenic effect of any sort remains to be demonstrated, although the recent apparent production of mutations in *Staphylococcus* by ultraviolet irradiation or chemical treatment (H_2O_2; nitrogen mustard) of the substrate (Stone, Wyss and Haas, 1947; Wyss, Stone and Clark, 1947) must excite great interest. It is quite possible that a variety of treatments that modify those specific substances which enter into the processes of gene growth and reproduction may turn out to be mutagenic. Yet it remains an extremely difficult technical problem to exclude the effects of selection which may also be produced by the same agents; and in the experiments mentioned this has not been done in an altogether convincing way. The readiness with which population dynamics and selective environments modify supposed mutations rates among bacteria is discussed below.

After the first positive results which showed that mustard gas acts as a mutagenic agent had been obtained, Auerbach and Robson (1947b) tried a number of other compounds, chemically related to mustard gas or analogous in some mode of physiological action. Three of these substances were nitrogen or sulfur mustards, one was mustard oil (allyl isothiocyanate), others included lewisite (a strong vesicant), chloroacetone and dichloroacetone (lachrymators), osmic and picric acids (protoplasmic fixatives), and ammonia. Mutation rates (for sex-linked lethals in *Drosophila*) were markedly increased by the nitrogen and sulfur mustards, and slightly by the mustard oil, whereas the other agents yielded doubtful increases or none. One X chromosome, treated with the nitrogen mustard $CH_3.N\ (CH_2.CH_2.Cl)_2$ not only carried a semi-lethal and also a sterility mutation, but segregated in a highly abnormal fashion at meiosis. It frequently underwent nondisjunction from its homologue, and even more frequently it got lost altogether (Auerbach, 1947a). Further tests showed that, like mustard gas, the nitrogen mustards can induce visible mutants and chromosome rearrangements.

Other workers have rapidly extended the work with these and similar agents. Mustard gas and nitrogen mustards have been shown to increase the mutation rate in *Neurospora* (Horowitz, Houlahan, Hungate and Wright, 1946; Bonner, 1946; McElroy, Cushing and Miller, 1948), *Aspergillus terreus* (Swanson and Goodgal, 1947), *Penicillium notatum* (Stahmann and Stauffer, 1947), and *E. coli* (Tatum, 1946). Strains of *E. coli* were so susceptible to the toxic effects of nitrogen mustard that they had first to be selected for resistance to it in gradually increasing concentrations, but after this had been done an increase in mutation rate upon treatment of the resistant strain was detectable (Bryson, 1947).

The mutagenic action of the mustards is related to their possession of an unsaturated N or S atom, which enables them to undergo intramolecular cyclization in a polar solvent to form a cyclic onium cation and liberate Cl^-, as follows: $R{-}S{-}CH_2CH_2Cl \rightarrow R{-}\overline{{}^{+}S{-}CH_2CH_2} + Cl^-$. The onium cation is highly reactive with anions and various uncharged nucleophilic molecules (Gilman and Philips, 1946). On the other hand, substances of very different structure are also proving to be mutagens. Demerec (1946, 1947a, b) has developed the use of the aerosol technique for the treatment of *Drosophila.* Of the first 20 substances tested for mutagenic activity, not only nitrogen mustard was effective, but also the carcinogen 1,2,5,6 dibenzanthracene, the latter to about half the effectiveness of the former. An extension of these studies to a score of carcinogens and related compounds is reported to show a considerable degree of correlation between mutagenic and carcinogenic activities (Demerec, Witkin, Newcombe and Beale, 1947). Strong (1947) has also reported the induction of a high frequency of mutations with a carcinogen, methylcholanthrene, in mice selected for high resistance to the tumor-forming action of injections of the carcinogen. The mutants obtained were visible in character, affecting coat color, eye color, or spotting pattern. The mutation rate was approximately 1 in 557, against 1 in 26,250 in related control animals. Somatic mosaics, as well as mutations in the germ cells, occurred and with a frequency that indicated that an unstable genetic state had been produced. Unfortunately, the genetic analysis is incomplete.

In an interesting development of technique, Hadorn and Niggli (1946) have excised ovaries from *Drosophila* females, treated them with dilute phenol, and then implanted them in untreated females. Mutations were reported to have been induced. This confirms the mutagenic action of phenol upon *Antirrhinum,* found by Stubbe in 1941. On the other hand, Demerec (1946) has been unable to induce mutations in *Drosophila* with phenol in aerosols, and further work will have to be done to determine whether or not phenol is a general mutagenic agent.

Of outstanding importance have been the recent studies upon the mutagenic action of desoxyribose nucleic acid, for this is a major component of chromosomes, and, it is conjectured, of genes. Avery, McCarty and their coworkers (see McCarty, 1946) have found that "smooth" (surrounded by a polysaccharide capsule) strains of *Pneumococcus* produce a substance that, when freed of all cells, will transform "rough," noncapsulated strains into smooth strains differing from their original specificity, and instead permanently retaining the specificity of the strain that supplied the "transforming principle" (TP). This substance, as shown by the fact that it can be inactivated by the purified crystalline enzyme desoxyribonuclease, is desoxyribose nucleic acid, existing in a highly polymerized state and differing specifically for each of the numerous *Pneumococcus* strains. Even 0.003 microgram of the total desoxyribose nucleic acid in the cell is enough to produce the transformation of rough cells. As many as 0.5 % of the rough cells are transformed, under optimum conditions, and this is so high a frequency as to make it very unlikely that the transformations are only spontaneous mutations brought out by the exposure to the transforming principle. Transformation takes place only in anti-R serum (rabbit or human), which must first sensitize the rough cells; and this action of the serum depends upon the presence in it of three constituents: an R antibody, another protein, and a dialysable substance (McCarty, Taylor, and Avery, 1946). Boivin and his collaborators have obtained parallel results in work with *E. coli,* with the difference that no sensitization of the cells is necessary as a preliminary step to transformation, and the presence of serum may therefore be dispensed with (Boivin, Delaunay, Vendrely and Lehoult, 1945, 1946; Boivin and Vendrely, 1947).

From this work on transformation of type specificity in bacteria, it is clear that the biological specificity of nucleoproteins may reside in the nucleic acid, as well as, or rather than, in the protein moiety. Since these transformations are permanently inherited, one may suppose that the specific desoxyribose nucleic acid which induces the transformation has actually become incorporated into the particular gene or genes "transformed," although other less direct modes of action are, of course, possible.

A remarkable mutation phenomenon has been reported by Mampell (1946). He found that a strain of *Drosophila pseudoobscura* characterized by a high mutation rate carries a mutator gene that, when a *Y* chromosome is present, produces a cytoplasmic mutator substance. Mutability is increased not only in flies that produce this substance but also in flies of another species (*D. melanogaster*) raised in the same cultures. Mampell has suggested that the mutator substance may be transmissible, like a virus. Confirmation of this work would be very important. Viruses have indeed been found in *Drosophila*. There is one that produces a fatal sensitivity of the infected strain to CO_2 (L'Héritier and Teissier, 1944; L'Héritier and Sigot, 1944, 1945); but no specific gene has been found to be necessary for the maintenance of that virus, nor has it apparently any effect upon mutation. In *Paramecium aurelia* (cf. Sonneborn, 1947a), a relation exists between a virus or plasmagene, "kappa," and a certain gene, *K*, without which kappa is unable to multiply. Here, too, no relation to mutation is known to exist. Still, in view of the nucleoprotein nature of viruses, it would not be too surprising to find that, like the desoxyribose nucleic acids discussed above, viruses might induce mutations.

2. *Physical Influences Upon Mutation*

At any rate, the study of the agents and influences that affect mutation can only be said to be beginning. Mutation varies so greatly in frequency from strain to strain within the species, from tissue to tissue within the organism, from gene to gene within the genome, and from allele to allele at a given locus that spontaneous mutation is hardly definable at all. It is actually mutation occurring under a great variety of unanalyzed influences, major and minor. Moreover, after the mutation has occurred, it is by no means always easy to separate the phenomena of mutation and the determination of rates of mutation from other factors. The studies of Braun (1947a, b) have revealed, for example, the difficulties of the problem in studying bacteria and the readiness with which population dynamics and selective environments modify supposed mutation rates. To make matters even more difficult, Lincoln (1947) has shown that a bacterial mutant which is nonadaptive in a broth environment may be adaptive in an altered environment. After the environment changes, previously "suppressed types of mutants that arise during growth may replace types adapted in the earlier environment." A similar instance has been reported in the occurrence of biochemical mutants in *E. coli* after x-ray treatment of resting cells (Roepke and Mercer, 1947). From plates poured shortly after treatment, 61 such mutants out of 4420 were obtained. When the suspensions were stored at 14°C. for 15 hours to 8 days before plating, no mutants at all were found among 1,091 colonies.

In the higher organisms there is a different sort of difficulty, one that arises because lethal mutations, the analysis of which has yielded most of the existing data on the mutation process, form a mixed category of changes. Many lethals are definitely associated with the chromosome breaks that are involved in large rearrangements or minute deficiencies, and the theory has been proposed that all lethals, at least those induced by x-rays, are located at the sites of chromosome breaks, many of which might thereafter be restituted so as to leave no trace of their occurrence except the presence of the lethal mutation (cf., Lea, 1947, pp. 154-160). Lea, Herskowitz (1946) and Kaufmann and Gay (1947) have all derived similar values for the frequency with which a break is accompanied by a lethal (Lea, 38%; Kaufmann and Gay, 32%; Herskowitz, 31%). From the data of earlier workers, Herskowitz has made calculations to show that chromosome breaks induced by x-rays increase linearly with the dosage at the same rate as the induced lethals. This implies that most x-ray induced lethals occur at chromosome breaks, though not all chromosome breaks are accompanied by a lethal mutation. It seems that very few lethals induced by x-rays can then be due to position effect alone or to intragenic change of any sort. Since most of the analysis of mutation and most of the conclusions regarding the nature of the gene have been based on the lethals induced by ionizing radiations, the indication that these are characteristically and regularly associated with chromosome breakage is highly important. Are lethals induced by ultraviolet radiation or chemical mutagens, or those arising spontaneously, also located at breakage points? This seems hardly likely, for the reasons discussed previously. Are the lethals produced at breakage points then different in nature from those arising without chromosome breakage? This question still cannot be answered. A clue might be supposed to exist in the capacity for reverse mutation, for if the association of lethals with breakage points implies that such lethals are deficiencies, they could hardly revert. But there is evidence not only that spontaneous lethals may revert, but also that at least some of those produced by x-rays and known to be associated with chromosome breaks are reversible (Plough, 1946; Suche, Parker, Bishop, and Griffin, 1939). Regarding the proportion of lethals which are reversible there is still no information. The biochemical mutants of *Neurospora* and bacteria may, however, be regarded as lethals, and reverse mutation seems to be possible for most of these (Ryan, 1946; Giles, 1948), yet not for all.

It needs to be kept in mind that the rates of mutation are very different in different tissues. Evidence has been gathered that in the mature spermatozoa of *Drosophila* lethal mutations accumulate in linear proportionality with the passage of time (Kaufmann, 1947). This occurs in unmated males aged up to 32 days, the increase being just four times the frequency in males mated in the first day or two of imaginal life. Muller (1946a, b) has reported that the rate of lethal mutations also increases in spermatozoa stored and aged in the female. These data provide evidence of constancy in the rate of mutation in a particular sort of nondividing cell. But spermatogonia, in contrast to mature spermatozoa, have a lower mutation rate

(Muller, 1946a, b; Ives and Andrews, 1946; Lamy, 1947). If the spermatozoa are expended as rapidly as they can be produced, a sharp periodicity in mutation rate becomes apparent. The rate is at first high, in those sperm cells formed in the pre-imaginal life; then it drops to a minimum; finally it rises again, although not to the original frequency. In females, on the other hand, chromosomes show a practically constant mutation frequency, regardless of age or metabolic activity; and this presumably means that mutations occur in females mostly at one or several definite stages, and not in the protracted "aging" of oögonia (Muller, 1946a, b).

X-rays have recently been used to produce mutations in bacteria in a dried state (Devi, Pontecorvo and Higginbotham, 1947). Doses of 35,000 to 50,000 *r* units, which leave 10^{-3} to 10^{-4} survivors, have yielded biochemical mutants of *Bacterium aerogenes* at rates up to 1%. Thus active growth and division are once again proved unnecessary for mutation, as in spores of fungi, dormant seeds of angiosperms, and spermatozoa of animals.

In recent years light on the nature of mutation has been sought by combining treatments of different sorts. King (1947) and Sax (1947) have each added to our knowledge of the supplementary influence of temperature upon the effects of x-rays. Earlier work left a highly confusing and conflicting picture. The work done on *Tradescantia,* chiefly by Sax and his students, seemingly showed that low temperatures, below about 15°C., when applied at the time of treatment with x-rays, considerably enhance the effects of the latter in inducing chromosome and chromatid rearrangements. Oft repeated and varied experiments on *Drosophila,* using cold at the time of x-ray treatment, were by some workers reported as yielding an increase in sex-linked lethals or translocations, and by others as not. The fog is at length beginning to lift. A reappraisal shows that whenever low temperatures of 5°C. or higher were used in the *Drosophila* experiments, there was, with but one exception, an absence of demonstrable effect. But whenever a low temperature of 0°C. has been applied, a definite effect has been found. King's experiments appear to clinch the matter. He has found that, for each of 5 doses from 600 up to 3,600 *r* units, treatment of *Drosophila* at 0°C. yields over twice as many sex-linked lethal mutations as treatment at 23-28°C. There seems to be, then, a critical temperature for the cold effect, and in *Drosophila* it is very low, quite close to 0°C. That a shock effect of the cold alone does not produce a detectable effect is clear from the lack of lethals in King's control series exposed to 0°C. but not irradiated.

Sax (1947) has found a similar increase due to cold, amounting to several times as many ring and dicentric chromosomes in *Tradescantia* microspores irradiated at 0°C. as at 36°C. Each such aberration arises from a coincidence of 2 or more breaks in the same cell, like the translocations in *Drosophila,* which have also been reported to be increased in number when the x-ray treatment is given at or near 0°C. Simple deletions, which arise from a single break, are, on the contrary, not increased in *Tradescantia* by the low temperature. Moreover, the temperature prevailing before or after the x-ray treatment has seemingly no effect. One may conclude that the low temperature has little if any effect upon chromosome breakage itself, but greatly affects the chance for a rearrangement to occur after breakage. On the other hand, if the theory that lethals are induced as a by-product of chromosome breaks is true, the increase of lethals observed in *Drosophila* by King must represent a real increase in breakage, and not just a shift from restituted breaks to breaks involved in chromosome rearrangements.

In *Drosophila,* ultraviolet has been used in conjunction with x-rays. It produced an increase in the frequency of dominant lethals due to single breaks but a decrease in the production of gross rearrangements (Kaufmann and Hollaender, 1946).

The use of short infrared radiation (of wavelength 10,000 A) has also been used in conjunction with x-rays. Given as a pretreatment of 24 to 72 hours duration before the x-ray treatment, the infrared increases the number of chromosome rearrangements produced in *Drosophila* by about 1.5 times (Kaufmann, Hollaender and Gay, 1946). Neither the frequency of dominant lethals, which result mainly from single breaks, nor that of sex-linked lethals (Kaufmann and Gay, 1947) is increased, however. On the other hand, a pretreatment of *Tradescantia* chromosomes with short infrared more than doubles the frequency of chromatids broken by x-rays, including single breaks as well as two-break rearrangements (Swanson and Hollaender, 1946). A delay of 96 hours between the pretreatment with infrared and the irradiation with x-rays makes no difference, and proves that the "sensitizing" effect of the infrared upon the chromosomes is quite lasting and carries over from interphase into prophase (Swanson, 1947). If the infrared is given just after the x-ray treatment instead of before, the frequency of 2-break deletions is unaffected by the infrared, and only the single breaks and interchanges are increased. When the infrared treatment is delayed another hour or two, translocations are still increased, but the frequency of single breaks is no longer affected. There is thus a progressive diminution in the types of changes which are susceptible of modification, until only the translocations remain; and this, it is to be noted, is the only sort of effect which is increased by infrared in conjunction with x-ray treatment in *Drosophila.*

Fungus spores pretreated with infrared before being irradiated with x-rays also yield an increased number of mutations over and above what would be expected from the same dose of x-rays alone (Hollaender and Swanson, 1947). This is also true for the supplementary effect of infrared with ultraviolet irradiation at high energy levels, although the interaction is complex (Swanson and Hollaender, 1946). Yet by itself infrared is as incapable of producing mutations in fungus spores as in the other organisms tested. Another striking interaction effect has been obtained by combining a pretreatment of fungus spores (*Aspergillus terreus*) with nitrogen mustard in a weak and non-mutagenic concentration (0.1%), with an irradiation with ultraviolet (Swanson and Goodgal, 1947). With weak doses of ultraviolet an increase of 300 to 400% in the mutation frequency was obtained from such sensitized spores.

Various ways of accounting for all these sorts of interaction effects have been suggested, but it is still too soon to be sure whether any of them are right. The significant thing, for the present, is that it is abundantly demonstrated that rates of mutation are not dependent simply and solely upon the amount of radiant energy applied to the biological target. In the last example, for instance, the nitrogen mustard or secondary products must have penetrated the nucleus and reacted with genic substances in such a way as to make the genes more mutable, more readily activated by the ultraviolet. And similarly, infrared radiation must exert some sort of effect, direct or indirect, upon chromosomes that either renders them more liable to break upon receiving an x-ray hit, or more liable to enter into chromosome rearrangements thereafter, or both.

It was a foregone conclusion that the mutagenic effects of radioactive isotopes would quickly be put to the test and verified. The first report of this sort, by Giles (1947), deals with radioactive phosphorus^{32}, which yields β radiation and has a half-life of 14.3 days. When introduced in solution into stems of *Tradescantia,* this isotope produces, in initial concentrations of 0.1 μc/ml. or greater, a detectable rise in the frequency of chromatid (and chromosome) aberrations. After 24 hours, chromatid breaks and exchanges begin to appear and thereafter increase in frequency up to 8 or 9 days. The one-hit breaks increase almost linearly with time for the first 4 days. The exchanges are relatively numerous and perhaps arise fairly often from a single hit rather than from two. Chromosome aberrations were not observed until the fourth day and were never more than about one-fourth so numerous as the chromatid aberrations. The most significant implication of this work, in its preliminary stages, is that even a very minute amount of a radioactive isotope produces an appreciable number of genetic changes. This ought to serve a warning to over-hardy experimenters. In addition, these results raise once again the question whether radioactive isotopes, produced by natural radiation—by cosmic radiation, in particular—can be a significant source of spontaneous mutations. Following the discovery of considerable natural radiocarbon (C^{14}) in methane from sewage, Grosse and Libby (1947) have made estimates of the number of particles discharged per minute by radioactive potassium and carbon in the human body. Because of the relatively enormous amount of carbon in protoplasm, as compared with potassium, the total radioactivity of the carbon is nearly half that of the potassium in the body. Nevertheless, if the calculations made by Muller and Mott-Smith (1930) for the effects of the potassium are correct, even the combined radioactive potassium and carbon can account for only a negligible fraction of the observed spontaneous mutations. Ultraviolet radiation in the sunlight has been shown to produce mutations in fungus spores at a rate of about 2 percent (Hollaender, Swanson and Posner, 1946). This type of natural radiation could, however, because of its very low powers of penetration, be of significance only in single-celled, air-borne organisms. The theory, attributable to Delbrück (Timoféeff, Ressoosky, Zimmer and Delbrück, 1935) that spontaneous mutations are due to statistical variation in thermal energies, which would carry certain genes at random beyond their threshold of stability, appears to be still in a strong position.

Considerable publicity has been given in the general press to the genetic effects of the atomic bomb, both of the two released in Japan and of the Bikini tests. No geneticist would doubt that genetic effects were indeed produced, but every geneticist would also appreciate the extreme difficulty of demonstrating that truth. It was timely to have a clear presentation of some of the obstacles before the Committee on Atomic Casualties in the undertaking to investigate the issue. The Genetics Conference of this Committee has pointed out (1947) that the median lethal dose for entire body radiation (500 *r* units) is a relatively low dose for the production of genetic effects. Most mutations will have been recessive and can only be expected to appear after some generations of inbreeding. Dominant lethals will eliminate themselves. For the estimation of abortions, stillbirths, and malformations caused by mutations there are no control figures reporting the previous frequency of such conditions in Japan. Registration of all inhabitants of Hiroshima and Nagaski, and a continued check on them and their descendants for several decades will be necessary if any useful information is to be secured at all. Haldane (1947) has calculated that the total number of recessive lethal mutations to be expected as a result of an atomic bomb explosion is about 4,000, and that the number of deaths from these would then be 2,000 spread over many generations. He warns that this may be a serious underestimate, and that the effect might amount to 20 deaths per generation instead of 2. Still, many of the lethals would probably kill in early embryonic life and consequently be of virtually no importance on any grounds. Nonlethal but detrimental mutations may well pose a greater humanitarian problem. The chief ground for optimism lies in the consideration that the aforesaid median lethal dose of 500 *r* units is only ten to a hundred times what an individual normally receives from natural radiation in a lifetime, anyway. On the other hand, we cannot be sure that man's genes are no more sensitive to radiation than those of *Drosophila,* on which such calculations are based. Comparative data from many species are needed. Meanwhile, the first reports regarding the animals and maize seed exposed at Bikini are beginning to confirm the expectations of geneticists.

3. Position Effect

The discovery that the effect of a gene may be radically altered merely by shifting its position in the chromosome, and quite without permanently changing the gene itself in any way, was thought, only ten years ago, to threaten a liquidation of the gene concept. There is certainly no question about the reality of position effects. What is disconcerting, however, to anyone inclined to stress their significance, is that position effects are so uncommon. Even in *Drosophila melanogaster,* after more than a decade of search, only a few gene loci can be demonstrated to undergo any change in action as a result of any change in position. And apart from *Drosophila,* only in one other species, *Oenothera blandina,* has a really well-established case been found (Catcheside, 1947a). This case, at least, is of virtually classic simplicity. A gene, P^s, which is responsible for sepals with broad, uniformly red stripes separated by narrow green ones, was affected by a translocation that involved a break in the chromosome near P^s. When P^s-*A* (that is, P^s affected by its interchanged position) is heterozygous, the stripes are broken up into patches of variegated red and green. Inasmuch as the P^s gene is some little distance from the point of chromosome breakage, it is possible for crossing over to occur in the interval, in about 1.7% of cases, so that P^s can be transferred to a normal chromosome with no rearrangement in the vicinity, and some other allele can be used to replace it in the translocation chromosomes. Whenever this was done, a total of 17 times, the P^s allele reverted to its normal original behavior. In turn, an allele P^r that produces solid red sepals, upon replacing P^s in the translocation chromosomes, became variegated whenever it was exposed to the position effect (7 times). The neighboring *S* gene (*S* = yellow petals; *s* = sulfur-colored petals), located 8.5 units from *P* and about 10 units from the interchange, is also affected by the new position, so as to produce variegated yellow and sulfur-colored petals with a pattern like that of the variegations in the P^s sepals. The *S* gene, like the P^s and P^r alleles, becomes once again normal in action whenever it is removed by crossing over from the translocation chromosome and transferred to a normal one.

The association of position effect with variegation is regularly connected, in *Drosophila* eye colors (e.g., white or brown), with a transfer of heterochromatin to the vicinity of the affected genes, and the homozygote is less variegated than the heterozygote. In the *Oenothera* case, too, the few translocation homozygotes that survive manifest a less extensive variegation than the heterozygote. However, there is no evidence yet that heterochromatin is concerned in this position effect; and the case cannot be said to clarify the nature of the forces involved in the production of position effects. The tremendous extension of the position effect, over a segment 10 crossover units in length, or of the order of many gene diameters, renders those hypotheses that rely on diffusion and competitive interaction between alleles appear inapplicable. On the other hand, the stress hypothesis elaborated by Ephrussi and Sutton (1944), a hypothesis which attributes position effects to unequal or subnormal extension within the gene brought about by the presence of the heterozygous structural rearrangement, fails to account for the variegation still evident, though reduced in amount, in homozygotes. In *Drosophila* this may be due to the action of nearby heterochromatin, with its penchant for nonspecific pairing attractions; but the presence of heterochromatin at the interchange point in the *Oenothera* position effect is still to be demonstrated, as was mentioned above. The stress theory, like all the present theories of the nature of position effects, also fails to account for the striking limitation of the variegation to particular stages in the ontogeny of the plant or animal. Inasmuch as these may be very different and highly specific for different variegated genes that affect the same structure or the same chemical substances (e.g., a pigment), it is indeed hard to see how stress due to somatic chromosome pairing can be the cause of the phenomenon. For one would suppose that in a given cell the chromosomes would be either paired or unpaired. Yet the theory explains so much that one is reluctant to abandon it. It may be to some degree correct.

A duplication of the P^r-*S* segment in *Oenothera blandina* has also been found (Catcheside, 1947b). It is of interest that the position effect is manifested by the P^r (or P^s) and *S* genes in the segment adjacent to the interchange, but fails to spread to the same genes in the contiguous but more distant duplicate segment. Nothing could better illustrate the nature of position effect!

The latest theory of the cause of position effects postulates that there is a reduced amount of available substrate for these genes and that the normally located allele has at least a partial priority on what substrate there is (Stern, MacKnight and Kodani, 1946). This theory was evolved to account for the fact that in *Drosophila* certain cubitus-interruptus (*ci*) position-effect heterozygotes are more extreme—that is, less normal—in wing venation than either the homozygous *ci ci* or the homozygous position-effect alleles. Although these facts could also be interpreted on the basis of the theory of stress due to somatic pairing, such an interpretation is discounted because in some rearrangements the position-effect gene is so relocated that pairing with its allele appears to be highly improbable, if not impossible, and has in fact never been observed in salivary gland nuclei. More study will certainly be required before either theory can be regarded as holding a very strong position.

The difference between the theories may be posed in the form of the alternatives: Is the gene itself temporarily modified by its new situation? Or, the gene itself remaining unchanged, is its altered access to those substances with which it reacts the key to the phenomenon? Two points seem worth making at the present time. The first is that since the removal of a particular susceptible gene from its original neighbors by no means regularly results in a position effect, but does so only when that gene is transferred to the vicinity of particular new neighbors (or of heterochromatin), the altered situation of the gene would seem to involve not so much a loss of access to its normal substrate as rather a reaction with new substances. One might imagine a "toxic" or inhibitory effect of certain genes (or of heterochromatin) upon certain other genes in their vicinity. The second point is that the two theories are not altogether incompatible but rather may be complementary. For, assuming that the gene is temporarily modified by stress, one must still account for the change which any such deformation introduces in the physiological action of the gene, and that changed action might be conceived in terms of an altered priority upon substrate. In any case, the analysis of position effects has so far yielded little positive information about either the nature of the gene or the nature of gene action.

4. *Multiple Alleles*

One of the most significant questions regarding the nature of gene action is whether each gene exercises only a single primary effect or whether it can exercise more than one. In those examples of gene action that are simplest and presumably most direct (such as the biochemical mutants of *Neurospora* and bacteria, the anthocyanin mutants of many blue or red flowers, and the genes that determine the antigens or vertebrate red blood cells), there is in general an apparent one-to-one relation between gene and effect. This has led so many geneticists to support the theory that a gene can have only one primary effect, that other biologists and biochemists have perhaps been inclined to accept it without question. Yet certain facts give pause.

Among such facts are the relations which exist among multiple alleles. Mutation at a single locus is capable of affecting a number of characters that in different alleles are combined independently. For example, in maize the changes at the *R* locus which are responsible for independent anthocyanin coloration of aleurone, seedling, mature seed leaf, margin or leaf blade, husk, glume and anther number 22 alleles (Stadler and Fogel, 1945). The R^r gene (colored aleurone, colored plant) mutates with a fairly high frequency (10^{-3} to 10^{-4}) both to r^r (colorless aleurone, colored plant) and to R^g (colored aleurone, colorless plant). It also mutates to r^g, representing a simultaneous change in both aleurone and plant characters. Although this type of mutation is much rarer than the first two, it nevertheless occurs more often than would be expected if it were only the chance coincidence of completely independent mutations. Furthermore, the mutation rate of colored aleurone (*R*) depends upon its respective combination with the factor for colored plant (^{r}) or with that for colorless plant (^{g}). For the mutation rates of the R^rR^g alleles have been tested within the identical heterozygous individuals, and it was found that the mutation of R^g to r^g was much lower than that of R^r to r^r [1 (or 0):12]. These facts speak strongly against the view that aleurone color and plant color depend upon distinct adjacent genes, or even upon a single gene with parts capable of completely independent mutation (Stadler, 1946).

Similar cases might be multiplied to a considerable number. In cotton, the changes at the *R* locus responsible for independent anthocyanin coloration of leaf and petal spot include two alleles at the R_1 locus and five alleles at the R_2 duplicate locus (Silow, 1946). In the mouse, the changes at the *A* locus responsible for agouti hair coloration, light belly, and a lethal effect number five alleles, and an occurrence of reverse mutation at a single step from *a*, non-agouti, to A^W, white-bellied agouti, makes it improbable that the light belly effect and the agouti hair color are due to different loci (Little and Hummel, 1947). In *Drosophila melanogaster,* the changes at the dumpy (*dp*) locus, numbering 23 alleles, responsible for wing curtailment, for vortices and comma-shaped depressions on the thorax, and for recessive lethal effects in various combinations, provide a classic case of separate effects still attributed to a single locus (see Bridges and Brehme, 1944).

In none of these cases, however, is it clear that the locus concerned actually governs more than a single primary process. One must turn to the field of human genetics for a more likely example of such a situation. The case is that of the Rh antigens and genes. In the years since the discovery of these red cell antigens, in 1940, much has been learned about their inheritance. In previous studies of red-cell antigens in man, in cattle, in doves, etc. (see review by Irwin, 1947b) each antigen has been found to be attributable to a separate gene. However, in the study of the Rh types, three varieties of antisera have been found which detect three distinct kinds of Rh antigens, known as Rh′/Rh_0/Rh″ (or *C, D, E*) respectively. These antigens, or in their absence their respective alternates Hr′/Hr_0/Hr″ (or *c, d, e*), occur in the population in all of the eight possible combinations of three pairs of alternates. One might therefore assume, with Wiener (1946; Wiener and Sonn, 1946; Wiener, Sonn-Gordon, and Handman, 1947), that there is a series of eight distinct alleles, each of which controls the production of a certain one of the eight combinations of antigens.

This theory, however, in establishing a single series of factors, fails to account for those three pairs of alternative relationships between the Rh and Hr antigens, relations which might be taken to imply that three distinct, separately mutable Rh antigens exist. Fisher, who was the first to notice these relationships, proposed, in order to explain them, that the inheritance of the Rh-Hr antigens depends, not on a single locus, but upon three closely linked loci, which he called *C/c, D/d,* and *E/e* (Race, 1944; Fisher and Race, 1946). This system of symbols shows admirably and at a glance all of the relations involved, the genetic as well as the serological ones. The eight antigen combinations (*CDE, CDe, CdE, Cde, cDE, cDe, cdE, cde*) are attributed to independent mutations at the *C, D,* and *E* loci, each of which modifies a single antigen. Thus the one-to-one relationship of gene to antigen is preserved in the present case, in agreement with the known relations between other genes and antigens. In addition, any new variant Rh antigen that replaces a particular Rh-Hr component (e.g., C^w, D^u —Callender and Race, 1946; Stratton, 1946) fits without difficulty into the *CDE* scheme, upon discovery. But each such new antigen requires the postulation of four new alleles according to the theory of multiple alleles.

In general support of Fisher's theory, it should be pointed out that numerous examples of duplicate or related loci in juxtaposition or in the close vicinity of one another are known. The three separate but closely linked loci producing taillessness (*T*), fused (*Fu*), and kinky tail (*Ki*) in mice cross over with frequencies of 2 to 5% (Dunn and Caspari, 1945). In *Drosophila melanogaster,* the striking case of the double or triple tandem duplications producing Bar eye is well known. The adjacent loci achaete (*ac*) and scute (*sc*), both of which affect the presence of bristles and hairs on the thorax of the fly, recombine by crossing over with a real but negligible frequency (see Bridges and Brehme, 1944). Such loci may also show a physiological interaction when each is heterozygous, in which case they have been termed "pseudo-alleles" by E. B. Lewis (1945, 1948), who has studied three examples in considerable detail: Star (*S*) and asteroid (*ast*), bithorax (*bx*) and bithoraxoid (bxd^D), and stubbloid-*2* (sbd^2) and Stubble (*Sb*). A fourth example is that of Bar (*B*) and Exaggeration of Bar (*Eb*), studied by Bonnier, Rasmuson and Rasmuson (1947).

The most practicable way of distinguishing experimentally between the two alternative situations of multiple alleles and multiple loci is that of finding, as Lewis has done, crossovers between pseudo-alleles; for in perhaps most such cases the chromosomes appear cytologically normal, even in the giant salivary gland chromosomes of the Diptera, so that analyses by means of the study of duplications or deficiencies that involve one but not the other of the adjacent loci would be far more laborious, if not quite impossible. Lewis has found crossover values, for the three pairs of pseudo-alleles he has studied, that range from 0.01 to 0.05%. *B* and *Eb* cross over with a frequency of less than 0.1%. It is especially interesting, in the latter case, that stocks established from different crossover individuals produce significantly different degrees of reduction in the size of the eye. This appears to indicate that either *B* or *Eb*, or both, can be fractionated by crossing over. It looks as if there may be very little distinction between a "gene" divisible into several serially arranged parts, on the one hand, and a series of several genes with similar functions, on the other. Bar is known to be a duplication. It may be suspected that *Eb* is one, too. The formation of duplications is rather common in the evolution of a species, and is a process which creates new loci that at first must have a very similar physiological effect to that of their originals, with which they will still interact as alleles, i.e., as pseudo-alleles.

If loci which cross over as frequently as in the examples cited, that is, once in ten thousand times or somewhat more, are yet close enough to behave physiologically as alleles, it would not appear hopeless to expect to detect crossing over between the Rh genes, if these really occupy three distinct loci. For example, a mating of $CDe/cde \times cde/cde$ will yield only phenotypically *CDe* and *cde* offspring in the absence of crossing over or mutation. Crossing over would yield, in addition to the parental types, recombinations phenotypically *Cde* and *cDe*, and those only;[1] whereas mutation, which would probably be much rarer, might yield those or a number of other types

[1]Fisher now suggests the order *DCE*, on indirect and inadequate evidence. This would not make any difference in the example given.

(e.g., *CDE, cdE,* etc.). The possibility of illegitimate births must of course not be overlooked, but it may be detected by checks of a sufficient variety of other inherited traits.

Meanwhile, exception must be taken to the statement in the Report of the Advisory Review Board of the U. S. Public Health Service (Castle, Wintrobe and Snyder, 1948) that the Fisher-Race nomenclature "is based on a genetic hypothesis which is purely theoretical and for which no clear proof exists—an hypothesis no more tenable on genetic grounds than Wiener's hypothesis." For Fisher's theory stands on the strongest of all scientific grounds, namely, that of predictions which have been experimentally verified. Of these the most notable were the predictions that anti-e and anti-d sera would be found and would give certain specific reactions with the various types of Rh red blood cells. The first of these sera was found by Mourant (1945) and its predicted reactions were confirmed. The second serum, anti-d, has more recently been found by Diamond (reference in Race, 1948).

One ought not to suppose, on the other hand, that even a very high number of postulated alleles is in itself any argument against the view that the Rh antigens depend on multiple alleles rather than on separate loci. *Oenothera organensis* has 45 known alleles of the *S* gene, each one specific and absolute in preventing self-fertilization in diploids (D. Lewis, 1947). *Trifolium* far exceeds even this magnificent variability of a single locus. From data collected by the late R. D. Williams, Bateman (1947) has calculated that each clover variety possesses 212 self-sterility (*S*) alleles (5% fiducial limits of 442 and 115). This is particularly significant because the self-sterility reaction between pollen and style in flowering plants has frequently been compared to an antigen-antibody reaction. Closest in character to the Rh antigens are the red-cell antigens of cattle (see Owen, Stormont and Irwin, 1946). Among the 30 antigens found with different frequencies in Holstein-Friesians and Guernseys, two series of "multiple alleles" have been detected.

One of these series of antigenic complexes numbers 80 different kinds. The characters making up any one of these antigenic complexes have never been observed to segregate in the offspring of an individual possessing it, so that Stormont, Owen and Irwin (1948) make the assumption that each complex is controlled by a single allele of the multiple series. These authors propose two explanations, either that individual alleles can produce up to as many as eight antigens, or that each produces only one, but that this has multiple serological properties. The latter view, which reconciles the theory of multiple alleles with that of the single primary effect, is equivalent to Wiener's theory of the Rh antigens and shows how it could apply to even a much more extensive series of alleles than the known Rh series. The first question that will have to be settled is whether such a complex is actually made up of a number of antigens or consists of but one with plural serological properties.

In short, Fisher's observation of the three pairs of reciprocal relationships between Rh and Hr antigens implies no more than that the three pairs of antigens are capable of independent recombination. This is quite consonant with the conception of a single gene possessing three parts capable of separate (yet not necessarily completely independent) mutation. One may plausibly conjecture, in other words, that a gene is a complex molecule with a number of separate sidechains or prosthetic groups (C, D, E) that are capable of separate mutation (Fig. 1A). Or a gene may be a linearly

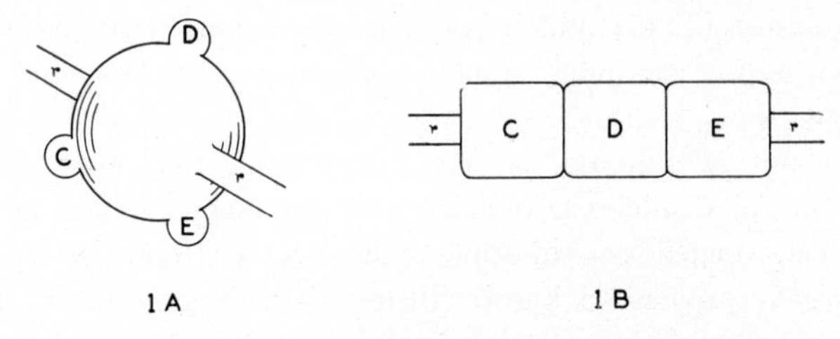

FIG. 1.

Diagrams of possible arrangements of a single gene capable of a number of independent mutations that can occur in all possible combinations. *C, D, E,* the independently mutable components of the gene; *r,* intergene linkages where crossing over may occur.

If the chromosome is a genetic continuum and if crossing over can occur anywhere along it, the concept illustrated in 1*B* becomes inapplicable, and *C, D,* and *E* must be reckoned separate genes. But if *C, D* and *E,* as illustrated in 1*A*, are in the same plane at 90° to the longitudinal extension of the chromosome, the distinction made must hold, even for a genetic continuum.

organized crossover unit composed of subsections (C, D, E) capable of separate mutation but not separable by crossing over (Fig. 1B). This would be just one step removed from pseudo-alleles, which do cross over. If there is indeed, as so many have thought, a close structural likeness between a gene and the specific antigen it produces, such conceptions will fall into line with the view expressed by Wiener (1946) that separate agglutination reactions need not imply corresponding separable components of the antigen. The *CDE/cde* concepts and symbols, however, can be applied equally well to separate loci or to separately mutable components of a gene. Ultimately we may expect the investigation of these phenomena to shed real light on the nature of the gene.

III. The Nature of Gene Action

Because this aspect of genetics has been extensively reviewed in the literature in both technical and nontechnical fashion in recent months, and because it is in itself so extensive a field, it seems wise not to attempt a complete review of the subject here. One may consult Irwin (1947a) and Beadle (1945, 1948) for more technical reviews, and Beadle (1946a, b, 1947) for excellent general discussions of the relation of genes to the chemistry of the organism. The Cold Spring Harbor Symposium on *Heredity and Variation in Microorganisms* (Vol. XI, 1946) is rich in papers covering aspects of this field, in particular the contributions of Anderson, Bonner, Lindegren and Lindegren, Lwoff, Pirie, Pontecorvo, Ryan, Spiegelman, and Tatum. Sonneborn (1946, 1947a) has also reviewed at length the genetics of *Paramecium* and *Euplotes*, including the highly interesting investigation of the relationship in *P. aurelia* between the killer gene (K), the plasmagene kappa and the production of a diffusible substance, the presence of which in the medium kills sensitive animals of non-killer phenotype.

It remains to add a few notes on recent highlights in the field. Regarding one of the all too few enzymes actually demonstrated to be gene-controlled, Lévy (1946) has confirmed and extended the work of Sawin and Glick (1943), which showed that tropanolesterase (atropinesterase), a diastase, is present in the blood serum of rabbits from birth, and is inherited as a simple autosomal dominant. Ginsburg and Kaplan (1947) have shown that an oxidase in mouse skin depends on the presence of the C gene. Caspari (1946a, b) has found that in the red-eyed mutant *aa* of the moth *Ephestia* tryptophan accumulates because its oxidation to kynurenine is blocked, and becomes incorporated in the proteins. Caspari next showed, by adding tryptophan to homogenized larvae, both *aa* and wild type, that a similar increase in respiration occurs for the two genotypes, so that the *aa* mutant must possess the enzyme that oxidizes tryptophane as well as tryptophane itself. The tryptophan $\longrightarrow$ kynurenine reaction is therefore not blocked for lack of enzyme, but in some way the action of the enzyme on its substrate is inhibited. The *a* gene also reduces the amount of ether-extractable substances in the tissues, and the entire biochemical reaction-system of the cell appears to be radically upset. Meanwhile it has been found that kynurenine is an intermediate in the formation of nicotinic acid from tryptophan by *Neurospora* (Beadle, Mitchell, and Nyc, 1947). If the biochemistry of *Ephestia* and *Drosophila* is like that of *Neurospora* in this respect, this affords a good example of those chemical interrelations which make a seemingly unimportant gene, that controls, to all appearances, only some superficial character such as eye color, nevertheless of vital importance, and lethal when deficient.

Growing attention is being directed to "suppressor" genes which inhibit the effects of mutants at other loci. Houlahan and Mitchell (1947) have found a gene in *Neurospora* that almost completely suppresses the effect of three mutants of separate origin that require pyrimidine, and are not at the locus of the suppressor gene. The latter does not, however, suppress two other pyrimidine-requiring mutants, so that the first three are probably alleles. The most interesting thing about the nature of the suppressor gene is that it cannot be a duplicate as to physiological action of the normal allele of the pyrimidineless mutants. For arginine suppresses the suppressor, but does not affect the wild type, which of course carries the normal allele of the pyrimidineless mutants. This behavior is exactly like that described by Glass (1944) for a suppressor in *Drosophila melanogaster*. In that case, x-ray treatment at 10 hours of development suppresses the suppressor of the eye mutant erupt, but has no effect upon the normal allele of erupt. Luria (1947a) has interpreted the influence of mutation at one locus on the frequency with which another locus mutates, in *E. coli,* as possibly due to the suppressor action of the first locus upon the second. Braun (1946) has elaborated upon the importance and generality of such mechanisms in gene action. He points out that desoxyribose nucleic acid, so intimately connected with gene and chromosome structure, has been shown by Greenstein to inhibit enzyme reactions (Greenstein and Chalkley, 1945; Greenstein, Carter, and Chalkley, 1947).

The phenomenon of "adaptation" in yeasts, bacteria, *Neurospora,* etc., has received much attention in recent years. For example, a *Neurospora* mutant that requires leucine for growth (l_1) sporadically becomes "adapted" so that it can grow without added leucine in the medium (Ryan, 1946). This has been explained on the basis of reverse mutations to wild types; but in other instances "adaptation" might result from the appearance by mutation of a suppressor gene at some other locus. Lederberg (1946) pointed out the similarity between the sudden release of growth in the reverted (or suppressed) mutant, on the one hand, and the unlimited increase of growth in the transformation of a normal tissue cell into a cancer cell. Virus infection, like mutation, might provide a missing link in an enzyme system, and thus could play a corresponding role in releasing growth.

The parallels between the plasmagenes of *Paramecium,* especially "kappa," and the milk agent, a virus which is active in the transmission of mammary cancer in mice, have become more and more striking as work on each has progressed. Sonneborn (1947b) has summed up the evidence in a unified theory of cancer, which is based upon the original suggestions of Darlington (1944) and Haddow (1944) that a virus is merely a plasmagene in a wrong host; that is to say, it is a foreign plasmagene. Sonneborn suggests that cancer may result either from the introduction of a virus into the cell or from the mutation of a plasmagene, and that carcinogenic agents either make the cells more sensitive to viruses or induce mutations in plasmagenes. The long interval which occurs between the application of a carcinogen and the appearance of the cancer may depend on the slow attainment of a high concentration of the mutant or the foreign plasmagene, just as it takes a high concentration of kappa to change a sensitive *Paramecium* to a killer.

This theory may prove to be as fruitful in increasing our knowledge of the gene and the mechanisms of gene action as in opening up a new approach to the conquest of the second, in present importance, among the causes of human death. Like kappa, the milk factor has been shown to depend upon one or more genes for its maintenance and perpetuation (Heston, Deringer and Andervont, 1945). A crucial question in genetics is that of the exact relationship between gene and plasmagene.

Spiegelman and Kamen (1946) have proposed a theory to relate gene activity and plasmagenes to the synthesis of enzymes and proteins. They have found that in yeast cells which are metabolizing but not growing or dividing the nucleoprotein phosphate turnover is negligible, but that in growing and dividing cells it is marked. This indicates, according to their view, that genes are continually producing partial replicas of themselves which enter the cytoplasm to act as plasmagenes. There, being nucleoprotein and at least to some degree self-reproducing, the plasmagenes control the synthesis of enzymes and proteins. (Up to this point the theory follows Wright, 1945). The plasmagenes compete with one another, and by competitive interaction determine the enzymatic make-up of the cytoplasm. Therefore, although genes determine the presence of specific enzymes, it need not follow that cells with identical genotypes will be identical as to enzyme constitution. This view unites the phenomena of classical genetics, cytoplasmic inheritance, cellular differentiation, and enzymatic adaptation.

IV. The Gene and the Chromosome

In conclusion, a brief mention should be made of certain important advances in the study of the chemical and structural nature of the chromosomes, although this review would be far too extended if it attempted to cover all of the recent advances in cytogenetics. The work on nucleic acid has been brought together in two outstanding symposia, one held in England in 1946, the other in the United States in 1947. These have been reported in the two volumes of contributed papers (Symposia of the Society for Experimental Biology, No. 1, 1947; Cold Spring Harbor Symposia on

Quantitative Biology, Vol. 12, 1947). Particularly interesting has been the report in the past year of a highly successful way of isolating chromosomes from tissue cells in large quantities, followed by an analysis of their chemical composition (Mirsky and Ris, 1947a, b). Contrary to previous opinion, it is now found that only 90 to 92% of the mass of the chromosome is desoxyribose nucleohistone. When this is dissolved off, there is left a coiled nucleoprotein thread that contains about five times as much ribose nucleic acid as desoxyribose nucleic acid. This coiled thread is presumably the basis of the linear order of the genes.

In an extensive review, Kaufmann (1948) has surveyed the advances of the past decade in our knowledge of chromosome structure in relation to the chromosome cycle. Among the problems of particular interest because of its relation to the nature of the gene and to gene action is the problem of the nature and role of heterochromatin. This has been discussed, in its relation to nucleic acid metabolism, and in a bold speculative way, by Darlington (1947) and Koller (1947) in contributions to the first of the two symposia. The theory first advanced by Caspersson, in 1941, that heterochromatin is concerned with simple protein synthesis has found wide acceptance, and is supported by Darlington and Koller through their studies of extra heterochromatic chromosomes, the effects of nucleic acid starvation of chromosomes, chromosome changes in differentiating and cancerous cells, relation to the nucleolus, etc. Caspersson himself has summarized and restated the now extensive and convincing chemical and histological results obtained by him and his coworkers on the relations between nucleic acid and protein synthesis (1947). Brachet (1947a, b) has gone far to relate the chromosome cycle and nucleic acid metabolism to embryonic differentiation. On the other hand, Caspersson's hypothesis that during mitosis chromosome composition changes has been disputed on the basis of recent cytochemical work (Ris, 1947). Schultz (1947) has reviewed the development of the heterochromatin concept and has pointed out the two major questions regarding it at the present time: what is the role of the genes responsible for the major intermitotic masses of heterochromatin? and what is the significance for gene function and metabolism of variations in amount and location of heterochromatin? Aside from two definite observations in *Drosophila,* (a) failure of spermatozoa to differentiate when heterochromatin (*Y*-chromosome) is reduced, and (b) variegations produced by position effect when certain genes are juxtaposed to heterochromatin, facts are lacking. Such views as that which assigns polygenic characters to the heterochromatin must be regarded as highly speculative. But that heterochromatin has certain functions in chromosome metabolism can scarcely be doubted. In the giant salivary gland chromosomes of *Drosophila* variation can be seen in the appearance of those bands where the genes showing variegation are located. These changes may be described as "heterochromatization" to a variable degree in different cells and tissues. Prokofyeva-Belgovskaya (1947) has supported her view that heterochromatization is a normal process for all chromosome regions as they enter mitosis, but that different regions vary characteristically in the synchronization of the process, by numerous cytological studies.

An elimination of chromatin from the nucleus has been shown for many decades to occur in various organisms. Recently Goldschmidt and Teh (1947) have explained the classic example of chromatin diminution in the somatic cell lineage of *Ascaris* as being an elimination solely of heterochromatin. By the use of the Feulgen stain it could be shown that the tips of the chromosomes in the first cleavage telophase are heteropycnotic, whereas the middle parts of the chromosomes, which are not lost, stain only lightly. Seshachar (1947) has related both the pinching off of buds from the macronucleus in certain ciliates and also the complete disintegration of the macronucleus before conjugation to the discharge of heterochromatin into the cytoplasm. The micronucleus of *Epistylis* is almost completely negative to Feulgen's stain, whereas the macronucleus is Feulgen positive. A discharge of the nucleic acid of the old macronucleus into the cytoplasm is envisaged as permitting the nucleic acid to reorganize upon a new euchromatic framework in the growth of a new macronucleus from the micronucleus which has been genetically reorganized by conjugation or autogamy. Since, as Sonneborn has shown (1947a), it is the macronucleus that directly governs the phenotype in *Paramecium,* the entire process is beginning to take on meaning.

Among other problems of great cytological interest are those concerning (a) the behavior of the centromere (or kinetochore) possessed by each chromosome, (b) abnormal segregation after treatment with mutagens or without treatment in the case of certain heterochromatic chromosomes, and (c) the normal and induced occurrence of polyteny and polyploidy in somatic tissues of plants and animals. But space fails for an adequate survey of biological progress in cytology.

V. Conclusion

To the worker in the field of genetics, this is truly a period of magnificent achievement. Bacterial and virus genetics have moved from a study of mutation to the demonstration of recombination phenomena resembling sex in higher organisms. Effective chemical mutagens have been discovered, and truly directed mutations appear to be at hand. The combination of mutagenic agents and influences, and the analysis of position effects and of the relations between multiple alleles promise to reveal new secrets about the nature of the gene. Genes, antigens, enzymes, and plasmagenes are being related to one another and may soon disclose how genes produce their effects—and perhaps how cancers arise. Finally, with rapid strides the chemistry of desoxyribose and ribose nucleoproteins is being related to the behavior of genes and chromosomes. One may be quite sure that the synthesis of all of these aspects of genetics lies not too far in the future. The greatest days still lie ahead.

References

Anderson, T. F. 1946. Morphological and chemical relations in viruses and bacteriophages. *Cold Spring Harbor Symposia on Quantitative Biology* **11**: 1-13.

Auerbach, C. 1946. Chemical induced mosaicism in *Drosophila melanogaster*. *Proc. Roy. Soc. Edin.* **B72**: 211-222.

Auerbach, C. 1947a. Abnormal segregation after chemical treatment of *Drosophila*. *Genetics* **32**: 3-7.

Auerbach, C. 1947b. The induction by mustard gas of chromosomal instabilities in *Drosophila melanogaster*. *Proc. Roy. Soc. Edin.* **B62**: 307-320.

Auerbach, C., and Robson, J. M. 1944. Productions of mutations by allyl isothiocyanate. *Nature* **154**: 81.

Auerbach, C., and Robson, J. M. 1946. The chemical production of mutations. *Nature* **157**: 302.

Auerbach, C., and Robson, J. M. 1947a. The production of mutations by chemical substances. *Proc. Roy. Soc. Edin.* **B72**: 271-283.

Auerbach, C., and Robson, J. M. 1947b. Tests of chemical substances for mutagenic action. *Proc. Roy. Soc. Edin.* **B72**: 284-291.

Auerbach, C., Robson, J. M., and Carr, J. G. 1947. The chemical production of mutations. *Science* **105**: 243-247.

Bateman, A. J. 1947. Number of S-alleles in a population. *Nature* **160**: 337.

Beadle, G. W. 1945. Biochemical genetics. *Chem. Rev.* **37**: 15-96.

Beadle, G. W. 1946a. The gene and biochemistry. In Currents in Biochemical Research (D. E. Green, ed.), pp. 1-12. Interscience, New York.

Beadle, G. W. 1946b. The gene. *Proc. Amer. Phil. Soc.* **90**: 422-431.

Beadle, G. W. 1947. Genes and the chemistry of the organism. In Science in Progress, Fifth Series (G. A. Baitsell, ed.), pp. 166-196. Yale Univ. Press, New Haven, Connecticut.

Beadle, G. W. 1948. Physiological aspects of genetics. *Ann. Rev. Physiol.* **10**: 17-42.

Beadle, G. W., Mitchell, H. K., and Nyc, J. F. 1947. Kynurenine as an intermediate in the formation of nicotinic acid from tryptophane by *Neurospora*. *Proc. Nation. Acad. Sci. U. S.* **33**: 155-158.

Boivin, A., Delaunay, A., Vendrely, R., and Lehoult, Y. 1945. L'acide thymonucléique polymérisé, principe paraissant susceptible de déterminer la spécificité sérologique et l'équipement enzymatique des bactéries. *Experientia* **1**: 334-335.

Boivin, A., Delaunay, A., Vendrely, R., and Lehoult, Y. 1946. Sur certaines conditions de la transformation du type antigénique et de l'équipement enzymatique d'un colibacille sous l'effet d'un principe inducteur de nature thymonucléique issu d'un autre colibacille (mutation "dirigée"). *Experientia* **2**: 139-140.

Boivin, A., and Vendrely, R. 1947. Sur le rôle possible des deux acides nucléiques dans la cellule vivante. *Experientia* **3**: 32-34.

Bonner, D. 1946. Biochemical mutations in *Neurospora*. *Cold Spring Harbor Symposia on Quantitative Biology* **11**: 14-24.

Bonnier, G., Rasmuson, B., and Rasmuson, M. 1947. "Gene divisibility," as studied by differences in Bar facet numbers in *Drosophila melanogaster*. *Hereditas* **33**: 348-366.

Brachet, J. 1947a. Nucleic acids in the cell and the embryo. *Sympos. Soc. Exptl. Biol.* **1**: 207-224.

Brachet, J. 1947b. The metabolism of nucleic acids during embryonic development. *Cold Spring Harbor Symposia on Quantitative Biology* **12**: 18-27.

Braun, W. 1946. Some thoughts on "gene action." *Science* **104**: 38.

Braun, W. 1947a. Bacterial dissociation. *Bact. Rev.* **11**: 75-114.

Braun, W. 1947b. Studies on bacterial variation and its relation to some general biological problems. *Amer. Nat.* **81**: 262-275.

Bridges, C. B., and Brehme, K. S. 1944. The Mutants of *Drosophila melanogaster*. *Carnegie Inst. Washington Publ.* **552**. 257 pp.

Bryson, V. 1948. Reciprocal cross resistance of adapted *Escherichia coli* to nitrogen mustard and ultra-violet light. *Genetics* **33**: 99.

Callender, S. T., and Race, R. R. 1946. A serological and genetical study of multiple antibodies formed in response to blood transfusion by a patient with lupus erythematosus diffusus. *Ann. Eugen.* **13**: 102-117.

Caspari, E. 1946a. On the effects of the gene *a* on the chemical composition of *Ephestia kuhniella* Zeller. *Genetics* **31**: 454-474.

Caspari, E. 1946b. Oxidation of tryptophane by homogenized a^+a^+ and aa *Ephestia* tissue. *Nature* **158**: 555.

Caspersson, T. 1941. Studien über den Eiweissumsatz der Zelle. *Naturwiss.* **29**: 33-43.

Caspersson, T. 1947. The relations between nucleic acid and protein synthesis. *Sympos. Soc. Exptl. Biol.* **1**: 127-151.

Castle, W. B., Wintrobe, M. M., and Snyder, L. H. 1948. On the nomenclature of the anti-Rh typing serums: Report of the Advisory Review Board. *Science* **107**: 27-31.

Catcheside, D. G. 1947a. The P-locus position effect in *Oenothera*. *Jour. Genet.* **48**: 31-42.

Catcheside, D. G. 1947b. A duplication and a deficiency in *Oenothera*. *Jour. Genet.* **48**: 99-110.

Darlington, C. D. 1944. Heredity, Development, and Infection. *Nature* **154**: 164-169.

Darlington, C. D. 1947. Nucleic acid and the chromosomes. *Sympos. Soc. Exptl. Biol.* **1**: 252-269.

Delbrück, M. 1945. Spontaneous mutations of bacteria. *Ann. Missouri Bot. Gard.* **32**: 223-233.

Delbrück, M., and Bailey, W. T. Jr. 1946. Induced mutations in bacterial viruses. *Cold Spring Harbor Symposia on Quantitative Biology* **11**: 33-37.

Demerec, M. 1945. Production of *Staphylococcus* strains resistant to various concentrations of penicillin. *Proc. Nation. Acad. Sci. U. S.* **31**: 16-24.

Demerec, M. (ed.). 1946. *Heredity and variation in microorganisms. Cold Spring Harbor Symposia on Quantitative Biology* **11**. 314 pp. The Biological Laboratory, Cold Spring Harbor, N. Y.

Demerec, M. 1946. Induced mutations and possible mechanisms of the transmission of heredity in *Escherichia coli. Proc. Nation. Acad. Sci. U. S.* **32**: 36-46.

Demerec, M. 1947a. Mutations in *Drosophila* induced by a carcinogen. *Nature* **159**: 604.

Demerec, M. 1947b. Production of mutations in *Drosophila* by treatment with some carcinogens. *Science* **105**: 634.

Demerec, M. (ed.). 1947c. *Nucleic acids and nucleoproteins. Cold Spring Harbor Symposia on Quantitative Biology* **12**. 279 pp. The Biological Laboratory, Cold Spring Harbor, N. Y.

Demerec, M., and Fano, U. 1945. Bacteriophage-resistant mutants in *Escherichia coli. Genetics* **30**: 119-136.

Demerec, M., and Latarjet, R. 1946. Mutations in bacteria induced by radiations. *Cold Spring Harbor Symposia on Quantitative Biology* **11**: 38-50.

Demerec, M., Witkin, E. M., Newcombe, H. B., and Beale, G. H. 1947. The gene. *Carnegie Inst. Washington Yearbook* **46**: 127-135.

Devi, P., Pontecorvo, G., and Higginbotham, G. 1947. X-ray induced mutations in dried bacteria. *Nature* **160**: 503-504.

Dienes, L. 1946. Complex reproductive processes in bacteria. *Cold Spring Harbor Symposia on Quantitative Biology* **11**: 51-59.

Dunn, L. C., and Caspari, E. 1945. A case of neighboring loci with similar effects. *Genetics* **30**: 543-568.

Ephrussi, B., and Sutton, E. 1944. A reconsideration of the mechanism of position effect. *Proc. Nation. Acad. Sci., U. S.* **30**: 183-197.

Fisher, R. A., and Race, R. R. 1946. Rh gene frequencies in Britain. *Nature* **157**: 48.

Genetics Conference, Committee on Atomic Casualties, N. R. C. 1947. Genetic effects of the atomic bombs in Hiroshima and Nagasaki. *Science* **106**: 331-333.

Giles, N. H., Jr. 1947. Chromosome structural changes in Tradescantia microspores produced by absorbed radiophosphorus. *Proc. Nation. Acad. Sci. U. S.* **33**: 283-287.

Giles, N. H., Jr. 1948. Induced reversions of biochemical mutants in *Neurospora. Genetics* **33**: 105-106.

Gilman, A., and Philips, F. S. 1946. The biological actions and therapeutic applications of the β-chloroethyl amines and sulfides. *Science* **103**: 409-415; 436.

Ginsburg, B., and Kaplan, F. 1947. Evidence for the presence of a gene controlled oxidase in mouse skin extracts. *Genetics* **32**:87-88.

Glass, B. 1944. The effect of x-rays upon the action of a specific gene in *Drosophila melanogaster. Genetics* **29**: 436-446.

Goldschmidt, R. B., and Teh, P. L. 1947. Note. *Science* **105**: 619.

Gray, C. H., and Tatum, E. L. 1944. X-ray induced growth factor requirements in bacteria. *Proc. Nation. Acad. Sci. U. S.* **30**: 404-410.

Greenstein, J. P., Carter, C. E., and Chalkley, H. W. 1947. Enzymatic degradation of ribosenucleic and desoxyribosenucleic acids with an addendum on the effect of nucleates on the heat stability of proteins. *Cold Spring Harbor Symposia on Quantitative Biology* **12**: 64-94.

Greenstein, J. P., and Chalkley, H. W. 1945. The influence of nucleic acid on dehydrogenase systems. *Ann. Missouri Bot. Gard.* **32**: 179-185.

Grosse, A. V., and Libby, W. F. 1947. Cosmic radiocarbon and natural radicactivity of living matter. *Science* **106**: 88-89.

Haddow, A. 1944. Transformation of cells and viruses. *Nature* **154**: 194-199.

Hadorn, E., and Niggli, H. 1946. Mutations in *Drosophila* after chemical treatment of gonads *in vitro*. *Nature* **157**: 162-163.

Haldane, J. B. S. 1947. The dysgenic effect of induced recessive mutation. *Ann. Eugen.* **14**: 35-43.

Hershey, A. D. 1946. Mutation of bacteriophage with respect to type of plaque. *Genetics* **31**: 620-640.

Hershey, A. D. 1946. Spontaneous mutations in bacterial viruses. *Cold Spring Harbor Symposia on Quantitative Biology* **11**: 67-77.

Herskowitz, I. H. 1946. The relationship of x-ray induced recessive lethals to chromosomal breakage. *Amer. Nat.* **80**: 558-592.

Heston, W. E., Deringer, M. K., and Andervont, H. B. 1945. Gene-milk agent relationship in mammary-tumor development. *Jour. Nation. Cancer Inst.* **5**: 289-307.

Hollaender, A., and Swanson, C. P. 1947. Modification of the x-ray induced mutation rate in fungi by pretreatment with near infrared. *Genetics* **32**: 90.

Hollaender, A., Swanson, C. P., and Posner, I. 1946. The sun as a source of mutation producing radiation. *Amer. Jour. Bot.* **33**: 830.

Horowitz, N. H., Houlahan, M. B., Hungate, M. G., and Wright, B. 1946. Mustard gas mutations in *Neurospora*. *Science* **104**: 233-234.

Houlahan, M. B., and Mitchell, H. K. 1947. A suppressor in *Neurospora* and its use as evidence for allelism. *Proc. Nation. Acad. Sci. U. S.* **33**: 223-229.

Irwin, M. R. 1947a. Physiological aspects of genetics. *Ann. Rev. Physiol.* **9**: 605-628.

Irwin, M. R. 1947b. Immunogenetics. *Advances in Genet.* **1**: 133-159.

Ives, P. T., and Andrews, M. B. 1946. Analysis of the sex-linked mutation rate in the Florida "high" stock. *Genetics* **31**: 220.

Kaufmann, B. P. 1946. Modification of the frequency of chromosomal rearrangements induced by x-rays in *Drosophila*. III. Effect of supplementary treatment at the time of chromosome recombination. *Genetics* **31**: 449-453.

Kaufmann, B. P. 1947. Spontaneous mutation rate in *Drosophila*. *Amer. Nat.* **81**: 77-80.

Kaufmann, B. P. 1948. Chromosome structure in relation to the chromosome cycle. II. *Bot. Rev.* **14**: 57-126.

Kaufmann, B. P., and Gay, H. 1947. The influence of x-rays and near infra-red rays on recessive lethals in *Drosophila melanogaster*. *Proc. Nation. Acad. Sci. U. S.* **33**: 366-372.

Kaufmann, B. P., and Hollaender, A. 1946. Modification of the frequency of chromosomal rearrangements induced by x-rays in *Drosophila*. II. Use of ultraviolet radiation. *Genetics* **31**: 368-376.

Kaufmann, B. P., Hollaender, A., and Gay, H. 1946. Modification of the frequency of chromosomal rearrangements induced by x-rays in *Drosophila*. I. Use of near infrared radiation. *Genetics* **31**: 349-367.

King, E. D. 1947. The effect of low temperature upon the frequency of x-ray induced mutations. *Genetics* **32**: 161-164.

Knaysi, G., and Baker, R. F. 1947. Demonstration, with the electron microscope, of a nucleus in *Bacillus mycoides* grown in a nitrogen-free medium. *Jour. Bact.* **54**: 4-5.

Koller, P. C. 1947. The experimental modification of nucleic acid systems in the cell. *Sympos. Soc. Exptl. Biol.* **1**: 270-290.

Lamy, R. 1947. Observed spontaneous mutation rates in relation to experimental technique. *Jour. Genet.* **48**: 223-236.

Lea, D. E. 1947. *Actions of Radiations on Living Cells.* 402 pp. Cambridge: at the University Press; Macmillan, New York.

Lederberg, J. 1946. A nutritional concept of cancer. *Science* **104**: 428.

Lederberg, J. 1947. Gene recombination and linked segregations in *Escherichia coli. Genetics* **32**: 505-525.

Lederberg, J., and Tatum, E. L. 1946a. Gene recombination in *Escherichia coli. Nature* **58**: 558.

Lederberg, J., and Tatum, E. L. 1946b. Novel genotypes in mixed cultures of biochemical mutants of bacteria. *Cold Spring Harbor Symposia on Quantitative Biology* **11**: 113-114.

Lévy, J. 1946. Transmission héréditaire de la tropanolestérase. *Compt. Rend. Soc. Biol.* **140**: 823-825.

Lewis, D. 1947. Competition and dominance of incompatibility alleles in diploid pollen. *Heredity* **1**: 85-108.

Lewis, E. B. 1945. The relation of repeats to position effect in *Drosophila melanogaster. Genetics* **30**: 137-166.

Lewis, E. B. 1948. Pseudo-allelism in *Drosophila melanogaster. Genetics* **33**: 113.

L'Héritier, P., and Sigot, A. 1944, 1945. Contribution à l'étude de la sensibilité au CO_2 chez la Drosophile. I, II, III, IV, V. *Bull. Soc. Phys. Biol. France* **18**: 108-109; **18**: 109-110; **18**: 119-120; **18**: 120-122; **19**: (No. 83).

L'Héritier, P., and Teissier, G. 1944. Transmission héréditaire de la sensibilité au gaz carbonique chez *Drosophila melanogaster. Publ. Lab. École Norm. Supér. Biol.* Fasc. **1**: 35-76.

Lincoln, R. E. 1947. Mutation and adaptation in *Phytomonas stewartii. Jour. Bact.* **54**: 745-758.

Lindegren, C. C., and Lindegren, G. 1946. The cytogene theory. *Cold Spring Harbor Symposia on Quantitative Biology* **11**: 115-129.

Little, C. C., and Hummel, K. P. 1947. A reverse mutation to a "remote" allele in the house mouse. *Proc. Nation. Acad. Sci. U. S.* **33**: 42-43.

Luria, S. E. 1945a. Mutations of bacterial viruses affecting their host range. *Genetics* **30**: 84-99.

Luria, S. E. 1945b. Genetics of bacterium-bacterial virus relationship. *Ann. Missouri Bot. Garden* **32**: 235-242.

Luria, S. E. 1946. Spontaneous bacterial mutations to resistance to anti-bacterial agents. *Cold Spring Harbor Symposia on Quantitative Biology* **11**: 130-138.

Luria, S. E. 1947a. Non-independent mutations in bacteria. *Genetics* **32**: 95.

Luria, S. E. 1947b. Reactivation of irradiated bacteriophage by transfer of self-reproducing units. *Proc. Nation. Acad. Sci. U. S.* **33**: 253-264.

Luria, S. E., and Delbrück, M. 1943. Mutations of bacteria from virus sensitivity to virus resistance. *Genetics* **28**: 491-511.

Lwoff, A. 1946. Some problems connected with spontaneous biochemical mutations in bacteria. *Cold Spring Harbor Symposia on Quantitative Biology* **11**: 139-155.

Mampell, K. 1946. Genic and nongenic transmission of mutator activity. *Genetics* **31**: 589-597.

McCarty, M. 1946. Chemical nature and biological specificity of the substance inducing transformation of pneumococcal types. *Bact. Rev.* **10**: 63-71.

McCarty, M., Taylor, H. E., and Avery, O. T. 1946. Biochemical studies of environmental factors essential in transformation of pneumococcal types. *Cold Spring Harbor Symposia on Quantitative Biology* **11**: 177-183.

McElroy, W. D., Cushing, J. E., and Miller, H. 1947. The induction of biochemical mutations in *Neurospora crassa* by nitrogen mustard. *Jour. Cell. and Comp. Physiol.* **30**: 331-346.

Mirsky, A. E., and Ris, H. 1947a. Isolated chromosomes. *Jour. Gen. Physiol.* **31**: 1-6.

Mirsky, A. E., and Ris, H. 1947b. The chemical composition of isolated chromosomes. *Jour. Gen. Physiol.* **31**: 7-18.

Mourant, A. E. 1945. A new rhesus antibody. *Nature* **155**: 237.

Muller, H. J. 1946a. Age in relation to the frequency of spontaneous mutations in *Drosophila*. *Yearbook Amer. Phil. Soc.* **1945**: 150-153.

Muller, H. J. 1946b. Physiological effects on "spontaneous" mutation rate in *Drosophila*. *Genetics* **31**: 225.

Muller, H. J. 1947a. The gene. *Proc. Roy. Soc. Lond.* B, **134**: 1-37.

Muller, H. J. 1947b. Genetic fundamentals: the dance of the genes. In Genetics, Medicine, and Man, pp. 35-65. Cornell University Press, Ithaca.

Muller, H. J., and Mott-Smith, L. M. 1930. Evidence that natural radioactivity is inadequate to explain the frequency of "natural" mutations. *Proc. Nation. Acad. Sci. U. S.* **16**: 277-285.

Oakberg, E. F., and Luria, S. E. 1947. Mutations to sulfonamide resistance in *Staphylococcus aureus*. *Genetics* **32**: 249-261.

Owen, R. D., Stormont, C., and Irwin, M. R. 1947. An immunogenetic analysis of racial differences in dairy cattle. *Genetics* **32**: 64-74.

Pirie, N. W. 1946. The state of viruses in the infected cell. *Cold Spring Harbor Symposia on Quantitative Biology* **11**: 184-192.

Plough, H. H. 1941. Spontaneous mutability in *Drosophila*. *Cold Spring Harbor Symposia on Quantitative Biology* **9**: 127-137.

Pontecorvo, G. 1946. Genetic systems based on heterocaryosis. *Cold Spring Harbor Symposia on Quantitative Biology* **11**: 193-201.

Prokofyeva-Belgovskaya, A. A. 1947. Heterochromatization as a change of chromosome cycle. *Jour. Genet.* **48**: 80-98.

Race, R. R. 1944. An "incomplete" antibody in human serum. *Nature* **153**: 771.

Race, R. R. 1948. The Rh genotypes and Fisher's theory. In The Rh Factor in the Clinic and the Laboratory (Hill, J. M., and Dameshek, W., eds.), pp. 27-42. Grune & Stratton, New York.

Ris, H. 1947. The composition of chromosomes during mitosis and meiosis. *Cold Spring Harbor Symposia on Quantitative Biology* **12**: 158-160.

Robinow, C. F. 1945. Nuclear apparatus and cell structure of rod-shaped bacteria. In The Bacterial Cell, by R. J. Dubois: Addendum, pp. 355-377. Harvard Univ. Press, Cambridge, Massachusetts.

Roepke, R. R., Libby, R. L., and Small, M. H. 1944. Mutation or variation of *Escherichia coli* with respect to growth requirements. *Jour. Bact.* **48**: 401-412.

Roepke, R. R., and Mercer, F. E. 1947. Lethal and sublethal effects of x-rays on *Escherichia coli* as related to the yield of biochemical mutants. *Jour. Bact.* **54**: 731-743.

Ryan, F. J. 1946. Back-mutation and adaptation of nutritional mutants. *Cold Spring Harbor Symposia on Quantitative Biology* **11**: 215-227.

Ryan, F. J., Schneider, L. K., and Ballentine, R. 1946. Mutations involving the requirement of uracil in *Clostridium*. *Proc. Nation. Acad. Sci. U. S.* **32**: 261-271.

Sawin, P. B., and Glick, D. 1943. Atropinesterase, a genetically determined enzyme in the rabbit. *Proc. Nation. Acad. Sci. U. S.* **29**: 55-59.

Sax, K. 1947. Temperature effects on x-ray induced chromosome aberrations. *Genetics* **32**: 75-78.

Schultz, J. 1947. The nature of heterochromatin. *Cold Spring Harbor Symposia on Quantitative Biology* **12**: 179-191.

Seshachar, B. R. 1947. Chromatin elimination and the ciliate macronucleus. *Amer. Nat.* **81**: 316-319.

Silow, R. A. 1946. Evidence on chromosome homology and gene homology in the amphidiploid New World cottons. *Jour. Genet.* **47**: 213-221.

Slizynski, B. M. 1947. Production of structural changes in somatic chromosomes of *Drosophila melanogaster*. *Nature* **159**: 66-67.

Society for Experimental Biology. 1947. Symposium Number I. *Nucleic Acid*. Cambridge Univ. Press, Cambridge, England. 290 pp.

Sonneborn, T. M. 1946. Experimental control of the concentration of cytoplasmic genetic factors in *Paramecium*. *Cold Spring Harbor Symposia on Quantitative Biology* **11**: 236-255.

Sonneborn, T. M. 1947a. Recent advances in the genetics of *Paramecium* and *Euplotes*. *Advances in Genet.* **1**: 263-358.

Sonneborn, T. M. 1947b. A new genetic mechanism and its relation to certain types of cancer. *Quart. Bull. Ind. Univ. Med. Cent.* **9**: (1-4).

Spiegelman, S. 1946. Nuclear and cytoplasmic factors controlling enzymatic constitution. *Cold Spring Harbor Symposia on Quantitative Biology* **11**: 256-277.

Spiegelman, S., and Kamen, M. D. 1946. Genes and nucleoproteins in the synthesis of enzymes. *Science* **104**: 581-584.

Stadler, L. J. 1946. Spontaneous mutation at the R locus in maize. I. The aleurone-color and plant-color effects. *Genetics* **31**: 377-394.

Stadler, L. J., and Fogel, S. 1945. Gene variability in maize. II. The action of certain *R* alleles. *Genetics* **30**: 23.

Stahmann, M. A., and Stauffer, J. F. 1947. Induction of mutants in *Penicillium notatum* by methyl-bis (β-chloroethyl) amine. *Science* **106**: 35-36.

Stern, C., MacKnight, R. H., and Kodani, M. 1946. The phenotypes of homozygotes and hemizygotes of position alleles and of heterozygotes between alleles in normal and translocated positions. *Genetics* **31**: 598-619.

Stone, W. S., Wyss, O., and Haas, F. 1947. The production of mutations in *Staphylococcus aureus* by irradiation of the substrate. *Proc. Nation. Acad. Sci. U. S.* **33**: 59-66.

Stormont, C., Owen, R. D., and Irwin, M. R. 1948. Gene action on cellular characters in cattle. *Genetics* **33**: 126.

Stratton, F. 1946. A new Rh allelomorph. *Nature* **158**: 25-26.

Strong, L. C. 1947. The induction of germinal mutations by chemical means. *Amer. Nat.* **81**: 50-59.

Stubbe, H. 1940. Neue Forschungen zur experimentellen Erzeugung von Mutationen. *Biol. Zbl.* **60**: 113-129.

Suche, M. L., Parker, D. R., Bishop M., and Griffen, A. B. 1939. Reversal of lethal factors. *Genetics* **24**: 88.

Swanson, C. P. 1947. The effect of infrared treatment on the production of x-ray induced changes in the chromosomes of *Tradescantia*. *Amer. Jour. Bot.* **34**: 12a.

Swanson, C. P., and Goodgal, S. H. 1948. The effect of nitrogen mustard on the ultra-violet induced mutation rate in *Aspergillus terreus*. *Genetics* **33**: 127.

Swanson, C. P., and Hollaender, A. 1946a. The frequency of x-ray-induced chromatid breaks in *Tradescantia* as modified by near infrared radiation. *Proc. Nation. Acad. Sci. U. S.* **32**: 295-302.

Swanson, C. P., and Hollaender, A. 1946b. Modification of the ultraviolet mutation rate by pretreatment with near infrared. *Amer. Jour. Bot.* **33**: 832.

Tatum, E. L. 1946. Induced biochemical mutations in bacteria. *Cold Spring Harbor Symposia on Quantitative Biology* **11**: 278-284.

Tatum, E. L., and Lederberg, J. 1947. Gene recombination in the bacterium, *Escherichia coli*. *Jour. Bact.* **53**: 673-684.

Timoféeff-Ressovsky, N. W., Zimmer, K. G., and Delbrück, M. 1935. Über die Natur der Genmutation und der Genstruktur. *Nachr. Ges. Wiss. Göttingen, Math.-Phys. Kl., VI, Biol.* n. f., **1**: 189-245.

Tulasne, R., and Vendrely, R. 1947. Demonstration of bacterial nuclei with ribonuclease. *Nature* **160**: 225-226.

Vendrely, R. 1947. La libération des deux acides nucléiques au cours de l'autolyse des bactéries et sa signification. *Experientia* **3**: 196-198.

Wiener, A. S. 1946. The Rh system in the chimpanzee. *Science* **104**: 578-579.

Wiener, A. S., and Sonn, E. B. 1946. The Rh series of genes, with special reference to nomenclature. *Ann. New York Acad. Sci.* **46**: 969-992.

Wiener, A. S., Sonn-Gordon, E. B., and Handman, L. 1947. Heredity of the Rh blood types. VI. Additional family studies, with special reference to the theory of multiple allelic genes. *Jour. Immunol.* **57**: 203-210.

Witkin, E. M. 1946. Inherited differences in sensitivity to radiation in *Escherichia coli*. *Proc. Nation. Acad. Sci. U. S.* **32**: 59-68.

Witkin, E. M. 1947. Genetics of resistance to radiation in *Escherichia coli*. *Genetics* **32**: 221-248.

Wright, S. 1945. Genes as physiological agents. General considerations. *Amer. Nat.* **79**: 289-303.

Wyss, O., Stone, W. S., and Clark, J. B. 1947. The production of mutations in *Staphylococcus aureus* by chemical treatment of the substrate. *Jour. Bact.* **54**: 767-772.

Tracer Methods in Biological Research

BY MARTIN D. KAMEN

Department of Chemistry and Mallinckrodt Institute of Radiology, Washington University, St. Louis, Missouri

SYNOPSIS

In the 25 years which have elapsed since Hevesy's first experiments, isotopic tracer methods have proliferated into biology at an ever increasing rate so that tracer methodology is now a firmly established feature of biological research. The recent spectacular advances in nuclear physics which now ensure an unlimited supply both of isotopic tracers and assay instrumentation would seem to presage a great expansion in the future scope of tracer research.

This article surveys some of the more salient features of tracer methodology using a restricted number of sample researches as foci for discussion of achievements and potentialities. An introductory section treats of the bases for the tracer techniques, including discussion of the isotopic composition of the elements and some of the limitations inherent in the nature of isotopes and instruments for their determination (Section II).

The discussion is organized to treat applications under the broad headings of biochemistry and physiology (Section III). Under biochemical applications there is a further subdivision into sections dealing with the concept of the "metabolic pool," precursor-product relations, metabolic cycles, detection of intermediates, reversibility of biochemical equilibria, and analysis by isotope dilution methods. The integration of such studies with others in the physiological field is noted in introducing a review of applications to studies in permeability, absorption and retention of metabolites, metabolic turnover, and transport of metabolites. Finally, there is passing mention of medical applications.

Specific researches are cited to illustrate each of these topics. Thus, research on biological precursors is elaborated with a discussion of the carbon sources found to participate in the formation of uric acid in pigeon excreta (Buchanan, Delluva, and Sonne, 1946) in which ureide carbons are found to originate primarily from fed acetate or formate, whereas the carbons of the 3-C skeleton appear to arise from carbonate and glycine. Quantitative aspects of precursor studies are delineated by discussion of the work of Shemin and Rittenberg on the biological synthesis of porphins in mammalian blood (1946). The application of these studies to a determination of the average life span of the human erythrocyte is described. Metabolic cycles and detection of intermediates are exemplified by the extensive researches involving participation of CO_2 in the tricarboxylic acid cycle (Wood, 1946) as well as in the formation of fatty acids from CO_2 in bacteria (Barker and Kamen, 1945).

Numerous examples are included for researches listed under the various other headings. Future trends and limitations of tracer methods are emphasized.

I. Introduction

Since the initial experiments of G. Hevesy in 1923, tracer methodology has become an established feature of modern biochemistry and physiology. This is due, on one hand, to the spectacular advances in nuclear physics and nucleonic engineering which have afforded a complete assortment of labeling isotopes and assay instrumentation to biologists, and on the other hand to the now classical pioneering researches of investigators such as Hevesy, Schoenheimer, Rittenberg, Du Vigneaud, Wood and many others. It is apparent that the outbreak of World War II marked the end of a decade (1931-1941) in which the use of tracers was the virtual monopoly of those few laboratories fortunate enough to be near sources of supply of both isotopes and assay apparatus. The emergence of the uranium pile reactor, the increase in commercial production of the important rare stable isotopes H^2, C^{13}, N^{15} and O^{18}, and the commercial availability of assay equipment would seem to guarantee a great expansion in the general use of tracers in the immediate future.

Despite the relatively small number of investigators employing tracer techniques in biological researches the literature available is very large, involving several thousand papers dealing directly with tracer research, not to mention many thousand more which are concerned more or less directly with the results of such research. Nor is there a dearth of review articles and monographs to enlighten the reader. A few such general references are included in the bibliography.[1]

It may be concluded that any survey in what may be considered a time of transition must be strictly circumscribed in its coverage of the literature and modest in its aims. This article will be concerned mainly with an examination of the status of tracer research especially with regard to potentialities. No attempt will be made to encompass the literature. A small number of examples from recent research will be included for clarification of the text whenever the discussion appears in danger of attenuation.

[1]A monthly magazine (*Nucleonics,* McGraw-Hill Publ. Co., N. Y.) devoted exclusively to nuclear technology is now being published. Many articles of timely interest, including some on tracer researches, may be found in the various issues which have appeared.

II. Bases of Tracer Methodology and Other Preliminaries

1. *Isotopic Composition of the Elements*

The composition of atomic nuclei can be specified in terms of two fundamental particles, the *neutron* and the *proton*. These two particles in the free state differ mainly in that the proton carries a unit positive electrical charge (4.8×10^{-10} electrostatic units) whereas the neutron is uncharged. The total nuclear charge is assigned to the nuclear protons, the total mass to the sum of all the neutrons and protons in the nucleus. For the purpose of this discussion the neutron and proton may be considered to have essentially identical mass ($\frac{1}{16}$ of the standard mass taken as 16.000 . . . for O^{16}). The nuclear charge is equal to the number of extranuclear electrons, which in turn determines the chemical behavior of the atom. Nuclei which have identical nuclear charge, and hence are identical chemically may possess different masses (differing ratios of neutrons to protons). Such nuclei are called *isotopes* of an element. The ratio of neutrons to protons is rather rigidly defined for stability, being very close to unity for the light elements and increasing somewhat for the heavy elements. After this stability limit is exceeded, radioactivity results. Although most elements are mixtures of isotopes, some elements possess but one stable isotope (Be^{9}, F^{19}, Na^{23}, P^{31}, etc.). In the usual notation as shown the superscript refers to the integral mass (mass number) of the nucleus involved.

It is found that samples of any given element gathered from whatever source, even those of extraterrestrial origin (meteorites), display constant isotopic content. This fact is basic for the tracer method. Thus, carbon from any natural source is invariably a mixture of two isotopes with mass numbers 12 and 13, the former being present to the extent of $98.9 \pm 0.02\%$. Hence any sample of carbon made up of a mixture of these two isotopes in different proportion can be distinguished from natural carbon. If an unstable radioactive isotope, such as one with mass 11 or 14, is prepared and included in a sample of carbon, such a sample can also be distinguished from natural carbon because negligible quantities of radioactive carbon isotopes occur in natural carbon (Anderson *et al.*, 1947). Only by the most arduous and exacting procedures is it possible to separate chemically isotopes of an element. Moreover no chemical procedures exist which influence the rate of radioactive decay. Hence, variation of isotopic content constitutes an ideal procedure for preparing labeled samples of any element. The labeling is accomplished either by changing the normal composition in terms of the stable isotopes or by adding a radioactive isotope. Either of these two types of isotopes are called "tracers." Inclusion of tracers in any aggregation of normal isotopic content produces a labeled sample of the element.

2. *Basic Limitations*

The foregoing well-known material has been included to supply a basis for a few remarks on the limitation in tracer research brought about by the physical nature of tracers. In connection with the constancy of isotopic composition, it may be noted that minor fluctuations have been reported for some elements such as carbon (Nier and Gulbransen, 1939) oxygen (Gilfillan, 1934; Birge, 1941) potassium (Brewer, 1938), and in particular, hydrogen. Detailed consideration of the evidence bearing on these fluctuations has been presented (see Kamen, 1946). These fluctuations determine the ultimate precision of work with samples enriched in rare stable isotopes. Waters of biological origin may fluctuate in density as much as 3 parts per million owing to variations in isotopic ratios of hydrogen and oxygen amounting to several percent (Emeleus *et al.,* 1934). In the case of carbon the maximum uncertainty appears to be a variation of ± 0.005 in the normal C^{13}/C^{12} ratio usually taken as 1/100. There is no evidence that any marked deviations occur in different specimens from the same organism (Swendseid *et al.,* 1942; Krampitz *et al.,* 1943). However, no careful investigation for isotopic fluctuations in hydrogen and oxygen have been reported using the most refined assay methods. It may be concluded that such fluctuations in the assay of stable tracers are outside the range of sensitivity of present methods. The natural radioactivity occurring in the elements lighter than lead is negligible with the exception of potassium, rubidium and some rare earths.

The chemical identity of isotopes is maintained in biochemical systems with the possible exception of hydrogen, for which extreme isotope mass ratios exist. Both the ultimate equilibria as well as the reaction rates in systems involving hydrogen transfer may be noticeably affected. The difference in activation energy for removal of the light common hydrogen isotope (H^1) as compared to that for the heavier hydrogen isotopes (H^2 and radioactive H^3) may well reach 1600 calories, as in certain photochemical reactions involving chlorine (Rollefson, 1934). For a discussion of isotopic equilibria the reader may be referred to a recent article by Urey (1946).

The dilution range available in tracer studies is another important factor and is determined by the concentration of isotope available or permissible, the constancy of the isotopic composition in the element studied and the precision of assay. Thus, the upper limit of dilution for the stable rare isotope of carbon (C^{13}) cannot exceed that resulting in an isotope ratio less than the error involved in determining the normal isotope ratio, which is given in one instance as 0.0110 ± 0.0002 (Nier and Gulbransen, 1939). Neglecting fluctuations introduced by isotopic differentiation, it is seen that a sample of 10% C^{13} cannot be diluted more than fifty-fold if a precision of $\pm 5\%$ is desired.

Radioactive isotopes in general offer much greater dilution factors because of the extreme sensitivity of radioactive assay methods. To compare directly with the example cited for stable isotopes (C^{13}) a sample 10% concentrated in C^{14} corresponds to an activity of 0.5 millicuries per mgm. The usual assay apparatus employed can detect approximately 1×10^{-8} millicuries with a precision $\pm 5\%$ so that a dilution of fifty-million-fold is possible. To obviate this advantage, however, it must be noted that such material is available only in milligram lots, so that for many researches considerable dilution is required before the tracer carbon is in the chemical form needed.

The ultimate concentration of tracer employed is limited for stable isotopes by the obvious fact that stable isotope concentrations cannot exceed 100%. For radioactive isotopes the concentration is limited to that above which radiation damage occurs in the organism studied. A discussion of this matter is beyond the scope of this article (see, however, Morgan, 1947). It may be stated that in general the concentration of radioactive tracers required for most biological studies can be lowered to a value at which normal physiological processes appear to remain undisturbed (Scott, 1937). The occurrence of both stable and radioactive tracer isotopes for the same element (i.e., C^{13} and C^{14}) affords the possibility of checking the system investigated for possible radiation effects. Thus, in researches with C^{14} occasional repetitions using the stable isotope C^{13} can be made. Deviations in experimental results obtained with the two isotopes may be interpreted as resulting from abnormalities in metabolic activity induced by radiation.

Other limitations arising from the physical nature of tracer isotopes are of minor importance and are discussed elsewhere (Kamen, 1947).

III. Survey of Tracer Methodology

1. *Significance of Tracer Methodology for Biological Research*

The central feature of tracer methodology is the preparation of labeled samples of elements involved in biological processes. Such samples can be used to distinguish and trace molecules or reactive atomic groups in the presence of similar unlabeled material. At the biochemical level, the biologist is interested primarily in questions associated with the term "intermediary metabolism." It is required in such research to determine the fate of a particular molecule in a given process, that is, the manner in which the molecule participates in any given phase of metabolism and is mobilized either as a source of energy or as a contributor to the structural elements of the living cell. It is to be expected that such knowledge can be utilized by the physiologist who is interested in the mechanisms which exist to integrate various metabolic processes into cellular economy so that differentiation and growth are regulated. From such researches one may hope among other things to establish a rationale for medical procedures in therapy and diagnosis.

There is little doubt that the potentialities of the tracer method for biological research are enormous and beyond the capacity of any individual to define at the present time. It is proposed in the sections which follow to review a number of general types of research which appear peculiarly suited to the tracer approach.

2. *Biochemical Applications*

a. Studies in Intermediary Metabolism. (1) The Concept of "Metabolic Pool." The major concept in modern biochemistry which is based primarily on the researches made possible by the tracer method is that of the "metabolic pool"—i.e., the existence of a circulating body of chemical substances in equilibrium, partial or total, with similar substances derived by continued release and uptake from cellular tissues. Thus, neither the classical comparison of a living being to a combustion engine nor the theory of independent endogenous and exogenous reactions popular with biochemists in the past can be reconciled with the finding that a rapid degeneration and resynthesis of all molecules occurs in biochemical processes involving constant interchange of specific atomic groups. This is true whether attention is focused on the relatively stable structural elements (fats, proteins) or on the relatively unstable energy-yielding substrates. As the late R. L. Schoenheimer so aptly put it (1941):

> "A simple analogy which may be taken as an incomplete illustration of this concept of living matter can be drawn from a military regiment. A body of this type resembles a living adult organism in more than one respect. Its size fluctuates only within various limits, and it has a well-defined highly organized structure. On the other hand the individuals of which it is composed are continually changing. Men join up, are transferred from post to post, are promoted or broken, and ultimately leave after varying lengths of service. The incoming and outgoing streams of men are numerically equal, but they differ in composition. The recruits may be likened to the diet; the retirement and death correspond to excretion. This analogy is necessarily imperfect as it relates to only certain aspects of the dynamic state of biological structure. While it depicts the continual replacement of structural units it takes no account of their chemical interaction."—*The Dynamic State of Body Constituents.*

The data which have led to this concept of the dynamic state have been derived for the most part from simple experiments in which a compound suitably labeled has been introduced into the biological system from which at some later time various biochemical fractions have been prepared and the location and nature of labeled compounds determined. In principle it is possible by such experiments or extensions of them to obtain data on a number of fundamental questions in intermediary metabolism. Generalized, these are:

1. What is the nature of molecules which are formed as precursors in the synthesis of the structural elements of living cells?

2. What molecular mechanisms are involved in the breakdown of substrates and mobilization of energy sources for synthetic reactions?

In practice there are three difficulties which exist to confound the researcher who would attempt to answer such questions in the present state of tracer research. First, it is necessary to isolate the intermediates formed in a pure state so that specific isotopic contents can be determined. Secondly, it must be assumed that the labeled material administered is in equilibrium with the same material already present in unlabeled form in the organism. Thirdly, it is necessary to prepare the labeled compounds and later to isolate the labeled products in pure form.

(2) *Precursor-Product Researches.* The demonstration that a substance B is derived from a substance A, that is, that a one-to-one correlation exists between appearance of tracer in B from A, has been achieved in many instances. R. Schoenheimer has described numerous such researches in his Harvey Lectures (1941). There will be recalled the reversible interconversion of the fatty acids, i.e., palmitic acid into stearic acid (Stetten and Schoenheimer, 1940) and the reverse (Schoenheimer and Rittenberg, 1937); the metabolic relation between various amino acids, i.e., the conversion of ornithine into arginine (Clutton, Schoenheimer and Rittenberg, 1940) and phenylalanine into tyrosine (Moss and Schoenheimer, 1940). It should be remarked that in any study of metabolism in which the organism is growing, it is possible to demonstrate possible relations between metabolites by nontracer feeding experiments. In the steady state when growth has ceased, the only method available is a tracer method.

Biological conversion of specific metabolites to normal structural entities as well as excretory products has been studied for a large variety of molecules of biochemical interest. A classical instance (Schoenheimer, 1941) is the demonstration of the biological synthesis of creatine from methyl (derived from methionine or choline), glycine (from protein degradation) and amidine (derived from arginine).

A few examples from the more recent literature are the demonstration of pregnandiol formation by degradation of cholesterol (Bloch, 1945), the synthesis of the carbon chain of cystine from serine (Binkley and du Vigneaud, 1942; Stetten, 1942) and the synthesis of adrenaline from phenylalanine (Gurin and Delluva, 1947). A demonstration of a negative nature is the proof using doubly labeled methionine (H_3 C–S* – C*H_2C*H_2 CHNH_2 COOH) that methionine contributes sulfur but not its carbon chain to cystine (du Vigneaud and associates, 1944).

There are few examples in the literature of what may be called "quantitative isotopy." Thus, for the most part one finds demonstrations of the qualitative relation between any two or more metabolites but few clear cut analyses of the extent to which the given relationship may be taken to account for the formation of a given metabolite from a given precursor. The fundamental difficulty has already been cited—the extent to which equilibration of ingested and circulating or storage material takes place. Another difficulty, of course, is that the actual number of molecules intervening between precursor and product cannot be specified merely from feeding experiments. Conditions for the precursor-product relationship in the simple case wherein a steady state obtains and in which there is no discrimination between storage material and similar ingested materials have been analyzed and applied in demonstrating the origin of liver phospholipid from plasma phospholipid (Zilversmit *et al.,* 1943). A more recent example of the same type of experiment concerns the demonstration of diiodotyrosine as a biological precursor of thyroxine in thyroid metabolism (Taurog and Chaikoff, 1947). A general discussion has appeared with suggestions for obviating through the use of multiple labels the difficulty that in any biological system a given product B is not exclusively derived from a given precursor A (Branson, 1946, 1947).

A recent example of research on biological precursors is concerned with carbon sources in the formation of uric acid (Fig. 1).

```
HN — CO
 |(1)  |(6)
             (7)
OC     C — NH  (8)
 |(2)  ||(5)     >CO
HN — C — NH
 (3)   (4)  (9)
```

FIG. 1.—Uric acid. The numbers in brackets distinguish the various atoms.

In these experiments using the rare stable isotope C^{13}, labeled carbonate, carboxyl-labeled acetate, carboxyl-labeled lactate, α-β labeled lactate, carboxyl-labeled glycine, and labeled formate have been studied as possible precursors for uric acid in pigeon excreta (Sonne, Buchanan and Delluva, 1946; Buchanan and Sonne, 1946). The isolation procedures and degradation reactions employed were as follows.

Uric acid was isolated from the excreta, purified and oxidized with alkaline MnO_2 to CO_2, urea and glyoxylic acid. In this degradation, the CO_2 is derived from carbon 6, urea from carbons 2 and 8 and aldehyde and carboxyl carbon of glyoxylic acid

(CHOCOOH) from carbons 4 and 5 (Fischer and Ach, 1899). CO_2 was recovered as $BaCO_3$, urea was determined as carbonate after treatment with urease, and glyoxylic acid isolated as the semicarbazone. The semicarbazone was degraded by oxidation with acid permanganate to carbonate and formate, thus determining as formate the aldehyde carbon of glyoxylic acid. A separate portion of the uric acid was split with $KClO_3$ thereby obtaining carbon 8 as urea carbon, the other reaction product alloxan being converted next to crystalline alloxantin which on oxidation yielded CO_2 and urea the latter containing the original carbon 2. The results of the isotopic analysis are shown in Table 1.

TABLE 1
(After Sonne *et al.*)

		C^{13}, *atom % excess*					
Compound fed	*Labeled carbons*	2	8	4	5	6	*Respiratory CO_2*
C^*O_2	8.13	0.00	0.00	0.07	0.00	0.25	0.28
CH_3C^*OOH	5.82	2.02	2.10	0.07	0.00	0.22	0.26
CH_3CHOHC^*OOH	8.80	0.00	0.00	0.37	0.00	0.26	0.25
$C^*H_3CHOHCOOH$	5.40	0.10	0.10	0.07	0.14	0.09	0.11
$NH_2CH_2C^*OOH$	5.20	0.00	0.00	1.16	0.14	0.11	0.13
H^*COOH	3.34	2.41	2.41	0.10		0.01	

In this table the isotopic concentrations are expressed in "atom-percent excess" which is the excess of percentage abundance of isotopes in the labeled element over that in the normal element. Thus, a sample of C^{13} labeled formate containing 3.34 atom percent C^{13} in its carbon actually contains 2.24 atom percent excess C^{13} because the normal C^{13} content of carbon is 1.10 atom percent.

It is immediately evident that all of these compounds are utilized in different ways. CO_2 appears to be a source for carbon 6. Decarboxylation of acetate and lactate yield carbon CO_2 which also appears in carbon 6 and is equilibrated with the respiratory carbon dioxide. Carboxyl from acetate also forms carbons 2 and 8, a fate not shared markedly by any other carboxyl carbon except that from formate. No appreciable decarboxylation of formate analogous to that of acetate occurs under the conditions noted. Glycine carboxyl appears to be a major contributor to carbon 4, as does the carboxyl from lactate. Recalling work on conversion of serine to glycine (Shemin, 1946) it is also possible that lactate may be converted to glycine or a derivative of glycine, thus explaining the contribution of lactate carboxyl to carbon 4. On this basis it is reasonable to suppose that carbon 5 comes from the α-carbon of glycine. Similar results have been obtained using N^{15}-labeled glycine in man (Shemin and Rittenberg, 1947).

It should be noted that glycine and acetate follow different metabolic pathways and are not interchangeable in the biological synthesis of uric acid in the pigeon. This is in good accord with work on carbon dioxide utilization in uric acid decomposition by the anaerobe *Cl. cylindrosporum* (Barker and Elsden, 1946) in which it is noted that the acetic acid and glycine formed in the presence of labeled CO_2 exhibit different isotopic distribution, the glycine being labeled only in carboxyl whereas the acetic is labeled in both carbons. Thus the two molecules appear to arise by different metabolic pathways in the degradation of uric acid as well as in the synthesis of uric acid. Another interesting conclusion follows from the observation that acetyl carbon is not involved in urea formation in the rat (Sonne *et al.*, 1946). It appears that despite the structural similarity of the ureide groups (carbon 2 or 8) in uric acid to that in urea, the two groups have different metabolic origins. It should also be noted that relatively little dilution of the isotope occurred in these experiments. This fact reflects primarily the large quantity of isotopic material fed and consequent low dilution with nonisotopic material in the animal. It still appears reasonable to conclude that compounds incorporated with such high resultant isotopic levels in product (i.e., acetyl carboxyl into carbons 2 and 8) must be involved as precursors quite directly.

To illustrate the possibilities of the more quantitative type of study involving time relations between precursor isotopic content and product isotopic content there may be considered briefly recent researches on the role of glycine in synthesis of blood heme in man and deductions therefrom considering the life span of the human erythrocyte (Shemin and Rittenberg, 1946). N^{15}-labeled glycine, glutamic acid, proline, leucine and ammonia as ammonium citrate were fed to rats on a protein-free diet. Two weeks later the same compounds as well as the hemin were re-isolated and tested for isotopic content. In Table 2 the various isotopic concentrations are compared.

TABLE 2
(After Shemin and Rittenberg)

Compd. fed			
Compd.	*N^{15} content* atom % excess	*Hemin N^{15}* atom % excess	*Hemin N^{15} assuming compd. fed contained 100% N^{15}* atom % excess
Glycine	11.6	0.108	0.93
"	19.0	0.169	0.89
Ammonium Citrate	13.0	0.012	0.09
dl—Glutamic Acid	18.6	0.032	0.17
dl—Proline	11.6	0.031	0.18*
"	11.6	0.028	0.15*
dl—Leucine	32.7	0.051	0.07*

*Corrected for ammonia liberation owing to degradation of *d*-isomers.

From this table it can be seen that regardless of whether N^{15}-labeled ammonia, glutamic acid, proline or leucine were fed, only a relatively small

N^{15} excess appeared in the porphyrin compared to that found after feeding the labeled glycine. From these experiments and others relating to the isotopic content of circulating glycine compared to heme it could be concluded that the nitrogen of glycine was directly utilized in the synthesis of the protoporphyrin of heme, the nitrogen of the other compounds being used only indirectly. Experiments using glycine labeled with isotopic carbon would be required to prove that glycine carbon is also utilized.

With these results established in rats, N^{15}-labeled glycine was used to build up labeled heme in a human subject. After cessation of feeding the variation of the isotopic concentration of heme as well as blood protein was followed. The isotopic concentration of heme continued to rise after the period of feeding (3 days) to a maximum reached after 25 days, remained relatively constant for nearly 75 days and then fell slowly along an S-shaped curve. Usually if labeled material were incorporated during the feeding period into material in a state of continual synthesis and degradation (as could be the case for utilization of most amino acids in tissue protein) there would occur a more or less immediate exponential drop of isotope concentration in the labeled product after administration of isotopic material. In the case of glycine, however, there was incorporation into heme which was fixed in the erythrocyte and not released until the whole cell was broken down. As a consequence, the N^{15} concentration in the heme rose to a maximum value, remained constant for a period approximating the average life of the cells and then declined. This behavior was precisely that which could be expected on the basis that none of the components liberated were reutilized. As a matter of fact, this reutilization did not take place with the glycine nitrogen contributed to heme although it does for the iron liberated by heme destruction, as demonstrated with labeled iron (Cruz, Hahn and Bale, 1942). The slow and prolonged rise after the end of feeding was due to the stability of freshly synthesized cells in circulation and the preferential destruction of the older unlabeled cells.

It was possible to analyze the results obtained quantitatively and arrive at a value of 127 days for the average half-life of the system (human erythrocytes) incorporating the labeled glycine. In this case as in the more general case of a system involving any number of intermediates and side reactions the analysis lead to integral equations which could be solved only by approximation methods. Analysis was possible only because a fortuitous set of circumstances obtained in this system, i.e., the glycine label was not metabolized away by general transamination reactions, but acted as a direct precursor molecule producing a stable product neither metabolized during the life of the system nor reutilized on breakdown.

One may conclude that precursor-product researches will remain an important aspect of tracer research despite the complexities introduced by the dynamic flux of the cellular constituents and equilibration difficulties in the test system, added to difficulties occasioned by synthesis of labeled material, administration, and then isolation and purification.

(3) *Metabolic Cycles and Detection of Intermediates.* The subject matter of the previous section may be considered a special aspect of the general study of mechanisms involved in anabolic and catabolic relations. The utilization of substrates proceeds stepwise, the necessary atomic fragments being passed along a chain of acceptors which usually are regenerated in a cyclic fashion, each step being controlled enzymatically. The tracer approach is particularly useful in ferreting out possible intermediates and participating molecules which are not evidently involved when the over-all chemistry is determined.

Many successful deductions from nontracer feeding experiments have been made concerning the origins and mode of synthesis of certain excretory products. A good example is the work on urea formation in tissue slices (Krebs and Henseleit, 1932) wherein it was deduced that urea was not formed directly from carbon dioxide and ammonia but rather by condensation of carbon dioxide and ammonia with ornithine to form citrulline which in turn condensed with ammonia to form arginine. The amidine group formed in arginine was assumed to be split off by an enzyme, arginase, to form urea and reform ornithine. This mechanism was investigated using labeled CO_2 and shown to be essentially correct (Evans and Slotin, 1940; Rittenberg and Waelsch, 1940. See also MacKenzie and du Vigneaud, 1948). In such experiments the considerations relating to direct participation of various constituents from an examination of their isotopic content are similar to those discussed in the previous section.

The tracer method of course can go far beyond feeding or nutritional balance experiments in uncovering mechanisms for substrate utilization. Thus, the origin of creatine could not be established by feeding various different amino acids and proteins, although some indirect evidence suggested that glycine might be involved (Brand *et al.*, 1929). In the case of creatine, no significant change in the level of creatine concentration could be induced in balance studies. The feeding of isotopic material was required to establish a mechanism for creatine formation.

In connection with creatine formation an important biochemical process, transmethylation, should be mentioned. The transfer of methyl groups could be demonstrated in liver tissue slices by non-tracer means using as a methyl source methionine, which was found to accelerate greatly the rate at which creatine could be formed from guanidoacetic acid (Borsook and Dubnoff, 1940). The direct proof of the methyl shift from methionine (to choline, in this case) was readily supplied by tracer experiments with methionine in which the active methyl group attached to sulfur was labeled using heavy hydrogen (du Vigneaud and associates, 1941). It appears that a balanced diet requires substrate material capable of supplying transferable methyl groups and that only a few substances such as methionine and choline are available biologically for this purpose in animal metabolism.

Undoubtedly the most extensive contribution to intermediary metabolism resulting from tracer studies has been the firm establishment of carbon dioxide as a metabolite important in an astonishing diversity of processes. That CO_2 may be utilized not only by autotrophic systems but also by heterotrophes in general is an idea with origins deep in the beginnings of microbiology. Definite evidence for CO_2 utilization by systems essentially heterotrophic began accumulating from a variety of nontracer studies in the middle of the last decade (Barker, 1936; Wood and Werkman, 1936; Woods, 1936). It remained for the tracer method to establish the general role of CO_2 in cellular metabolism. The reader will find numerous excellent reviews of the status of this field (Van Niel and associates, 1942; Buchanan and Hastings, 1946; Wood, 1946). For this discussion it will suffice to mention a few experiments which show certain unique features of tracer research.

The majority of heterotrophic organisms which respire or ferment organic substrates produce CO_2 as an end product. The demonstration that CO_2 may also be utilized can be deduced only when utilization reactions outweigh CO_2 excretion resulting from degradation of cellular material or substrate, as in the glycerol fermentation by propionic acid bacteria (Wood and Werkman, 1936). It was possible to deduce from indirect evidence that CO_2 absorption occurred in some bacterial systems (Barker, Ruben and Beck, 1940). Direct proof of CO_2 utilization merely involved maintaining the respiring or fermenting systems in the presence of labeled carbonate. The appearance of labeled carbon in cellular material and in excretory products other than carbon dioxide could then be demonstrated with comparative ease. Thus, consider the fermentation of purines by *Clostridium acidi-urici*. It had been established (Barker and Beck, 1940) that uric acid, xanthine and hypoxanthine were fermented as follows:

$$\begin{array}{l} \text{HN—CO} \\ \;\;|\qquad | \\ \text{OC}\;\; \text{C—NH} \\ \;\;|\qquad \|\quad >\text{CO} \\ \text{HN—C—NH} \\ \text{(uric acid)} \end{array} + 5.5\,H_2O \longrightarrow 0.75\,CH_3COOH + 4NH_3 + 3.5CO_2$$

```
HN—CO
 |   |
OC  C—NH + 6 H2O   ⟶ CH3COOH + 4NH3 + 3CO2
 |   ||    >CH
HN—C—N
(xanthine)

HN—CO
 |   |
HC  C—NH + 6.5 H2O ⟶ 1.25 CH3COOH + 4NH3 + 2.5CO2
 ||  ||    >CH
 N—C—N
(hypoxanthine)
```

The decrease in CO_2 production from hypoxanthine compared to the other purines together with the apparently abnormal quantity of acetic acid found (one could expect at most only one mole from simple fission of the C_3 chain) indicate CO_2 absorption might be involved at least in the case of hypoxanthine.

The organisms were allowed to ferment the three purines in the presence of labeled carbonate. Isolation of cell material and of the acetic acid revealed appreciable utilization of CO_2 to form acetic acid as well as some cellular material. Both carbons of the acetic acid were found to be labeled.

In this type of experiment only qualitative results could be obtained, that is, the precise extent to which CO_2 entered into the synthesis reactions could not be inferred. As an example of a more quantitative study more recent work on another fatty acid producing anaerobe may be cited (Barker and Kamen, 1945). *Cl. thermoaceticum* had been found to ferment glucose almost entirely to acetic acid, a very small percentage of the glucose being assimilated as cell material. The complete absence of the usual one carbon type of product (CO_2, CH_3OH, CH_2O, etc.) was indicative of a possible CO_2 assimilation although the over-all reaction, $C_6H_{12}O_6 \longrightarrow 3\ CH_3COOH$, gave no indication of CO_2 participation. By conducting the fermentation in the presence of labeled CO_2, it could be shown that although no net change occurred in the amount of CO_2 present throughout the fermentation, labeled carbon disappeared from the CO_2 and reappeared in the product acetic acid, both carbons of the acetic acid being labeled nearly equally. Thus there was a situation in which a metabolite, CO_2, was absorbed and excreted at the *same* rate, so that its participation in the metabolism of glucose by this organism could not be detected except by a labeling method. It was comparatively simple to obtain precise dilution data, analysis of which showed that the number of molecules of CO_2 utilized and excreted (turned over) during fermentation of one molecule of glucose was two. This fact could be expressed most simply by the set of equations:

$$C_6H_{12}O_6 + 2H_2O \longrightarrow 2CH_3COOH + 2CO_2 + \text{“8H”}$$
$$\text{“8H”} + 2CO_2 \longrightarrow CH_3COOH + 2H_2O,$$

where "8H" represents reducing hydrogen made available by the glucose degradation. The over-all reaction obtained by summing these two reactions was thus $C_6H_{12}O_6 \longrightarrow 3\ CH_3COOH$, in accordance with the nontracer balance experiments on the fermentation process. Hence, the fermentation appeared as a combination of a normal type of glycolysis superimposed on a condensation reaction involving CO_2 or some one-carbon intermediate in equilibrium with it. From the high isotopic content of the two acetic carbons produced it appeared reasonable to suppose that the CO_2 was very close in the reaction chain leading to the precursor carbon fragment. In this process, at least one third of the acetic acid must have arisen through this condensation mechanism, a fact which would have continued to escape observation if tracer were not available.

Many more instances of similar researches on a wide variety of biochemical processes could be mentioned, such as the great number of studies which have been concerned with elaboration of the intermediates in the Krebs tricarboxylic acid cycle, interrelations between fat and carbohydrate metabolism (particularly verification of glycolytic mechanisms) and interactions of protein components in protein synthesis (see reviews by Wood, 1946; Shemin and Rittenberg, 1946). Indeed the literature on the biochemical utilization of tracer methods is made up so far largely of studies in the metabolism of CO_2 and the simpler fatty acids and amino acids. The general finding is that the large molecules characteristic of the fat, carbohydrate and protein of living systems can be pictured as synthesized continually from relatively simple units in partial or total equilibrium with the simple acids such as acetic acid and pyruvic acid. An example of synthesis at least in part of a large molecule has already been presented, namely the incorporation of glycine in heme. The nature of the active two-carbon fragment derived from acetate in syntheses of the higher fats is still a matter for speculation (Bloch, 1947; Bloch and Rittenberg, 1944).

The tracer approach has also indicated the erroneous nature of speculations about a number of fundamental biochemical processes. Thus, experiments with C^{13} on acetoacetate production in kidney slices have shown that ketone bodies arising in fatty acid oxidation could not be produced by "multiple alternate" oxidation of the fatty acid chain but must arise by coupling of β-oxidation with condensation (Weinhouse, Medes and Floyd, 1944; see also MacKay *et al.*, 1940). Another good example may be cited from study of intermediates involved in photosynthesis (Ruben, Kamen and Hassid, 1940). The technique employed was to add quantities of suspected intermediates as unlabeled material to extracts of photosynthetic organisms (algae, higher plants) which had been exposed to labeled CO_2 as substrate and allowed to photosynthesize at known rates for different periods. The labeled material formed in the first few minutes was fractionated in the presence of "carrier" material, the latter being added to aid in isolation of labeled material. None of the postulated intermediates (formaldehyde, simple organic acids, amino acids, etc.) could be demonstrated to contain significant quantities of labeled material. The general characteristics of the isotopically labeled intermediates could be shown, however by chemical tests for general reactive groups (carboxyl, hydroxyl, carbonyl), sedimentation and diffusion studies. Some kinetic data on the change in acid solubility of the labeled intermediates were also obtained indicating that a primary reaction involved a thermal reversible carboxylation followed by reduction with compounds formed photochemically.

This type of labeling experiment illustrates a general procedure in tracer research. When the labeled material to be isolated is present in quantities too small to be handled chemically, one may add a sufficient quantity of the same material unlabeled as "carrier" which on mixing with the labeled material yields a labeled mixture lower in isotopic content but sufficient in amount for convenient chemical analysis. When examining systems with intermediates of unknown nature, it is, of course, necessary to guess what substance to add. A serious difficulty is the one mentioned so often in previous sections, that is, when working with intact cellular systems equilibration must be assumed between carrier and intermediate. Furthermore one must guess *precisely* what carrier to add. One may add a carrier not identical with the intermediate but one which is sufficiently identical so that the two will react quite similarly and be mistaken as identical. Hence in all experiments with tracer, it is of the utmost importance to verify exhaustively purity of isolated samples (invariance of isotopic content as well as chemical constants) by all chemical procedures conceivable. The extreme sensitivity of the method when radioactive tracers are employed places much more rigorous demands on chemical purification procedures than those to which chemists have been accustomed in the past.

(*4*) *Reversibility of Biochemical Equilibria.* An important phase of biochemical research concerns the investigation of isolated reaction systems *in vitro.* Most enzymatic studies on single reactions studied *in vitro* are carried out with systems in which the reaction proceeds predominantly in one direction. Thus, in studying peptide syntheses *in vitro* using component reagents (amino acids), the equilibrium lies far in the directon of dissociation.

Some drastic (usually unphysiologic) means of removing product peptides is required to displace equilibria sufficiently to bring about observable utilization of the reagents. However, it is simple in principle to demonstrate reversibility of degradation reactions by employing labeled reagents (in this case, labeled amino acids) because, even if there be a net decrease of peptide or protein during the course of the reaction, labeled peptide will be formed if the reaction is at all reversible. The appearance of labeled peptide constitutes positive evidence for reversibility, provided, of course, that the proper control chemistry is done to obviate the possibility that the isotopic content of the products as isolated is not due to contamination by mere absorption or reactions other than direct peptide formation. Such an approach has been used in demonstrating protein synthesis *in vitro* using methionine labeled with S^{35}, the test system being rat liver homogenates (Melchior and Tarver, 1946). An example of spurious results gotten when labeled cystine was employed is also available in the same researches.

The procedure described has been generalized and applied to a great variety of systems the reversibility of which may be considered crucial in many metabolic cycles. One may mention a few cases at random, i.e., the reversibility of the "phosphoroclastic" split of pyruvic acid in the presence of phosphate to acetyl phosphate and formate (Lipmann and Tuttle, 1945; Utter, Werkman and Lipman, 1944), the reversibility of phosphate transfer from phosphopyruvate to adenosinediphosphate in muscle extract (Lardy and Ziegler, 1945), the synthesis of glutathione from glycine in rat liver slices (Bloch and Anker, 1947) and the reversibility of enzymic degradation of cysteine (Smythe and Holliday, 1944). The extension of this method to dipeptide synthesis *in vivo* has been reported for leucylglycine synthesis from labeled glycine and unlabeled leucine (Friedberg, Winnick, Greenberg, 1947). An important finding relating the mechanism of enzymatic synthesis of sucrose to a general glucose transferring enzyme, based partly on the exchange of inorganic phosphate with Cori ester (glucose-l-phosphate) in the presence of this enzyme has also been reported (Doudoroff, Barker and Hassid, 1947).

A major contribution from studies of this type has been the demonstration that enzymatic decarboxylation of a variety of important organic acids is reversible. Thus, extracts of liver have been obtained which can be shown to catalyze the reversible decarboxylation of oxalacetate (Kramptiz, Wood and Werkman, 1943; Utter and Wood, 1945). Similar results are available with fumarate and lactate (Wood and associates, 1945). Most recently, conclusions regarding the reversibility of the oxidative decarboxylation of isocitric acid (Ochoa, 1945) have been confirmed in pigeon liver extracts using labeled CO_2 (Grisolia and Vennesland, 1947). The ability to establish CO_2 fixation in isolated enzyme systems wherein the net reaction involves an output of CO_2 is of obvious importance in the study of systems such as those involved in photosynthetic fixation. It should be possible to use the tracer technique to monitor the isolation of enzyme extracts from photosynthetic organisms so that eventually cell-free extracts capable of CO_2 fixation are obtained.

b. Analysis by Isotope Dilution. The concentration of any given component in a biochemical mixture can be ascertained by adding a known quantity of the same component with known isotopic content, isolating a quantity of pure component after thorough mixing and noting the isotopic content obtained in the isolated product. If X_2 represents the grams of unknown (unlabeled) component, X_1 the grams of labeled component added, C_1 the isotopic content (atom percent excess or specific radioactivity) of the final product, C_2 the isotopic content of added component, M_2 the molecular weight of added component and M_1 the normal molecular weight, then

$$X_2 = \left[\frac{C_1}{C_2} - 1 \right] X_1 \left(\frac{M_2}{M_1} \right).$$

It is necessary only to isolate a quantity of sample sufficient for isotopic analysis, so that large losses incidental to complete purification can be tolerated. This method has been developed as a useful analytical tool, particularly in the analysis of protein hydrolyzates and fatty acids (Rittenberg and Foster, 1945; Foster, 1945; Shemin, 1945, see also Gest, Kamen and Reiner, 1947).

This method is the reverse of that used to isolate biological intermediates described previously in that, for detection of intermediate, unlabeled carrier is added whereas in the isotope dilution procedure it is the carrier which is labeled. However, a useful variant of the isotope dilution method using unlabeled carrier has been described (Keston, Udenfriend and Cannan, 1946) which permits very high sensitivity. In this method the mixture of unknowns is converted to some well-characterized derivative using labeled reagent under conditions in which the conversion to derivative is complete. An excess of unlabeled derivative is added, the resultant mixture separated, a pure sample of the derivative obtained and the dilution measured. Thus, in the analysis of a protein such as γ-globulin for glycine, the reagent used was *p*-iodophenyl sulfonyl-chloride ("pipsyl") the labeling being accomplished by the use of I^{131} (radioactive, half-life 8.0 days). Since the method involves dilution of material with high specific activity, any impurity of high specific activity which is difficult to separate chemically will lead to high results. It has been found (Keston and associates, 1947) that in separation of a mixture of such derivatives simple repeated crystallization from one solvent is inadequate because of formation of solid solutions between pipsyl derivatives, but that extraction from a variety of solvents accomplishes a satisfactory purification. The extension of the method in conjunction with partition chromatography on filter paper has a bright future (Keston, Udenfriend and Levy, 1947).

c. Concluding Remarks. The discussion of biochemical applications presented has been far from complete. It is hoped nevertheless that the reader will have obtained some impression of the manner in which the tracer method proliferates throughout the field of biochemistry. In the following discussion a brief survey of the tracer method as it applies to certain aspects of physiology and medicine will be attempted. As a bridge to this discussion, it may be remarked that the labors and interests of the biochemist merge continuously with those of the physiologist so that most physiological researches will be found to contain a large component of pure biochemistry. The major difference would appear to lie in that the physiologist is interested primarily in the organism as a whole. Thus, physiology is concerned not with isolated enzyme systems so much as with the interaction between enzyme systems and the integration of all component chemical systems into the efficient functioning of cellular economy and mechanisms of regulation. An attempt will be made to discuss the significance of tracer methodology in helping to obtain some insight into these problems.

3. Applications to Physiology

a. Permeability, Absorption and Retention. The interaction between the living cell and its environment presents the physiologist immediately with a number of processes grouped under the term "permeability." The rate at which mineral and organic metabolites are incorporated into the cell is related to the cellular metabolism in a manner which is obscured by one major characteristic of cells—that in the steady state and under normal physiological conditions the cell does not vary its composition discernibly despite relatively large changes in environmental conditions. A technique is necessary for tracing ingestion and distribution of metabolite under conditions where there is no net transfer. Thus the interchange of sodium ions between the cell and its surrounding medium cannot be studied by conventional analytical procedures because there is no net transfer. The problem is strictly comparable to that involved in studying self-diffusion in purely chemical systems. Some means must be found to distinguish atoms in one part of a homogenous system from the same kind of atoms elsewhere in the system. It is obvious that the tracer method satisfies this need. Thus, biologists for the first time are in a position to make some inroads into the important problem of how the cell in the steady state governs uptake of material from its environment. A special field, the metabolism of the "trace" elements, e.g., those elements required in micro amounts for normal cell function, is also rendered more accessible by the availability of tracer methods. Another advantage inherent in the high sensitivity of the method is the possibility of ascertaining accumulation at specific sites in the organism despite the extremely small concentrations involved. One may also inquire into the chemical combinations in which an element is fixed during transport and localization.

The procedure for investigation of such problems in mineral metabolism involves introduction of the labeled mineral (usually in ionic form) into the medium. At appropriate times thereafter, the metabolizing organism is withdrawn, washed free of adherent medium and examined for labeled material. The presence of such material is positive proof for the entry of the labeled material. Since the first experiment of this type (Hevesy, 1923) there have been innumerable such experiments done with a variety of elements. Extensions of absorption experiments to include distribution of elements at various sites in the organism are also numerous (for a review, see Hevesy, 1940). The general result has been to confirm the view that permeability is not governed simply by diffusion laws, but is influenced primarily by cellular metabolism (Krogh, 1946). Accumulation of any given mineral, for instance, potassium, is not brought about in the living cell because of some purely physico-chemical "selective" permeability effect based on membrane potentials but results from specific chemical processes in the cell which are most probably directly mediated by enzyme action.

It may be noted that extensive data have become available for the first time on distribution of "trace" elements and factors affecting their absorption. One may cite work on antimony (Ness and associates, 1947) cobalt (Copp and Greenberg, 1941; Comar and Davis, 1947; Sheline, Chaikoff and Montgomery, 1946), copper (Yoshikawa, Hahn and Ball, 1942; Havinga and Bykerk, 1947) and zinc (Sheline and associates, 1943). Certain toxic elements have also been studied, notably among the newer elements resulting from nuclear fission (Hamilton, 1947). Although many interesting facts about the circulatory mechanisms involved in distribution of such elements have been recorded, it is premature to attempt any correlation of the data with metabolic patterns in the various organs. It may be expected that a large number of tracer researches in the future will center around the integration of such distribution studies with studies in metabolism.

The successful application of tracer techniques to absorption phenomena requires careful consideration of the physiology of the system in addition to observation of coexisting metabolic patterns. That much of importance can be learned from properly designed experiments even of a simple type is obvious from the literature (i.e., Stout and Hoagland, 1939; Overstreet and Broyer, 1940; Arnon, Stout and Sipos, 1940; Jenny, Overstreet and Ayers, 1939) particularly when relating to aspects important to agriculture such as the effect of various physical factors on uptake of nutrient minerals (Spinks and Barber, 1947).

Caution is necessary in making statements with respect to the success which may attend the use of tracer methods in establishing the nature of the chemical combinations involved in metabolite transport and particularly in cellular entry. Difficulties arise from two sources, one the washing or decontamination techniques, and the other the possibility of chemical artifacts occasioned by extraction procedures. The latter difficulty is superimposed on the standard complication of assuming chemical purity in extraction of intermediates. It should be remarked that administration of any given labeled molecule followed by the mere appearance of labeled atoms in the cell does not constitute proof the molecule entered as such. Dissociation of the labeled portion of the molecule in the complex region defined by the cell interface can take place, so that constituent atomic groupings rather than the molecule as a whole enter the cell.

One may consider briefly a typical problem: entry of phosphate (present as orthophosphate in the environment) into the yeast cell during fermentation of glucose. The mechanism of entry is usually pictured as a diffusion of the orthophosphate into the cell followed by its esterification and utilization. However, an alternative mechanism might involve esterification of the phosphate at the cell interface, the compound formed being a component in cellular metabolism. On this supposition intracellular orthophosphate would originate primarily from breakdown of internal organic phosphate. Hence there need be no direct connection between external and internal orthophosphate. Some evidence for this latter view has been presented recently, based on studies of uptake of labeled phosphate as affected by various metabolic poisons such as azide and iodoacetic acid (Spiegelman and Kamen, 1947). The extension of such studies to elaborate the precise nature of the phosphate involved in entry may be obviated by chemical difficulties in isolation of the compounds involved because of instability and loss during extraction procedures.

b. Metabolic Turnover in Relation to the Intact Organism. The dynamic flux of metabolites in and out of the structural elements of the living cell is regulated so that no net change occurs in composition or structure. To understand how this comes about, it is necessary to study the interaction between enzyme systems under physiological conditions. From the discussion in previous sections it will be obvious that the tracer method may be used effectively to aid in unraveling regulation mechanisms by following transfer of atomic groupings from one cellular fraction to another and by validating inferences drawn from researches conducted in unregulated isolated enzymic systems as exemplified by cell extracts and homogenates.

Some researches have been reported dealing with the sites of synthesis of various metabolites. An example is the study of the origin of plasma phospholipid. When labeled inorganic phosphate is administered, it is found that the liver phospholipid reaches a higher isotopic content than phospholipid from any other organ in the relatively short time of 10 hours (Hevesy and Hahn, 1940; Artom and associates, 1937, 1938). In other experiments, labeled phospholipid produced in one rabbit was isolated and introduced into the plasma of another (Hevesy and Hahn, 1940) and found to disappear rapidly, appearing at the greatest rate in the liver. Although these experiments could be interpreted as evidence for the primary involvement of the liver in phospholipid synthesis (turnover) a more direct approach was tried in somewhat later researches using hepatectomized animals (Fishler and associates, 1943). The animals (dogs) with excised livers showed a very low rate of plasma phospholipid recovery from plasma compared to control animals, despite the appearance of large amounts of labeled phospholipid in kidney and small intestine of both groups. Apparently escape of phospholipid from these organs was blocked, so that, although there was plenty of lipid synthesized, little got into the circulation. It appeared therefore quite certain that liver was the major contributor to phospholipid in plasma. The synthesis of lipid in the organs other than liver proceeded at about the same rate whether the animals had livers or not, so that one might conclude that phospholipid synthesis in these organs did not require a liver factor. Further researches on *in vitro* systems (surviving liver and kidney slices) demonstrated that phospholipid formation in the isolated synthetic system required coupled oxidation reactions (Fishler and associates, 1941). This latter type of research is another example of tracer investigation into reversibility of enzymatic degradation. In these experiments the synthesis of phospholipid was detected in a system in which there was a net degradation of lipid. Much work on phospholipid metabolism has appeared in the literature, which should be consulted for further details (Chaikoff, 1942).

The two elements the physiological utilization of which has been most widely investigated are iodine and iron. As in the case of phosphate, the available literature is so large as to render futile any attempt in a limited space to elaborate its content. One finds again the application of methodology similar to that already ascribed for phosphate. The researches by Chaikoff and his group as well as LeBlond and his associates have resulted in many contributions to knowledge concerning the physiology of the thyroid particularly with regard to the formation of diiodotyrosine and thyroxine under a variety of physiological conditions. The remarkable efficiency of the thyroid gland in utilization of very small doses of iodine has been noted. It is found that iodine excretion and distribution outside of the special thyroid fraction parallels that of other halides. The thyroid can fix 50%

or more of a physiological dose of iodine (<1 mg. in a normal man). Larger doses are less well assimilated. Under physiological conditions, the iodine appears to enter into thyroxine through diiodotyrosine as precursor (this fact has been mentioned in an earlier section). Large doses of iodine remain in the inorganic form in the thyroid, being synthesized slowly into the thyroid metabolites. Storage appears to occur mainly in the colloid follicle. These are only a few facts among many available from tracer researches with labeled iodine (see LeBlond, 1942).

One should note that recently an inquiry into the significance of protein-bound iodine in blood plasma of rats as experimental animals has been reported. The depressing effect of thyroidectomy in the incorporation of labeled iodide into this protein fraction coupled with the augmenting effect of thyrotropic hormone suggests the use of such iodine bonding as a good index of thyroid activity (Chaikoff, Taurog and Reinhardt, 1947). One further example of the peculiar advantages of the tracer approach which may be cited in connection with iodine metabolism is the demonstration that appreciable synthesis of thyroxine and diiodotyrosine may occur in organs other than thyroid, such as muscle and intestine (Morton and associates, 1943).

Researches in iron metabolism have stemmed primarily from the work of Hahn and his associates in Whipple's laboratory. The major finding with respect to iron utilization is that absorption in the dog is regulated by iron reserves, primarily through a mucosal factor. The animal body is very efficient in utilizing iron, reutilizing iron resulting from degradation of blood heme continuously and maintaining excretion at a low level. The nature of the reservoir iron in tissues appears to be defined by recent work as the iron protein "ferritin" (Granick and Michaelis, 1943; Hahn and associates, 1943; Granick, 1946). A scheme for the mechanism of iron absorption, transport, storage and utilization has been postulated as involving entry of ferric iron into the gastro intestinal tract as food, reduction to the ferrous state, absorption as ferrous iron in the intestinal mucosa, and combination with the apoenzyme component to form ferritin. Regulation of iron absorption is maintained by the equilibrium between ferritin, plasma iron in serum and ferrous iron in the mucosa, the latter being fixed by oxidation-reduction equilibria.

The investigation of metabolic mechanisms in intact cellular systems has been often undertaken using various agents as inhibitors more or less specific for one or another type of cellular reaction. The mechanisms involved in the operation of such inhibitors is amenable to the tracer approach. An example of such work is the demonstration of inhibition of phospholipid synthesis by oxidation inhibitors such as azide and cyanide (Fishler and associates, 1941). More recently, the effect of azide in uncoupling anaerobic glycolysis from synthesis (Winzler, 1944) has been suggested, partially on the basis of work with tracer phosphate, as arising from the splitting of acyl phosphate in diphosphoglycerate immediately upon formation of the ester phosphate by coupled oxidation (Spiegelman, Kamen and Sussman, 1948).

The interpretation of turnover experiments in which the labeled material must enter the cell from the surrounding substrate is complicated by the ever present factor of nonequilibration. Thus, the specific activity of labeled orthophosphate in yeast never attains the same value as that of the outside labeled orthophosphate (Mullins, 1942) unless the cell is killed. The physiological heterogeneity of cellular fractions isolated as identical chemical fractions has already been shown for the case of yeast metaphosphate (Juni and associates, 1947). Limitations in the use of tracer techniques arising from nonequilibration between intracellular components and between intracellular and extracellular material may be noted more frequently in the future as more investigators enter into researches on metabolic turnover. The most well-known instance in which such difficulties have arisen in past work is the study of phosphorylation equilibration in muscle between the various phosphate esters involved in the Meyerhof-Parnas scheme for glycolysis (Furchgott and Shorr, 1943); ambiguities in interpretation are caused by lack of equilibration of intracellular and extracellular orthophosphate.

The understanding of the effect of radiation on metabolism in the intact organism is another aspect of physiology aid in the elucidation of which may be expected from the use of tracer methods (Kamen, 1947). One may mention in this connection the pioneering investigations on x-ray inhibition of desoxyribose nucleic acid synthesis as measured by labeled phosphate incorporation (von Euler and Hevesy, 1942, 1944; Ablstrom, von Euler and Hevesy, 1945). Here the obvious advantage of the measurement of turnover in tissues metabolizing in the steady state before and after irradiation may be turned to good account.

c. Brief Comment on Transport Studies. The movement of metabolites in living organisms is a subject very widely studied using tracer techniques in plant and animal physiology. The procedures employed are similar to those already described in the section on permeability studies. The researches on plant nutrition reported to date have dealt mainly with the movement of such elements as potassium, sodium, phosphorus, iron, bromine and rubidium. The movements of labeled growth stimulators and inhibitors are, of course, also amenable to study. Although most of the work to date is still very much in the pioneering stage, a number of rather surprising observations have been reported, i.e., movement of ions from roots upward many feet in very short time intervals ($\sim$15 minutes), rapid lateral transfer of solutes from wood to bark, and dynamic flux of nutrient in and out of roots even during intervals of accumulation. It is evident that the availability of tracer material possesses marked advantages for research of this type because of its great sensitivity and because movement under true physiological conditions can be studied (Stout and Hoagland, 1939).

Turning for a single example to animal physiology, it may be noted that recently deuterio-labeled fatty acids have been used to establish the flow of these compounds across rat placenta. It has been shown that when body fluids of pregnant rats are enriched with heavy water, there results rapid incorporation of deuterium into the glycogen, fatty acids and cholesterol of the fetus, the conclusion being that synthesis of these compounds occurs in the fetus (Goldwater and Stetten, 1947).

d. Passing Mention of Medical Matters and Concluding Remarks. From the considerations presented in this all too brief survey one may conclude that the development of tracer research in the coming years must inevitably exert a profound effect on biological research, particularly because of elaboration of fundamental phenomena at the biochemical and physiological level. Application of the methodology to practical matters particularly in the medical arts is already marked, and some procedures involving therapy with radioactive isotopes have already become routine. Thus, there may be cited treatment of various hematologic dyscrasias and malignant neoplastic diseases in which radioactive isotopes are used as extensions to radio therapy. It is established that the use of radioactive phosphate offers advantages over x-ray dosage in the treatment of polycythemia vera and some types of leukemia (Reinhard and associates, 1940). The use of radioactive iodine as a therapeutic agent in treatment and even cure of hyperthyroidism is common (Hertz and Roberts, 1946). Some success has even attended its use in therapy of certain metastatic carcinomas of the thyroid (Seidlin and associates, 1946).

In medical research, a number of important contributions have been noted. The factors involved in blood storage have been assessed using labeled iron (Gibson and associates, 1946). It is found that the labeling technique can be used to determine survival of preserved human erythrocytes under a variety of conditions and to investigate the merits of various preservative solutions proposed in the past. Optimal conditions for storage of whole blood have been given, i.e., ratio of whole blood to diluent not less than 4:1; concentration of citrate in diluted plasma between 0.4 and 0.6 g. per 100 ml; dextrose concentration about 0.5 g. per 100 ml, final *p*H not higher than 7.0 in plasma and 6.8 in cells, etc. Other conclusions relate to the rapid removal of nonviable stored erythrocytes after transfusion, necessity for refrigeration and the reliability of hematocrit determinations. An accurate measurement of the total circulating blood volume using the two available radioactive iron isotopes has been described. The extension of tracer experimental methods in iron physiology has been extended to the study of iron absorption in various clinical conditions (Balfour and associates, 1942). Thus, it is noted that pregnancy induces increased iron uptake. Diseased states in which iron stores are abundant, such as pernicious anemia and hemachromatosis show much less than normal absorption. Chronic infections in spite of associated anemia result in no utilization of radio iron. It appears that reserve stores, not anemia, control iron absorption. Other researches have dealt with the mechanism of anemia of infection which appears ascribable to impaired hemoglobin production (Wintrobe and associates, 1947). An interesting finding with which to conclude this list is that the efficiency of iron absorption depends on the valence form in which it is administered in man but not in dogs. The former can use ferrous iron much more efficiently than ferric (Moore and associates, 1944).

Some researches on the use of tracer methods in localization of inflammation (Moore, Tobin and Aub, 1942) may be taken to indicate possible practical application to diagnostic procedures. The use of labeled sodium in the study of vascular diseases and peripheral circulation has been reported. Thus, in congestive heart failure there appears to be marked interference with sodium excretion, a condition relieved by administration of mercurial diuretics (Reaser and Burch, 1946). The use of labeled sodium in assessing the efficiency of vasodilators such as papaverine and histidine has been reported most recently (Mufson, Quimby and Smith, 1948). Isotope dilution techniques for the estimation of blood volume (Moore, 1946; Nylin, 1945) under a variety of clinical conditions are being employed in numerous hospitals.

It is evident that instances of ingenious applications of tracer isotopes to practical medical problems will multiply rapidly. However, fundamental advances at the medical level as well as for all biology require continued and painstaking researches on the fundamental biochemical problems with which tracer methodology is concerned primarily.

References

General References

Conference on Applied Nuclear Physics, 1941. *Jour. Applied Phys.* **12**: 259-350.

Kamen, M. D. 1947. Radioactive Tracers in Biology. Academic Press, New York.

Schoenheimer, R. 1941. Dynamic State of Body Constituents. Harvard Univ. Press, Cambridge, Massachusetts.

Wilson, D. W., ed. 1946. Preparation and Measurement of Isotopic Tracers. Edwards Bros., Ann Arbor, Michigan.

Literature Cited

Ahlstrom, L., Euler, H. V., and Hevesy, G. 1945. *Svenska, Vet. Akad. Arkiv. f. Kemi.*, **19A**: No. 13.

Anderson, E. C., Libby, W. F., Weinhouse, S., Reid, A. F., Kirschenbaum, A. O., and Grosse, A. V. 1947. *Physiol. Rev.* **72**: 931.

Arnon, D. I., Stout, P. R., and Sipos, F. 1940. *Amer. Jour. Bot.* **27**: 791-798.

Artom, C., Sarzana, G., Perrier, C., Santangelo, M., and Segre, E. 1938. *Arch. intern. physiol.* **45**: 32-39.

Balfour, W. M., Hahn, P. F., Bale, W. F., Pommerenke, W. T., and Whipple, G. H. 1942. *Jour. Exptl. Med.* **76**: 15-30.

Barker, H. A., and Elsden, S. R. 1946. *Jour. Biol. Chem.* **167**: 619-620.

Barker, H. A. 1936. *Arch. Mikrobiol.* **7**: 404-419.

Barker, H. A., Ruben, S., and Beck, J. V. 1940. *Proc. Nation. Acad. Sci. U. S.* **26**: 477-482.

Barker, H. A., and Beck, J. V. 1941. *Jour. Biol. Chem.* **141**: 3-27.

Barker, H. A., and Kamen, M. D. 1945. *Proc. Nation. Acad. Sci. U. S.* **31**: 219-225.

Binkley, F., and du Vigneaud, V. 1942. *Jour. Biol. Chem.* **144**: 507-511.

Birge, R. T. 1941. *Repts on Progress in Phys.* **8**: 90-134.

Bloch, K. 1945. *Jour. Biol. Chem.* **157**: 661-666.

Bloch, K. 1948. Symposium on Isotopic Tracers in Biology. Univ. of Wisconsin Press, Madison, Wisconsin.

Bloch, K., and Rittenberg, D. 1944. *Jour. Biol. Chem.* **155**: 243-254.

Bloch, K., and Anker, H. S. 1947. *Jour. Biol. Chem.* **169**: 765-766.

Borsook, H., and Dubnoff, J. W. 1940. *Jour. Biol. Chem.* **132**: 559-574.

Brand, E., Harris, M. M., Sandberg, M., and Ringer, A. I. 1929. *Amer. Jour. Physiol.* **90**: 296-297.

Branson, H. 1946. *Bull. Math. Biophys.* **8**: 159-163; **9**: 93-98.

Branson, H. 1947. *Science* **106**: 404.

Brewer, A. K. 1938. *Ind. Eng. Chem.* **30**: 893-896.

Buchanan, J. M., and Sonne, J. C. 1946. *Jour. Biol. Chem.* **166**: 781.

Buchanan, J. M., and Hastings, A. B. 1946. *Physiol. Rev.* **26**: 120-155.

Chaikoff, I. L. 1942. *Physiol. Rev.* **22**: 291-317.

Chaikoff, I. L., Taurog, A., and Reinhardt, W. O. 1947. *Endocrinology* **40**: 47-54.

Chapman, E. M., and Evans, R. D. 1946. *Jour. Amer. Med. Assoc.* **131**: 86-91.

Clutton, R. F., Schoenheimer, R., and Rittenberg, D. 1940. *Jour. Biol. Chem.* **132**: 227-231.

Comar, C. L., and Davis, G. K. 1947. *Jour. Biol. Chem.* **170**: 379-389.

Copp, D. H., and Greenberg, D. M. 1941. *Proc. Nation. Acad. Sci. U. S.* **27**: 153.

Cruz, W. O., Hahn, P. F., and Bale, W. F. 1942. *Amer. Jour. Physiol.* **135**: 595-599.

Doudoroff, M., Barker, H. A., and Hassid, W. Z. 1947. *Jour. Biol. Chem.* **168**: 725-732.

du Vigneaud, V., Kilmer, G. W., Rachele, J. R., and Cohn, M. J. 1944. *Jour. Biol. Chem.* **155**: 645-651.

du Vigneaud, V., Cohn, M., Chandler, J. P., Schenck, J. R., and Simonds, S. 1941. *Jour. Biol. Chem.* **140**: 625-641.

Emeleus, H. J., James, F. W., King, A., Pearson, T. G., and Briscoe, H. V. A. 1934. *J. Chem. Soc.* **136B**, 1207-1219.

Euler, H. V., and Hevesy, G. 1944. *Svenska Vet. Akad. Arkiv. f. Kemi.*, **17A**: No. 30.

Evans, E. A., Jr., and Slotin, L. 1940. *Jour. Biol. Chem.* **136**: 805-806.

Fischer, E., and Ach, F. 1899. *Ber.* **32**, 2745.

Fishler, M. C., Entennan, C., Montgomery, M. L., and Chaikoff, I. L. 1943. *Jour. Biol. Chem.* **150**: 47-55.

Fishler, M. C., Taurog, A., Perlman, I., and Chaikoff, I. L. 1941. *Jour. Biol. Chem.* **141**: 809-818.

Foster, G. L. 1945. *Jour. Biol. Chem.* **159**: 431.

Friedberg, F., Winnick, T., and Greenberg, D. M. 1947. *Jour. Biol. Chem.* **169**: 763-764.

Furchgott, R. F., and Shorr, E. 1943. *Jour. Biol. Chem.* **151**: 65-86.

Gest, H., Kamen, M. D., and Reiner, J. M. 1947. *Arch. Biochem.* **12**: 273-281.

Gibson, J. G., II, Aub, J. C., Evans, R. D., Peacock, W. C., Irvine, J. W., Jr., and Sack, T. 1946. *Jour. Clin. Invest.* **26**: 704-714.

Gibson, J. G., II, Evans, R. D., Aub, J. C., Sack, T., and Peacock, W. C. 1946. *Jour. Clin. Invest.* **26**: 715-738, 739-746.

Gibson, J. G., II, Peacock, W. C., Seligman, A. M., and Sack, T. 1946. *Jour. Clin. Invest.* **25**: 838-847.

Gibson, J. G., II, Weiss, S., Evans, R. D., Peacock, W. C., Irvine, J. W., Jr., Good, W. M., and Kip, A. F. 1946. *Jour. Clin. Invest.* **25**: 616-626.

Gilfillan, E. S., Jr. 1934. *Jour. Amer. Chem. Soc.* **56**: 406-408.

Goldwater, W. H., and Stetten, D. W., Jr. 1947. *Jour. Biol. Chem.* **169**: 723-738.

Graff, S., Rittenberg, D., and Foster, G. L. 1940. *Jour. Biol. Chem.* **133**: 745-752.

Granick, S. 1946. *Chem. Rev.* **38**: 379-403.

Granick, S., and Michaelis, L. 1943. *Jour. Biol. Chem.* **147**: 91-97.

Grisolia, S., and Vennesland, B. 1947. *Jour. Biol. Chem.* **170**: 461-465.

Gurin, S., and Delluva, A. M. 1947. *Jour. Biol. Chem.* **170**: 545-550.

Hahn, P. F., Granick, S., Bale, W., and Michaelis, L. 1943. *Jour. Biol. Chem.* **150**, 407-412.

Hamilton, J. G. 1947. *Radiology,* 325-343.

Havinga, E., and Bykerk, R. 1947. *Rec. Trav. Chim.* **66**: 184-188.

Hertz, S., and Roberts, A. 1946. *Jour. Amer. Med. Assoc.* **131**: 81-86.

Hevesy, G., 1923. *Biochem. Jour.* **17**: 439-445.

Hevesy, G. 1940. *Ann. Rev. Biochem.* **9**: 641-662.

Hevesy, G., and Hahn, L. 1940. *Kgl. Danske Videnskab. Selskab. Biol. Medd.* **15**.

Jenny, H., Overstreet, R., and Ayers, A. D. 1939. *Soil Sci.* **48**: 9-24.

Juni, E., Kamen, M. D., Spiegelman, S., and Wiame, J. 1947. *Nature* **160**: 717-718.

Kamen, M. D. 1946. *Bull. Amer. Mus. Nat. Hist.* **87**: 105-138.

Kamen, M. D. 1947. *Radiology,* **49**: 223-230.

Keston, A. S., Udenfriend, S., and Cannan, R. K. 1946. *Jour. Amer. Chem. Soc.* **65**: 1390.

Keston, A. S., Udenfriend, S., Levy, M., and Cannan, R. K. 1947. Private communication.

Keston, A. S., Udenfriend, S., and Levy, M. 1947. *Jour. Amer. Chem. Soc.* **69**: 3151-3152.

Krampitz, L. O., Wood, H. G., and Werkman, C. H. 1943. *Jour. Biol. Chem.* **147**: 243-253.

Krebs, H. A., and Henseleit, K. 1932. *Z. Physiol. Chem.* **210**: 33-66.

Krogh, A. 1946. *Proc. Roy. Soc. Lond.,* Series B **133**: 140-200.

Lardy, H. A., and Ziegler, J. A. 1945. *Jour. Biol. Chem.* **159**: 343-351.

LeBlond, C. P. 1942. *Rev. Canadienne de Biol.* **1**: 402-453.

Lipmann, F., and Tuttle, L. C. 1945. *Jour. Biol. Chem.* **158**: 521-531.

MacKay, E. M., Barnes, R. H., Carne, H. O., and Wick, A. N. 1940. *Jour. Biol. Chem.* **135**: 157-163.

MacKenzie, C. G., and du Vigneaud, V. 1948. *Jour. Biol. Chem.* **172**: 353-354.

Melchior, J. B., and Tarver, N. 1946. *Arch. Biochem.* **12**: 301-315.

Moore, F. D., Tobin, L. H., and Aub, J. 1943. *Jour. Clin. Invest.* **22**: 155-159; **22**: 161-167.

Moore, F. D. 1946. *Science* **104**: 157-160.

Moore, C. V., Dubach, R., Minnich, V., and Roberts H. K. 1944. *Jour. Clin. Invest.* **23**: 755-767.

Morgan, K. Z. 1947. *Jour. Phys. Coll. Chem.* **51**: 984-1003.

Morton, M. E., Chaikoff, I. L., Reinhardt, W. O., and Anderson, E. 1943. *Jour. Biol. Chem.* **147**: 757-769.

Moss, A. R., and Schoenheimer, R. 1940. *Jour. Biol. Chem.* **135**: 415.

Mufson, I., Quimby, E. H., and Smith, B. C. 1948. *Amer. Jour. Med.* **4**: 73-82.

Mullins, L. J. 1942. *Biol. Bull.* **83**: 326-333.

Ness, A. T., Brady, F. J., Cowie, D. B., and Lawton, A. H. 1947. *Jour. Pharmacol. and Exptl. Therap.* **90**: 174-180.

Nier, A. O., and Gulbransen, E. A. 1939. *Jour. Amer. Chem. Soc.* **61**: 697-698.

Nylin, G. 1945. *Arkiv. Kemi. Mineral, o. Geol.* **A20**: No. 17, 1-16

Ochoa, S. 1945. *J. Biol. Chem.* **159**, 243.

Overstreet, R., and Broyer, T. C. 1940. *Proc. Nation. Acad. Sci. U. S.* **26**: 16-24.

Reaser, P. B., and Burch, G. E. 1946. *Proc. Soc. Exptl. Biol. and Med.* **63**: 534-546.

Reinhard, E. H., Moore, C. V., Bierbaum, O. S., and Moore, S. 1946. *Jour. Lab. and Clin. Med.* **31**: 107-218.

Rittenberg, D., and Waelsch, H. 1940. *Jour. Biol. Chem.* **136**: 799-800.

Rittenberg, D., and Foster, G. L. 1940. *Jour. Biol. Chem.* **133**: 737-744.

Rittenberg, D., and Shemin, D. 1946. *Ann. Rev. Biochem.* **15**: 247-272.

Rollefson, G. K. 1934. *Jour. Chem. Phys.* **2**: 144-145.

Ruben, S., Kamen, M. D., and Hassid, W. Z. 1940. *Jour. Amer. Chem. Soc.* **62**: 3443-3450.

Schoenheimer, R., and Rittenberg, D. 1937. *Jour. Biol. Chem.* **120**: 155-165.

Scott, C. M. 1937. *Brit. Med. Research Council Rept.*, 223.

Seidlin, S. M., Marinelli, L. D., and Oshry, E. 1946. *Jour. Amer. Med. Assoc.* **132**: 838-847.

Sheline, G. E., Chaikoff, I. L., and Montgomery, M. L. 1946. *Amer. Jour. Physiol.* **145**: 285-290.

Sheline, G. E., Chaikoff, I. L., Jones, H. B., and Montgomery, M. L. 1943. *Jour. Biol. Chem.* **147**: 409-414; **149**: 139.

Shemin, D. 1945. *Jour. Biol. Chem.* **159**: 439.

Shemin, D. 1946. *Jour. Biol. Chem.* **162**: 297-307.

Shemin, D., and Rittenberg, D. 1946. *Jour. Biol. Chem.* **166**: 621-635.

Shemin, D., and Rittenberg, D. 1947. *Jour. Biol. Chem.* **167**: 875-876.

Smythe, C. V., and Holliday, D. 1942. *J. Biol. Chem.* **144**, 237.

Sonne, J. C., Buchanan, J. M., and Delluva, A. M. 1946. *Jour. Biol. Chem.* **166**: 395-396.

Spiegelman, S., and Kamen, M. D. 1947. *Cold Spring Harbor Symposia on Quantitative Biology* **12**: in press.

Spiegelman, S., Kamen, M. D., and Sussman, M. 1948. *Arch. Biochem.* **18**, 409-436.

Spinks, J. W. T., and Barber, S. A. 1947. *Sci. Agric.* **27**: 145-156.

Stetten, DeW., Jr. 1942. *Jour. Biol. Chem.* **144**: 501-506.

Stetten, DeW., Jr., and Schoenheimer, R. 1940. *Jour. Biol. Chem.* **133**: 329-345.

Stout, P. R., and Hoagland, D. R. 1939. *Amer. Jour. Bot.* **26**: 320-324.

Swendseid, M. E., Barnes, R. H., Hemingway, A., and Nier, A. O. 1942. *Jour. Biol. Chem.* **142**: 47-52.

Taurog, A., and Chaikoff, I. L. 1947. *Jour. Biol. Chem.* **169**: 49-56.

Urey, H. C. 1947. *Jour. Chem. Soc.,* 562-581.

Utter, M. F., Werkman, C. H., and Lipmann, F. 1944. *Jour. Biol. Chem.* **154**: 723-724.

Utter, M. F., and Wood, H. G. 1945. *Jour. Biol. Chem.* **160**: 375-376.

Van Niel, C. B., Ruben, S., Carson, S. F., Kamen, M. D., and Foster, J. W. 1941. *Proc. Nation. Acad. Sci. U. S.* **28**: 8-15.

Weinhouse, S., Medes, G., and Floyd, N. F. 1944. *Jour. Biol. Chem.* **155**: 143-151.

Wintrobe, W. M., Greenberg, G. R., Humphreys, S. R., Aschenbrucker, H., Worth, W., and Kraemer, R. 1947. *Jour. Clin. Invest.* **22**: 155-159.

Winzler, R. J. 1944. *Science* **99**: 327-328.

Wood, H. G., and Werkman, C. H. 1936. *Biochem. Jour.* **30**: 48-53.

Wood, H. G. 1946. *Physiol. Rev.* **26**: 198-246.

Wood, H. G., Vennesland, B., and Evans, E. A., Jr. 1945. *Jour. Biol. Chem.* **159**: 153-158.

Woods, D. D. 1936. *Biochem. Jour.* **30**: 515-527.

Yoshikawa, H., Hahn, P. F., and Ball, W. F. 1942. *Jour. Exptl. Med.* **75**: 489.

Zilversmit, D. B., Entenman, C., and Fishler, M. C. 1943. *Jour. Gen. Physiol.* **26**: 325-332.

Zilversmit, D. B., Entenman, C., Fishler, M. C., and Chaikoff, I. L. 1937. *Jour. Gen. Physiol.* **20**: 333-340.

Nutrition and Reproduction

BY KARL E. MASON

*University of Rochester, School of Medicine and Dentistry,
Rochester, New York*

SYNOPSIS

Growth and reproduction constitute the two vital powers of protoplasm that distinguish it from non-living substances. Growth is the sum of the available nutrient supply plus the capacity of the organism to utilize it. In unicellular organisms cell growth is a prerequisite for cell multiplication. In multicellular organisms, the capacity for perpetuation of the species resides only in certain cells (germ plasm) which, during early stages of development, become segregated from other cells of the body (body plasm). These relatively unspecialized germ cells undergo rapid growth and maturation during the period of reproductive activity. The general body cells differentiate and specialize during fetal life and many cannot reproduce themselves in the mature organism. There has long been a natural curiosity as to whether the sequestered and potentially immortal germ cells possess a more primitive or a more complex nutritive requirement than that exhibited by the body cells concerned with promoting growth and well being of the organism as a whole.

The nutritive needs of invertebrate organisms, and of lower vertebrates (fishes, amphibia, reptiles), are little understood. In protozoa encystment and conjugation are recognized responses to unfavorable nutrition. In higher invertebrates inadequate food supply tends to favor sexual over asexual reproduction, where both exist. The role of food in determining sexual and social status in insects, the placenta-like structures elaborated by certain fishes for nurture of their young *in vivo,* and the internal metabolic rearrangements and sex gland changes associated with seasonal breeding seasons in many species, are but examples of the complex relationships that exist. In lower, as well as in higher vertebrates, the gonads usually exhibit remarkable resistance to inanition during the period of sexual activity.

Studies on the domestic hen have provided much interesting information on such questions as: what nutrients are transferred from maternal tissues to the eggs?; how do varying levels of these nutrients in the diet modify the efficiency of transfer?; how essential are these for normal development of the egg?; can certain essential nutrients be synthesized by the developing embryo? The proper answers to such questions, in addition to their purely scientific value, are of practical importance to the dietitian, consumer, and poultryman. The diet of the hen has little or no influence on the protein or fat content of the egg. Most vitamins are transferred to the egg in limited amounts when the diet is adequate; this transfer is increased only a few-fold when a great dietary excess is provided. This restricted transfer may be looked upon as a mechanism of nature to prevent unnecessary waste, or as one to protect the developing embryo against deleterious effects of an excess. If the diet of the hen be deficient in certain vitamins (riboflavin, biotin, and others) or in the element manganese, defective embryos and lowered hatchability result; in some instances these conditions can be prevented by direct injection of the missing substance into the egg. This affords presumptive evidence that many specific nutrients play a vital role in metabolic processes of the developing chick embryo. With the exception of vitamin C, there is no convincing evidence of vitamin synthesis by the chick embryo.

It has long been recognized that inanition in man or animals, if sufficiently severe and prolonged, may diminish sexual activity, lower the incidence of conception, cause involution of the sex glands, or interfere with the course of established pregnancy. Low protein and low caloric intakes may be largely responsible for these effects, some of which may be mediated through an underfunctioning anterior pituitary gland. It is important to bear in mind these inanition effects when considering disturbances of reproduction in vitamin deficiency states where loss of appetite and of body weight frequently precede or parallel the appearance of deficiency symptoms. The practice, in some countries, of "flushing" domestic animals before the breeding season undoubtedly has merit in compensating for a prior state of suboptimal nutrition. The lay beliefs that overfeeding causes infertility, or increases infant birth weight beyond normal limits, are erroneous.

The relation between diet and reproduction in mammals has long been a matter of great practical importance and concern to animal breeders, and one of particular interest to the experimental nutritionist studying the effects of deprivation of specific nutrients upon laboratory animals; only recently has it received much consideration by students of reproductive physiology and endocrine interrelationships. Extensive research has revealed that the gonads of mammals are relatively resistant to deficiency of specific nutrients, even when moderate inanition is involved, that rather critical degrees of vitamin depletion or of inanition may arise before fetal injury or intrauterine death occur, and that reproductive disturbances characterizing specific deficiency states in certain laboratory animals do not necessarily have a strict counterpart in domestic animals or in man.

One of the most interesting developments in nutritional research in recent years has been the experimental production of congenital defects in farm and laboratory animals deprived of specific nutritive factors, chiefly vitamin A and riboflavin, with determination of the stage of gestation at which these deficiencies exert their effect upon the fetus. Many of the effects observed closely resemble those encountered in clinical medicine. The question of the manner and extent to which specific substances are transferred across the placental barrier to the fetus has been given much attention in recent years and has provided much useful information. The concept that the mammalian fetus is essentially a parasite upon the maternal organism has come to be replaced by a picture of the placenta serving to regulate nutrient exchange to the best advantage of both organisms. Clinical experience in European countries during and after the last war, and carefully planned clinical studies in this country, have demonstrated a close correlation between quality of the maternal diet and the health and vigor of the infants during the first year or more of life, and the beneficial effect of vitamin and mineral supplementation of low quality diets upon the incidence of stillbirths and neonatal mortality.

The general findings add up to the fact that the animal organism seems to be capable of making an heroic effort to maintain the mechanisms for perpetuation of the species in the face of inadequate general or specific nutrient supply, that no single "panacea" can correct for these ills, and that conditions which just barely permit the production of viable offspring and those required to produce offspring capable and worthy of perpetuating the species represent quite diverse extremes of nutritional status.

I. Introduction

Historically speaking, scientific interest in the relationship of nutrition to reproduction is essentially a twentieth-century development. To be sure, the folk lore of different civilizations is replete with superstitious beliefs that certain articles of diet can enhance or depress sexual libido, fertility or fecundity. On a more factual plane are scattered observations over past centuries regarding the effects of partial starvation upon procreative functions in man and animals, especially during periods of prolonged war, siege and famine. Yet, until about one hundred years ago, it was believed that there was a single "universal aliment" or nutrient substance absorbed from foods by the digestive tract. Differentiation between nitrogenous and non-nitrogenous foods, glorification of proteins and emphasis upon calories and energy aspects of metabolism characterized nutritional science from the middle of the past century to the second decade of the present century. This was also a period of intensive exploration of the anatomical and histological features of the reproductive organs, and the morphological changes involved in embryonic development and placentation, in vertebrate forms of life.

Beginning about 1915 the sciences of vitaminology and endocrinology had their humble beginning. Attention was focused upon the "little things" (vitamins, minerals) in nutrition, and upon the hormonal factors so vital to a proper understanding of the physiological control and regulation of the complex phenomena of reproductive and other endocrine activities. Each phase of study underwent a substantial but relatively independent development during the next 10 years. With the recognition of a special nutritive factor required for successful reproduction in the rat (vitamin E), about 10 years later, it became apparent that the investigator of reproductive physiology might well afford to give particular consideration to nutritional status of his experimental animals and that students of nutrition should give more attention to the effect of other dietary deficiencies upon reproductive processes.

The last mentioned type of approach, spurred both by purely academic inquiry and economic interest, has formed most of the bridges between the two sciences. Too often, because of the nutritionist's lack of interest in or understanding of reproductive mechanisms, the gaps have been rather weakly spanned. Consequently, the literature on this subject is replete with mention of "impaired reproduction," "lowered fertility," or "sterility" in one or the other sex, or both sexes, with no data presented or efforts made to ascertain the nature or locus of the dysfunction. Often no distinction is made between the effects of nutritive states upon fecundity (the capacity of the organism to produce functional gametes) and fertility (the capacity of the organism to produce viable offspring); often consideration is not given to the fact that reproductive rate or activity is determined by both of these factors. The problem is further complicated by two other difficulties largely inherent in the experimental method. First, but of lesser importance, is the fact that diets designed to be adequate except for deficiency of a specific factor may be, or subsequent developments in nutrition may demonstrate them to have been, deficient in other unrecognized factors or defective in some other manner; hence the constant problem of re-evaluating, and sometimes re-investigating, previous studies in the light of newer advances. Second, specific nutritional deficiencies are frequently associated with retarded growth, physical debility, diminished appetite and lowered intake of other essential nutrients of the diet. This vicious circle of events induces the factor of "inanition" which, in itself, has a profound influence upon sex interest and reproductive functions. To a certain extent the inanition effect may be overcome experimentally by forced feeding of the deficient diet, or evaluated by comparing deficient animals with others fed the control diet but restricted to the same body weight or the same caloric intake as the experimental animals. Too frequently in studies dealing with reproductive dysfunctions the inanition factor has been disregarded and the data presented do not enable one to even estimate its possible influence upon the observations and results reported.

Because of the complex nature of the processes under discussion, the essential phases of each that shall receive consideration in the discussion to follow should be defined and outlined. Under the term *nutrition* reference will be made to the two major types of malnutrition—(1) *inanition,* referring in a general way to quantitative inadequacy of diet and of calories, which may range from total inanition or starvation to lowered intake of adequate or inadequate diets, and (2) *deficiency states,* usually implying qualitative inadequacy of a single essential nutritional factor whether it be vitamin, mineral, protein or fat. The term *reproduction,* reduced to its simplest terms, will include (1) development and maintenance of structural integrity of the gonads of both sexes, (2) liberation, transport, and union of gametes, (3) implantation and development of the fertilized ovum, whether it be extrauterine or intrauterine, and, to a certain extent, (4) the delicately balanced hormonal interrelationships between the anterior pituitary, gonads and accessory reproductive organs, necessary for cyclic and other changes in the genital tract.

In addition to calling attention to the general accumulation of knowledge on the subject of nutrition and reproduction, some effort will be made to indicate certain gaps and deficiencies that exist. To accomplish these ends it seems most expedient to discuss the general status of the subject in animals grouped in phylogenetic order. Such stereotype treatment has certain drawbacks but is justified largely by the great divergence in sex organs, reproductive functions, and nutritive requirements in various phyla and classes of animals. Brevity necessitates many generalizations based upon review articles covering certain sectors of the subject. Limited reference will be made to specific reports representing more important contributions not covered by the reviews mentioned.

Long before the recognition of vitamins and other specific dietary factors much interest had developed in the effects of starvation and of general underfeeding upon many types of invertebrates and vertebrates. The vast literature accumulated on this question as well as that on the effects of deficiency of vitamins and other dietary essentials, up to 1929, has been thoroughly reviewed by Jackson (1925, 1929). Much of the existing information concerning the effects of specific vitamin and other deficiencies upon the sex glands and reproduction in vertebrates, up to 1939, has also been extensively reviewed (Mason, 1939; Phillips *et al.,* 1939). Since that time many new contributions have been made; certain of these have been discussed and correlated in other review articles dealing with more specific phases of nutritional research, which will be referred to later. Especially noteworthy is the rapid advance of the past 10 years in elucidation of the many components of the vitamin B complex, and the need for separate consideration of many vitamins in this formidable list even though knowledge of their relation to reproduction is still rather fragmentary. For more detailed information on current knowledge of the vitamins and manifestations of their deficiency states the reader is referred to other sources (Wolbach and Bessey, 1942; Bicknell and Prescott, 1947; Follis, 1948).

II. Invertebrates

1. *Protozoa*

There is considerable, although not too conclusive, evidence that starvation or severe underfeeding in protozoa tends to promote conjugation. It is, in fact, on the basis of such evidence that there arose the interesting postulation that sex is a primitive form of hunger, driving organisms to engulf each other. Investigation of specific nutrient needs of protozoa has received considerable attention during the past 10 years but has been handicapped by technical difficulties in developing adequate media and in variations in the transfer technique. The literature has been reviewed by Trager (1941) and by Hall (1943). It should be emphasized that distinctions between needs for growth and those for reproduction are difficult to make in these lower forms of life. Likewise, when growth is used as a measure of response to specific nutrient factors it is usually impossible to determine from the procedures used whether this is the result of fission or of prolongation of the life of individual organisms. There is no conclusive evidence that any protozoan can synthesize vitamins, although some forms seem to be able to utilize the two components of the thiamine molecule—thiazole and pyrimidine. Certain protozoa do require thiamine, ascorbic acid, hematin and cholesterol. In none has there been demonstrated a specific need for riboflavin, pyridoxine, pantothenic acid, nicotinic acid or biotin. Many of them undoubtedly require for vital functions certain vitamin and other factors, many of which are provided by microorganisms of their normal habitat.

2. *Metazoa*

In the metazoa, or higher invertebrates, inanition and other adverse environmental conditions usually favor sexual reproduction over the asexual type (budding, fission, parthenogenesis) in forms possessing both mechanisms. Furthermore, in certain species (hydra, rotifers, daphnids, aphids) there is strong evidence of nutritional sex determination, inanition favoring a preponderance of males, a phenomenon noted also in the plant world. The gonads themselves, together with the nervous system, are usually the last organs to show involution; this is also a common finding in vertebrates. The most extensive studies have been carried out on forms such as hydra, planaria, snails, crustacea and insects. Considerable data on the composition of the eggs of various invertebrates have been summarized by Needham (1942) but the relation of these facts to developmental processes has received little or no attention.

Considerable attention has been given to the effect of nutrition upon sex development in certain insects. For instance, the special diet of "royal jelly" is essential for transforming the rudimentary reproductive tract of the "worker" bee into the functional tract of the "queen." Also, in certain species of ants, where similar determining factors operate, variations in the size of "workers" seem to depend upon quantitative differences in food received, and differences between workers and soldiers depend upon qualitative differences in diet. Various insects studied have shown the need for, but the inability to synthesize, many of the factors of the vitamin B complex and certain fat-soluble substances of vitamin-like nature. Some show nutritional requirements as complex as those of vertebrates.

III. Fishes, Amphibia, Reptiles

At the outset, distinction should be made between "nutritional inanition" and certain types of "physiological inanition" which, in certain vertebrate species, are affiliated closely with seasonal reproductive activity. Of the latter type, perhaps the most striking is the extensive loss of muscle and adipose tissue, associated with marked growth of the gonads, occurring in fasting salmon prior to the spawning season. Similar phenomena have been observed in the male fur seal and in the gander (Jackson, 1925). Their restriction to so few and quite unrelated species has received no adequate explanation. Somewhat different from this is the phenomenon of *hibernation*. Here there is usually a special accumulation of food reserves coupled with a striking diminution in the general body metabolism. Gonadal changes appear to be correlated more closely with pituitary changes (which, in turn, are influenced by light, temperature, and other environmental factors) than with nutritive conditions. For example, testis regression usually precedes, often by some months, the phenomenon of hibernation, and testicular regeneration usually occurs during the latter phases of the hibernation period. It must be assumed that certain of the storage materials, if not other tissues of the organism, are specifically allocated for this important metabolic event.

The effects of starvation or lack of specific nutrients upon the reproductive organs of fish have received little or no attention. Numerous studies on frogs and salamanders, mostly carried out prior to 1918, indicate that the gonads in both sexes are highly resistant to fasting during the breeding season but at other periods respond by involution and resorption of the more mature sex cells. As in higher forms, the capacity for recovery after refeeding is quite remarkable. Likewise, starvation at the larval stage inhibits both body growth and gonad development, but the latter to a lesser extent (Jackson, 1925).

In both the elasmobranch and teleost fishes there exist oviparous, ovoviviparous and viviparous forms providing varying degrees of relationship between the embryo and maternal tissues. In some the embryo is nourished by uterine secretions similar to the "histotrope" or "uterine milk" of mammals possessing epitheliochorial placentas; at the other extreme are forms with rather elaborate yolk-sac types of placentas which actually invade the uterine wall. There are also interesting correlations between the dependence of the embryo upon the maternal organism and the histology, lipid content and diminishing size of the liver, suggesting that this organ serves as a special storehouse of reserve nutrients for the embryo. A similar though less obvious alteration of the liver during pregnancy has been postulated for mammals. Needham (1942) gives an excellent discussion of the known morphological and biochemical features of these interesting embryo-mother relationships of fishes, as well as those of certain insects and lower invertebrates. The extent to which they may be influenced by nutritional deficiencies is unknown.

It is to be regretted that we know so little about the requirements for vitamin and other factors in the large group of cold-blooded vertebrates. We are aware of the relatively great storage of vitamins A and D in the cod and other species of fish, and the extensive transfer of vitamin A to the gonads during the spawning season. Whether this represents a special provision for developmental processes in the ovum has not been established. The feeding and other habits of these lower vertebrates are such that experimental dietary studies are very difficult to carry out. A few studies have been made on trout, guppy fish and tadpoles. There is evidence that vitamin E may be necessary for development and structural integrity of the testis in the guppy fish (Mason, 1944).

IV. Birds

1. *Nutrition and Sex Glands*

It has long been recognized that the testis and ovary of birds are especially susceptible to starvation, diminishing in weight about twice as rapidly as the body as a whole and showing quite profound histologic damage.

Restoration after refeeding is astonishingly rapid (Jackson, 1925). There is also evidence that the testes of birds, unlike those of mammals, are peculiarly sensitive to lack of thiamine (Mason, 1939). Extensive damage occurs even when forced feeding prevents loss of body weight. Ovarian effects due specifically to lack of thiamine are negligible. Gonadal injury due to lack of other factors of the vitamin B complex has not been reported; on the other hand, testicular degeneration has been described in domestic fowl deficient in vitamin A (Seifried and Köcher, 1943) and in vitamin E (Mason, 1939).

During the past 10 years it has become apparent that the vitamin B complex consists of ten or more components. Disturbances caused by their absence may vary widely in birds and mammals and may be considerably modified by the presence or absence of other dietary constituents. Certain of them are synthesized by bacteria in the gastrointestinal tract, to a variable extent in different forms; many of them are also growth factors for bacteria. Increased knowledge of these latter functions, and the capacity of sulfa drugs to inhibit their bacterial synthesis, have played an important role in their identification. For further details the reader is referred to three comprehensive reviews of these bacteria-vitamin relationships (Najjar and Barrett, 1945; Knight, 1945; Daft and Sebrell, 1945). At least six of the vitamin B complex components (thiamine, riboflavin, nicotinic acid, pyridoxine, pantothenic acid, biotin) function through their capacity to combine, in phosphorylated form, with specific proteins to form tissue enzymes capable of effecting catalysis of known reactions, and perhaps as yet unknown reactions, in intermediary metabolism. The role of other members of this group (*p*-aminobenzoic acid, folic acid, choline, inositol) are less well understood. Current knowledge of the nature and functions of the newest member of this group, folic acid, has been presented in an exhaustive review (Jukes and Stokstad, 1948). Reproduction in chicks seems not to be influenced by deficiency of this vitamin.

2. *Egg Storage and Hatchability*

Studies on birds have been concerned largely with transfer of essential nutrients to the egg, hatchability and defects in embryonic development. An excellent review of the subject up to 1941 has been presented by Cruickshank (1941); newer findings are discussed by Hertz (1946). The total protein and fat content of the egg is not much influenced by the diet, but unsaturated fats of the diet are readily transferred to the egg. Thiamine and nicotinic acid are transferred in small amounts even when the diet is low in these factors. Vitamin C is not present in the egg but can be synthesized by the developing embryo, beginning about the fourth day. Evidence that pantothenic acid, riboflavin and biotin undergo no material change, whereas nicotinic acid and inositol are synthesized to a considerable extent during incubation, requires further investigation (Romanoff and Bauernfeind, 1942). On diets low in vitamin A, maternal needs are satisfied before transfer to the egg occurs. On normal diets the latter amounts to about one-fourth of the maternal intake. The efficiency of this transfer diminishes rapidly as the intake is increased, because of buffering action of the liver; great excess increases the egg content only about five times that observed on normal diets. In the case of vitamin D this buffering action is negligible and transfer to the egg is more proportional to that present in the diet. The other fat-soluble vitamins, E and K, are usually present in moderate amounts when hens are fed adequate diets.

Hatchability of the chick egg, which may be influenced by a variety of nondietary factors (genetic characteristics, egg size, porosity of shell), is especially dependent upon an adequacy of specific nutrients. These include riboflavin, biotin, pantothenic acid, vitamin A, vitamin D, vitamin E and manganese. Direct injection of riboflavin or manganese into eggs from hens deficient in these substances promptly improves hatchability. It is also of interest that a dietary excess of vitamin D or strontium, and direct injection of strontium or nicotinic acid into the egg, can greatly depress or abolish hatchability. Some of the effects appear to be rather nonspecific; others result in rather characteristic, structural modifications at certain stages of embryonic development.

Mortality at about the fourth day of incubation, caused by formation of a "lethal ring" of proliferating mesoderm shutting off the vitelline circulation, has been observed in eggs from hens deficient in vitamin E or in riboflavin. At later stages riboflavin deficient embryos may show marked stunting, edema, anemia, clubbed down, shortening of extremities and lower mandible, and degenerative changes in developing kidney and liver (Romanoff and Bauernfeind, 1942). Biotin deficiency results in high mortality during the last 3 days of hatching, associated with perosis, shortening of bones in leg and wing, and parrot beak. The bone defects may be secondary to defects in metabolism and development of the muscles (Couch, *et al.*, 1948). In manganese deficiency the embryo frequently shows short, thick legs and wings, globular heads, and parrot beaks (Cruickshank, 1941; Underwood, 1940). An excess of selenium causes inhibition of embryonic growth, "wing" down, and defective development of cartilage and bone. It is still impossible to relate these developmental defects to specific metabolic functions of the nutrient factors concerned.

Egg yolk normally contains small amounts of biotin, a rather universal constituent of plant and animal cells. On the other hand, egg white contains a basic protein "avidin" which, unless denatured by heat, is capable of combining with biotin to form an avidin-biotin complex resistant to the action of digestive enzymes. Uncooked egg white may thus inactivate dietary biotin and produce in animals the symptomatology first termed "egg white injury" but now recognized as biotin deficiency. No other protein capable of inactivating biotin in this way has been found, and avidin has been found only in the egg white of birds and in the egg jelly of amphibia (Hertz, 1946). It is still a mystery why nature provided in the egg white of birds about twice as much avidin as is necessary to inactivate the biotin present in the yolk. Avidin is a normal product of the albumen-secreting portion of the oviduct in hens, and its formation may be induced prematurely in the oviduct of young chicks by administering stilbestrol combined with progesterone. Its presence in the egg jelly of amphibia adds further weight to the suggestion that it, as well as biotin, may play some important role in embryonic development of the extrauterine type. One might speculate as to whether avidin might have been provided by nature to discourage, by virtue of its capacity to inactivate their biotin supply, the growth of microorganisms that might effect premature dissolution of the jelly or albumen of the amphibian and avian egg. It would be of interest to know more about the fate of biotin and avidin during early stages of development of these eggs. Avidin cannot be demonstrated in the oviduct secretions of mammals (Hertz, 1946). Whether biotin occurs in the ova of mammals remains to be determined.

V. Mammals

Nutritive conditions that maintain good health and vigor in adult mammals generally provide the essentials for good reproduction. Vitamin E constitutes the major exception to this rule. It must also be kept in mind, however, that gestation and lactation place special metabolic demands upon the maternal organism. Furthermore, numerous body dysfunctions influencing absorption, storage, distribution, tissue utilization and excretion of certain essential nutrients, and "conditioning" or "stress" factors that increase nutritional requirements for specific nutrients, may cause malnutrition even when diets are presumably adequate. An excellent discussion of these factors is given in a recent review (Ershoff, 1948). The problem is further complicated by the fact that failures of reproduction can be due to a great variety of non-nutritional causes; genetic factors, endocrine dysfunctions, congenital and other anatomical defects as well as pathological changes in the reproductive tract, mechanical injury to female genital tract or to fetus, or combinations of any of these. Furthermore, the normal course of events may be interrupted by failures in gamete formation, in copulation because of lack of sex desire, in fertilization, in implantation, in placental or fetal development and in lactation capacity of mother or lactation performance of offspring.

1. *Relation to Sex Glands*

a. Inanition. Inanition in mammals affects the reproductive organs somewhat differently from that observed in birds. The germinal epithelium of the testis shows considerable resistance to degenerative change, more so in adult than in sexually immature animals, and the ovary exhibits only moderate suppression of follicular development with increased follicular atresia. Functionally, however, the effect is more marked and may be related in part to diminished production of gonadotropic hormones by the anterior pituitary. The accessory reproductive organs in both sexes show extensive atrophy and cyclic changes in the female genital tract are prolonged or suppressed; yet their capacity to respond to hormonal stimuli is not impaired and their rapid return to normality after restoration of a complete diet is quite remarkable. Depending upon the stage of pregnancy at which underfeeding becomes effective and the severity of the latter, inanition in rodents may induce fetal resorption, abortion, stillbirth or delivery of puny offspring after prolonged gestation (Jackson, 1925 and 1929; Mason, 1939).

It is common knowledge that periods of war and famine are associated with varying degrees of infertility in man and domestic animals. Males usually show testicular atrophy, suppression of spermatogenesis and diminished libido. Women exhibit scanty or infrequent menses, ovarian and uterine atrophy and greatly lowered incidence of conception. If pregnancies are not terminated by miscarriage, abortion or stillbirth, the impoverished offspring rarely survive if dependent upon breast feeding because of the impaired lactation of the mother. In the concentration camps of World War II history repeated itself and much the same conditions were observed; so also, but to a lesser extent, in civilian populations suffering prolonged deprivation of calories. This is essentially the same picture as encountered in experimental animals subjected to inanition. In both experimental and clinical situations it is difficult to determine what qualitative deficiencies may have also existed. However, it is generally held that in states of lowered caloric intake the requirement for vitamins and other essential nutrients is appreciably lowered. Furthermore, the increased use of vegetable foods in times of general food shortage, which most frequently involves meat and poultry foods, usually assures a reasonably good vitamin intake. This is strikingly illustrated by experiences of the past war, with almost no evidence of frank vitamin deficiency in peoples of any of the occupied or warring countries despite the dietary restrictions often necessary.

On the other side of the ledger is the question of overfeeding and its influence on mother and fetus. The practice of "flushing" ewes before the mating season is an example. It would seem that any benefits derived from the procedure are dependent upon degrees of suboptimal nutrition existing prior to flushing. Beliefs have arisen that overfeeding may cause infertility and may also increase birth weights far beyond normal limits. These are not supported by experimental studies or general experience. Overfeeding in pregnancy is reflected largely in increased maternal weight. The fetus seems capable of exercising relatively independent control of its own metabolism with considerable capacity to adjust to dearth or excess of nutritive materials in the maternal organism.

b. Proteins. The effects of lowered protein intake upon reproductive organs are considered to be quite similar to those resulting from inanition. To a certain extent the same seems to be true of deficiency of certain of the "essential" amino acids. The rat is unable to synthesize sufficient amounts of about ten of these to meet its requirements for growth and maintenance. One might assume that these protein units are as essential for reproduction as for growth. However, this postulation receives only partial support from the rather fragmentary evidence recorded to date.

Considerable interest has centered around a possible role of arginine in reproduction. The relatively high content of this amino acid in nucleoproteins of the sperm head has long been recognized. The newer interest originated largely with the report that arginine deficiency in man causes a marked reduction in sperm count, which is repaired by return to an adequate diet, and also induces considerable testicular degeneration in rats. Restudy of this problem in the rat indicates that an exogenous source of arginine is not necessary for reproduction in rats of either sex (Williams and Watson, 1944). However, these studies do not exclude the possibility that the endogenously produced arginine, which in the adult rat is sufficient to meet all needs except those for new growth, may be utilized for reproductive functions, or that it may be insufficient for testis development during adolescence.

Deficiency of phenylalanine, leucine and histidine in the rat is said to induce testicular atrophy of somewhat more severe degree than observed in "paired-feeding" controls (Maun *et al.*, 1946). Contrary to findings previously reported, uncomplicated deficiency of tryptophan in young rats, lasting as long as 20 days, does not induce subsequent sterility in either sex (Berg and Rohse, 1947). It is to be regretted that so little attention has been given to the effect of specific amino acid deficiencies upon pregnancy and fetal development.

c. Carbohydrates. Deficiency or excess of carbohydrates exerts no deleterious effect upon the reproductive organs of either sex. However, the secondary effects of maternal diabetes upon fetal development and mortality are well recognized, but there is no general agreement as to the mechanisms involved.

d. Fats. It is generally accepted, though based chiefly upon feeding experiments with rats, that the mammalian organism can provide its own fats through synthesis from carbohydrates and proteins, except for certain long-chain unsaturated fatty acids (linoleic, arachidonic) which are very essential as components of cell phospholipids and must be procured through the diet. In the absence of these unsaturated fatty acids the seminiferous epithelium of the testis undergoes extensive degeneration and pregnancy may terminate in resorption, prolonged labor, excessive hemorrhages and birth of dead offspring (Mason, 1939; Burr, 1942; Quackenbush *et al.*, 1942). Little has been added to this subject during the past seven years.

e. Minerals. The literature on inorganic salt requirements up to 1940 has been reviewed by Underwood (1940), and current knowledge of deficiency effects has been presented by Follis (1948) and Warkany (1945). It is now accepted that five metals (Co, Cu, Fe, Mn and Zn) have particular metabolic significance in the sense that they represent indispensable constituents of enzyme systems. The needs of Ca, P, Fe and other minerals for fetal development are of course well recognized. Of these only Mn has been shown to have specific relation to reproductive functions. On manganese-low diets male rats exhibit testicular atrophy which is apparently not an inanition effect, whereas female rats ovulate and conceive but produce a high proportion of nonviable young or young that show motor incoordination and paralysis and succumb within 48 hours even when suckled by control rats. Contrary to previous reports, nesting instincts and lactation capacity of the mother are not seriously impaired. Some of the offspring show skeletal abnormalities, involving shortening and bowing of the forelegs. A biochemical lesion involving decreased activity of liver arginase, which requires Mn for proper activity, has been postulated.

f. Vitamin B Complex. The general relation of vitamins to reproduction has been discussed rather extensively in several reviews (Mason, 1939; Phillips *et al.*, 1939; Warkany, 1945). Discovery and differentiation of many components of the vitamin B complex has taken place largely during the past 10 years. There is reason to consider the existence of other as yet unrecognized factors. Time has not permitted much exploration of their role in reproduction. This is especially complicated by the fact that deficiency symptoms, in practically all instances, are associated with considerable anorexia, growth impairment and general debility.

Thiamine deficiency in the rat and other experimental animals seems to have no direct effect upon reproductive organs but may interfere with the normal completion of pregnancy. Deficiency states severe enough to cause general debility and loss of sex interest may be compatible with normal testis structure unless inanition effects arise. Delayed sexual maturity, prolonged or suppressed estrus, and atrophy of ovaries and uteri after thiamine deficiency are also inanition effects. Considering the complicating factors of anorexia, cachexia, pituitary underfunction and diminished function of the genital tract, sometimes referred to as a state of "pseudohypophysectomy," it is understandable why so little concrete evidence can be brought forth concerning any specific role of thiamine in pregnancy. The literature on gestational polyneuritis and infantile beriberi in man is quite extensive but not particularly illuminating.

Testis damage has been observed in a few studies with rodents deprived of riboflavin, pantothenic acid and pyridoxine but the possible influence of inanition has not been entirely eliminated. In the female rodent deficiency of pantothenic acid may cause fetal resorption or birth of weak offspring and impair lactation (Nelson and Evans, 1946). A similar sequence of events occurs after riboflavin deficiency and is associated with skeletal defects in the offspring (Warkany, 1945), as discussed in a later section. Biotin deficiency may give similar results but here the inanition effect is quite marked and has not been carefully evaluated by paired-feeding experiments. There is as yet no evidence to indicate whether fetal death in utero or weakness of offspring can be correlated with a deficiency, in the fetal tissues of enzymes, of which the vitamin in question constitutes an integral component.

The ruminants need no consideration here since they represent a special group of mammals whose needs for the various components of the vitamin B complex are adequately met by bacterial synthesis in the rumen, the first of the four compartments of the stomach. The many observations on sheep, goats, and cattle have been reviewed by Goss (1943). In other mammals, there is a variable but much more limited synthesis of certain of these factors by intestinal bacteria. The inhibition of this synthesis by the sulfanilamide drugs is well recognized and is one of the means of inducing a deficiency of certain factors (biotin, pantothenic acid, *p*-aminobenzoic acid).

The recent reviews of Hertz (1946) and Biskind (1946) discuss current concepts of interrelationships between the B vitamins and endocrinological aspects of reproduction. The first of these gives particular attention to growth responses of tissues, especially those of the reproductive system, as influenced by the B vitamins and hormonal factors. The second deals especially with the influence of thiamine deficiency, riboflavin deficiency, and nutritional cirrhosis upon impaired capacity of the liver to inactivate estrogenic hormones, a subject which still remains controversial because of the complicating factor of associated inanition (Drill and Pfeiffer, 1946), and also gives consideration to clinical observations regarding beneficial effects of vitamin B therapy in overcoming hormonal and metabolic dysfunctions that relate to reproductive disturbances in both sexes. The subject matter of both reviews indicates some of the newer trends of investigation dealing with the interplay of nutritive and hormonal factors upon the reproductive system.

g. Vitamins C and D. Neither vitamin C nor vitamin D has been shown to have any specific relationship to structural or functional integrity of the reproductive organs in either sex. Only the guinea pig, monkey and man require an extraneous source of vitamin C. Certain cellular components of the sex glands and pituitary are relatively rich in vitamin C, but this seems to be related to high levels of metabolic activity in these tissues. Despite numerous studies carried out to determine whether the mammalian fetus can synthesize its own supply of vitamin C, and whether pregnancy accentuates or attenuates the manifestations of scurvy in the maternal organism, opinions are generally divided on the issues. Several clinical studies carried out during the past few years indicate quite clearly that the vitamin C content of fetal cord blood at delivery is normally higher than that of maternal blood. This has been interpreted not as synthesis by the fetus but rather as an indication that vitamin C needs of the fetus may be met and maintained, if need be, at the sacrifice of the maternal reserves. To the extent that this may be true, the fetus may be considered a parasite on the maternal organism. In the rat pregnancy is not seriously affected by diets deficient in vitamin D and containing wide variations in calcium and phosphorus content, or by diets containing great excess of vitamin D. In man the state of pregnancy is quite compatible with frank manifestations of osteomalacia (the latter is frequently precipitated by pregnancy) excepting in so far as parturition may be complicated by pelvic deformities incident to the deficiency state.

h. Vitamin A. One of the major functions of vitamin A is to maintain and permit proper differentiation of epithelial tissues. Since the reproductive tract in both sexes is composed of numerous epithelial-lined structures, it is not surprising that deficiency of vitamin A affects reproduction, directly or indirectly, in a variety of ways. The characteristic histopathologic changes observed in laboratory rodents, especially the rat, have been reviewed in considerable detail (Mason, 1939). Briefly, they are as follows: In the male there occurs a progressive loss of germ cells from the seminiferous epithelium. The more mature cells are first affected; the basal spermatogonia and primary spermatocytes are relatively more resistant. The histological changes differ from those of vitamin E deficiency and inanition. Repair following vitamin A therapy, although less rapid than that after inanition and refeeding, is quite remarkable and is not greatly retarded if body weight is held constant or even diminished by restriction of caloric intake during therapy. The lining of the efferent sex ducts may exhibit keratinizing metaplasia which, through blockage with desquamated cells or infection and abscess formation, may constitute a secondary factor in sterility in instances of prolonged and rather severe deficiency.

In the female rodent one of the earliest indications of vitamin A deficiency is keratinizing metaplasia of the vaginal mucosa, producing a condition simulating persistent estrus. This promptly disappears following vitamin A therapy. It is of particular interest that the vaginal epithelium of rodents should respond in much the same manner to either lack of vitamin A or a certain level of estrogenic hormone. Furthermore, this vaginal epithelium when under the influence of inadequate vitamin A loses its capacity to undergo mucification in response to progesterone. This suggests a suppression of mucoprotein formation and an exaggerated production of albuminoids on the part of the A-deficient epithelium. Despite the continuous vaginal cornification, rhythmic changes (ovulation, estrus) occur in the genital tract and are of normal duration unless associated inanition effects some irregularity and lengthening of the cycle. Fertilization and implantation are usually successful but, depending on the severity of the deficiency, pregnancy culminates in fetal death and resorption, stillbirth, prolonged and difficult parturition and high mortality of viable offspring. Fetal death seems to be due to foci of infection and necrosis in the placenta fostered by lowered resistance of uterine epithelium and stroma to invading organisms. The possibility that congenital defects may also account for some of these intrauterine deaths will be discussed later. Keratinization of the vaginal epithelium throughout pregnancy has recently been noted in A-deficient monkeys (van Wagenen, 1948).

Much attention has also been given to the relation of vitamin A to reproduction in dairy cattle, and to a lesser extent in sheep, pigs and other farm animals. The literature to 1940 has been reviewed by Hart (1940); many of the later studies are referred to elsewhere (Warkany, 1945; Ellis, 1946; Hodgson *et al.*, 1946). This represents a problem of great economic importance. The failure of the dairy cow to conceive when bred means delayed calving and maintenance for several months without any financial return. The fault may lie with the herd sire or the cows. Many factors interfere with normal reproductive performance. As a rule, vitamin A is a matter of concern only when cattle have been maintained under conditions of prolonged drouth or the feeding of very poor roughage over considerable periods of time. Temporary periods of poor nutrition have little effect providing that previous nutrition has permitted an adequate liver storage of vitamin A. Many experimentally induced deficiencies of vitamin A in cattle have also been carried out. The findings differ in certain respects from those on rodents. Blindness, due to constriction of the optic nerve through overgrowth of bone around the orbital fissures, and cysts of the pituitary with variable degrees of damage to the anterior lobe, are frequent phenomena. It has been reported (Hodgson *et al.*, 1946) that bulls sufficiently deficient to show blindness, incoordination, weakness, diarrhea, edematous joints, low concentration of semen, cystic pituitaries and degenerate testes were still fertile and capable of siring normal calves. The fact that supplements of cod liver oil were supplied at variable periods to prevent the bulls from succumbing completely to the deficiency may account for preservation of some seminiferous tubules and capacity to inseminate some of the cows which the animals served. The regenerative capacity of the testes of vitamin A deficient bulls, following A-therapy, has been repeatedly demonstrated. It is of particular interest that fertility is possible in the face of cystic destruction of so much anterior pituitary tissue. Vitamin A deficiency in cows does not interfere with conception, unless extreme, but moderate deficiency may cause stillbirth or delivery of blind and weak calves. Sheep respond in much the same manner. Pigs show estrous irregularities and high incidence of abortions and stillbirths.

i. Vitamin E. The existence of vitamin E (or tocopherol) was established on the basis of its need for reproductive function in the male and female rat. Subsequent studies have revealed other equally, and perhaps more, important functions of this vitamin in fat stabilization, muscle metabolism and other tissue functions. These may prove to reflect a vital role of vitamin E as a general intracellular antioxidant. These latter trends of investigation, coupled with the difficulties in securing convincing evidence that reproductive failure in man or in domestic animals is in any way related to inadequacy of vitamin E, have served to de-emphasize the antisterility aspects of the vitamin. Various aspects of vitamin E functions have been discussed in several reviews (Bicknell and Prescott, 1947; Mason, 1944; Hickman and Harris, 1946).

It has been repeatedly demonstrated that the testicular damage in rats deprived of vitamin E is quite different from that encountered in any other deficiency state, both with respect to the sequence of cellular changes and the irreversibility of the injury. Prolonged deficiency causes no injury to the mouse testis even though the female mouse responds to E-depletion as does the female rat. Testicular damage has been demonstrated, however, in the E-deficient guinea pig, rooster, and guppy fish but its irreversibility has not been determined. The recent finding that testicular degeneration in the E-deficient hamster can be repaired by E-therapy (Mason, unpublished studies) suggests that perhaps too much emphasis has been placed on the irreversibility of testicular injury in the rat. Although it has been reported that administration of vitamin E can effect a marked increase in sperm count and correct in large measure barren marriages due to infertility in the human male, which in recent years has come to be recognized as a very common phenomenon, other studies carried out in a more carefully controlled manner do not support this belief.

Intrauterine death and resorption of the fetus, which constitutes the classic manifestation of vitamin E deficiency, has been produced with regularity only in the rat and mouse. A similar phenomenon has been observed in the hamster. The precocious and severe dystrophy of the skeletal musculature that occurs in herbivorous laboratory animals renders them rather unsuitable for studies of reproductive function. As in the case of the testis, the intrauterine changes differ from those observed after other nutritive deficiencies. The animals appear healthy and vigorous, at least during the first few months of life, and all events up to and including placentation are normal until fetal death and autolysis occur, usually during the second week of the 3-week gestation period. Fetal death has been attributed to failure of mesodermal derivatives, especially those concerned with hematopoiesis, and to abnormalities of the vascular system characterized by stasis, distension, thrombosis, hemorrhage and generalized tissue ischemia. It is not known which represents the primary lesion or what the underlying cellular dysfunctions may be. Suboptimal levels of vitamin E produce all gradations between early resorption and viable fetuses. The latter rarely survive the first few days of life unless the maternal intake of E is several times that required for successful gestation. Although unknown dysfunctions in the fetal tissues leading to death and autolysis of the latter have generally been regarded as the basis of resorption sterility of E-deficiency, there is considerable evidence that with increasing age and continued deficiency the amount of the vitamin required for successful gestation increases and the incidence of established pregnancies after fertile matings diminishes greatly (Kaunitz and Slanetz, 1947). There is also a progressive deposition of inert pigment in the uterine smooth muscle (Mason, 1944). All these facts suggest possible dysfunction of uterine, and possibly placental, tissues. In this connection it is of interest that alloxan diabetes in the rat causes death and resorption of the fetus beginning about mid-pregnancy (twelfth day), yet the placentas are retained and delivered at parturition (Davis *et al.*, 1947); in E-deficiency, on the other hand, placentas always undergo rapid regression to a structureless blood clot before term even when fetal death occurs at the sixteenth day or later.

It is perhaps natural that the unusual types of reproductive impairment in vitamin E deficiency should lead to a rather extensive literature attributing these changes to dysfunction of the anterior pituitary, ovary, and thyroid, and ascribing estrogenic as well as anti-estrogenic and other properties to the vitamin. These postulations, and the more critical observations which deny the existence of such endocrine interrelationships, have been reviewed in detail elsewhere (Mason, 1944).

Evidence concerning a role of vitamin E in reproductive functions of man and domestic animals is either negative or circumstantial. Efforts to interfere with reproduction by feeding E-deficient diets to sheep, goats and cattle have, as yet, been unsuccessful. Such experiments are difficult because of the occurrence of small amounts of the vitamin in almost any component of a diet that would be tolerated and capable of maintaining the animal in a good state of nutrition, unless subjected to solvent extraction or oxidative treatment which may cause other deleterious effects. On the other side of the ledger is the reputed improvement in fertility in cattle, especially in the reported efficacy of vitamin E in reducing the incidence of noninfectious abortions in cattle, and in treating habitual abortion, threatened abortion, premature separation of the placenta and certain types of pregnancy toxemia in women. Statistical analysis, by Bacharach, of the clinical data reported up to 1939 suggests that the results are highly significant (Mason, 1944). It is to be regretted that we have acquired so little information regarding the reproductive needs of most mammalian organisms for a vitamin discovered more than thirty years ago on the basis of rather distinctive types of reproductive impairment in the rat. We have every reason to believe that a dietary source of vitamin E is essential for vital processes in all mammals, and in lower animals as well. On the basis of present evidence, we must assume either that vitamin E is not necessary for reproduction in some mammals (e.g., the male mouse), or that the experimental methods so far applied have, for one reason or another, failed to demonstrate this need.

j. Vitamin K. The primary function of vitamin K seems to be in stimulating production of plasma prothrombin, so important in the mechanism of blood clotting. The prothrombin level of infants at birth is normally low and may diminish further during the first few days of life. If these values fall low enough, hemorrhagic disease of the newborn results. Such hemorrhagic tendencies may have some bearing upon the high incidence of cerebral hemorrhage in the large number of infants born each year who do not survive. Vitamin K, when administered to the parturient mother or to the infant at birth, promptly overcomes the low prothrombin levels and lowers the incidence of infant mortality. It is usually assumed that after the first 4 or 5 days of postnatal life an adequate supply of vitamin K is provided through bacterial syntheses in the gastrointestinal tract.

There is no evidence that a comparable situation prevails in any other mammalian form. It is usually quite difficult to induce a state of vitamin K deficiency in experimental animals because of the extent of intestinal syntheses and the potential sources through microorganisms in the external environment (food, water, feces, etc.). One series of studies with rabbits (Moore *et al.,* 1942) indicates that dietary lack of vitamin K may cause abortion during early or midpregnancy, associated with hemorrhages in the placenta not unlike those seen in retroplacental hemorrhage in man.

2. *Developmental Anomalies*

In other sections of this review it has been noted that severe underfeeding as well as dietary deficiencies of specific vitamins, essential fatty acids, and to a lesser extent minerals, in the rat and other laboratory animals may lead to intrauterine fetal death and resorption, abortion, stillbirth or delivery of puny and weak offspring. Too often there has been failure to examine the uterus, placentas and fetuses either macroscopically or microscopically. Undoubtedly the causes of fetal death at any stage of gestation are manifold. Some of these may be purely biochemical, others may involve structural defects in growth and differentiation of tissues or organs which are incompatible with continued survival of the fetus, still others are probably combinations of both causative factors. Although many fetuses that succumb in utero are undoubtedly congenitally defective, the mechanism of resorption (or abortion) can scarcely be regarded as a mechanism designed to rid the organism of defective conceptuses; at least, if this be so, it is not an efficient mechanism for many congenitally defective offspring are viable at term.

Except for a number of early observations in the field of animal husbandry, there existed very little evidence that congenital anomalies in the mammalian fetus could be correlated with specific nutritional deficiencies in the mother (this subject, as far as it applies to avian development, has been discussed in an earlier section). One of the most interesting developments in nutritional research in recent years has been the experimental production of congenital defects in farm and laboratory animals deprived of specific nutritive factors, chiefly vitamin A and riboflavin, with determination of the stage of gestation at which these deficiencies exert their effect upon the fetus. No claims are made that congenital anomalies in man, though closely resembling those experimentally produced, are due to the same causes. Certain developmental defects may be due to a variety of factors operating at a particular stage of gestation. In any case, the observations so far recorded are highly significant. An excellent summary has been given by Warkany (1945) who has contributed much to this new phase of nutritional research.

In female rats deprived of riboflavin there exists between states of fertility and sterility a stage in which a high percentage of defective offspring develop. These defects involve shortening of long bones of the extremities and the mandible, tendency to fusion of ribs and digits, and cleft palate; similar skeletal defects in chick embryos deficient in riboflavin were referred to earlier. These are due to special need for riboflavin on the thirteenth and fourteenth days of gestation which is a critical period in the process of chondrification of the skeleton in the rat. These changes are quite different from those that may occur in the late fetus and newborn of animals fed certain types of rachitogenic diets.

Fifteen years ago Hale observed that pigs severely depleted of vitamin A prior to and during the first month of gestation, and subsequently given an abundance of the vitamin to assure successful completion of gestation, produced offspring with varied developmental defects. These included harelip, cleft palate, subcutaneous cysts, malformation of the extremities and retention of kidneys and sex glands in an embryonic condition (Mason, 1939; Warkany, 1945). Warkany has produced equally striking developmental defects in rats by careful restriction of the vitamin A and carotene intake throughout gestation. Although many embryos succumbed, considerable numbers of viable fetuses were carried to term or were removed from the uteri at various periods prior to parturition. Especially striking were eye abnormalities, involving absence or poor development of the anterior chamber, ciliary body, and iris, replacement of the vitreous by a fibrous retrolenticular membrane, eversion of the retina, defects of cornea and conjunctival sacs and failure of fusion of the eyelids. Further study of such fetuses has revealed general underdevelopment of many of the soft tissues (lungs, myocardium, kidneys, ureters) as well as subcutaneous hemorrhage, edema, undescent of the testes, diaphragmatic hernia and variable degrees of fusion of the kidneys (Warkany and Roth, 1948; Wilson and Warkany, 1948). Many embryos show keratinizing metaplasia of the epithelial lining of the urethra distal to the termination of the genital ducts, which constitutes one of the first examples of specific tissue effects of vitamin deficiency in the adult being traced back to prenatal stages of development (Wilson and Warkany, 1947). It is of interest that this localized area exhibiting A-deficiency metaplasia is also one which readily undergoes keratinization metaplasia under the influence of estrogenic hormones. More recent findings by Wilson and Warkany (1949) center around interesting anomalies of the vascular system, pertaining especially to derivatives of the aortic arches; these are indicative of dysfunctions arising between the 10th and 15th days of embryonic development. It should be kept in mind that degrees of deficiency of a specific nutritive factor necessary to induce developmental anomalies in experimental animals usually result in considerable retardation of fetal growth, and that care must be used in differentiating between deficiency effects and associated inanition effects.

Apart from any bearing that such studies may have in clinical medicine or in animal husbandry, they offer means of experimental approach to fundamental problems in mammalian development. Undoubtedly more attention will be given in the future to (1) the effects of nutritive deficiencies up to a specified stage of development followed by restoration of the missing dietary factor for the remainder of gestation, in order to determine reactiveness of certain tissues, organs, and systems at different stages of development, (2) the use of "paired controls" to permit better analysis of the concomitant influence of induction upon growth and differentiation of tissues and (3) application of histochemical and other special techniques to provide a better understanding of cellular mechanisms in normal as well as in abnormal development.

It has been pointed out (Wilson and Warkany, 1948) that abnormal processes of development may be considered as being of four major types, and those observed in deficiency states so far studied are variably distributed in these categories. Briefly they are as follows: *Aplasia,* or complete failure of development of a structure because of suppression of differentiation of its embryonic primordia, usually a late phenomenon in development; e.g., failure of development of vagina or cowpers gland. *Paraplasia,* or aberrant process resulting in a condition entirely foreign to, and not simulated in, normal development; e.g., fused ribs, accessory ear growths, hypospadias, retrolenticular membranes in eyes, kidney fusions. These are relatively few. *Hypoplasia,* or incomplete development because of arrest of a process short of completion, whether it be a progressive or a regressive type of change. Arrest of progressive changes is most common; e.g., tardy appearance of mullerian ducts or slow differentiation of urogenital sinus, failure of descent of testis. The regressive types are less frequent; e.g., persistence of genital ducts of opposite sex, retention of urethral plate. *Hyperplasia,* or overgrowth of certain structures or parts. No anomalies of this type have been encountered in deficiency states.

Addendum

Since this mansucript was prepared an interesting booklet has appeared (Appraisal of Human Dietaries by Animal Experiment: A conference under the auspices of the Williams Waterman Fund for the Combat of Dietary Diseases; Research Corporation; March, 1947: edited by R. R. Williams) with several chapters containing data pertinent to the topic of this review and justifying brief comment here.

In one chapter, "Mammalian Species Variation in Nutritional Requirements for Reproduction," Dr. H. E. Robinson emphasizes marked variations in the capacity of certain diets to maintain good reproduction in different species of animals. For instance, three diets (a 25% protein stock diet, a canned cereal-meal, and a dehydrated cereal-meal) which proved quite adequate for dogs, gave decidedly inferior results with rats and proved quite inadequate for cats unless supplemented by fresh animal protein. Although reproduction here is used in a very broad sense (as the capacity to successfully perpetuate the species through three generations), and reflects more the capacity to rear offspring than the events in reproduction that precede parturition, the results emphasize the need for caution in transferring data on reproductive needs of one species to another species.

Dr. R. H. McCoy, in a chapter dealing with the "Effect of Protein Level of Diet on Reproduction and Lactation" presents evidence that in rats a protein level of 40% was superior to levels of 25% or 15% for the production of offspring, but that the 25% protein level was more optimal for lactation.

Another chapter on "Vitamin Requirements of Swine during Reproduction and Lactation," by Dr. T. J. Cunha, describes results obtained with the "Wisconsin ration" fed to both rats and pigs. In both, there was a lowered incidence of conception. The pigs showed a high incidence of deformities in the offspring (chiefly involving extremities, tail and eyes). In rats there was considerable resorption of fetuses, stillbirth, and early postnatal death. The occurrence of these phenomena could be diminished or prevented by dietary additions of alfalfa, fish meal, soybean lecithin or preparations from liver. Other studies presented by Dr. Cunha deal with premature farrowing in pigs fed diets low in thiamine or riboflavin, associated with leg weakness in the thiamine-deficient offspring and front-leg edema and hairlessness in those deficient in riboflavin.

References

Bacharach, A. L. 1940. Vitamin E and habitual abortion. *Brit. Med. J.* **1**, 890.

Berg, C. P., and Rohse, W. G. 1947. Is sterility induced in growing rats on a tryptophane-deficient diet. *Science* **105**: 96.

Bicknell, F., and Prescott, F. 1947. Vitamins in Medicine. 2nd ed. Heinemann, London.

Biskind, M. S. 1946. Nutritional therapy of endocrine disturbances. *Vitamins and Hormones* **4**: 147.

Burr, G. O. 1942. Significance of the essential fatty acids. *Federation Proceedings* **1**: 224.

Couch, J. R., Cravens, W. W., Elvehjem, C. A., and Halpin, J. G. 1948. Relation of biotin to congenital deformities in the chick. *Anat. Rec.* **100**: 29.

Cruickshank, E. M. 1941. The effect of diet on the chemical composition, nutritive value and hatchability of the egg. *Nutr. Abstr. and Rev.* **10**: 645.

Daft, F. S., and Sebrell, W. H. 1945. Sulfonamides and vitamin deficiencies. *Vitamins and Hormones* **3**: 49.

Davis, M. E., Fugo, N. W., and Lawrence, K. G. 1947. The effect of alloxan diabetes on reproduction in the rat. *Proc. Soc. Exptl. Biol. and Med.* **66**: 638.

Drill, V. A., and Pfeiffer, C. A. 1946. Effect of vitamin B complex deficiency, controlled inanition and methionine on inactivation of estrogen by the liver. *Endocrinology* **38**: 300.

Ellis, N. R. 1946. The vitamin requirements of swine. *Nutr. Abstr. and Rev.* **16**: 1.

Ershoff, B. H. 1948. Conditioning factors in nutritional disease. *Physiol. Rev.* **28**: 107.

Follis, R. N. 1948. The Pathology of Nutritional Disease. Charles C. Thomas, Springfield, Ill.

Goss, H. 1943. Some peculiarities of ruminant nutrition. *Nutr. Abstr. and Rev.* **12**: 531.

Hall, R. P. 1943. Growth-factors for protozoa. *Vitamins and Hormones* **1**: 249.

Hart, G. H. 1940. Vitamin A deficiency and requirements of farm animals. *Nutr. Abstr. and Rev.* **10**: 261.

Hertz, R. 1946. Effect of B vitamins on the endocrinological aspects of reproduction. *Vitamins and Hormones* **4**: 135.

Hickman, K. C. D., and Harris, P. L. 1946. Tocopherol interrelationships. *Advances in Enzymology* **6**: 269.

Hodgson, R. E., Hall, S. R., Sweetman, W. J., Wiseman, H. G., and Converse, H. T. 1946. The effect of vitamin A deficiency on reproduction in dairy bulls. *Jour. Dairy Sci.* **29**: 669.

Jackson, C. M. 1925. The Effects of Inanition and Malnutrition upon Growth and Structure. Blakiston's Son & Co., Philadelphia.

Jackson, C. M. 1929. Recent work on the effects of inanition and of malnutrition on growth and structure. *Arch. Path.* **7**: 1042; **8**: 81, 273.

Jukes, T. H., and Stokstad, E. L. R. 1948. Pteroylglutamic acid and related compounds. *Physiol. Rev.* **28**: 51.

Kaunitz, H., and Slanetz, C. A. 1947. Influence of alpha tocopherol on implantation in old rats. *Proc. Soc. Exptl. Biol. and Med.* **66**: 334.

Knight, B. C. J. G. 1945. Growth factors in microbiology. *Vitamins and Hormones* **3**: 105.

Mason, K. E. 1939. Relation of the vitamins to the sex glands: in Allen, E., Danforth, C. H., Doisy, E. A., Sex and Internal Secretions. 2nd ed., Chap. 22. Williams & Wilkins Co., Baltimore.

Mason, K. E. 1944. Physiological action of vitamin E and its homologues. *Vitamins and Hormones* **2**: 107.

Mason, K. E. Unpublished studies.

Moore, R. A., Bittenger, I., Miller, M. L., and Hellman, L. M. 1942. Abortion in rabbits fed a vitamin K deficient diet. *Amer. Jour. Obstet. and Gynec.* **43**: 1007.

Maun, M. E., Cahill, W. M., and Davis, R. M. Morphologic studies of rats deprived of essential amino acids. I. Phenylalanine; II. Leucine; III: Histidine. *Arch. Path.* **39**: 294; 1945; **40**: 173, 1945; **41**: 25, 1946.

Najjar, V. A., and Barrett, R. 1945. The synthesis of B vitamins by intestinal bacteria. *Vitamins and Hormones* **3**: 23.

Needham, J. 1942. Biochemistry and Morphogenesis. Cambridge University Press, Cambridge, England.

Nelson, M. M., and Evans, H. M. 1946. Pantothenic acid deficiency and reproduction in the rat. *Jour. Nutrition* **31**: 497.

Phillips, R. W., Friedman, M. H., and Turner, W. A. 1939. The relation of diet to reproduction; in Food and Life, Yearbook of Agriculture, p. 476, Gov't. Printing Office, Washington, D. C.

Quackenbush, F. W., Kummerow, F. A., and Steenbock, H. 1942. The effectiveness of linoleic, arachidonic, and linolenic acids in reproduction and lactation. *Jour. Nutrition* **24**: 213.

Romanoff, A. L., and Bauernfeind, J. C. 1942. Influence of riboflavin deficiency in eggs on embryonic development (Gallus domesticus). *Anat. Rec.* **82**: 11.

Seifried, O., and Köcher, E. 1943. Die Veränderungen der Geschlechtsorgane bei A-avitaminotische Hühnern. *Ztschr. Infektionskr.* **95**: 32.

Trager, W. 1941. The nutrition of invertebrates. *Physiol. Rev.* **21**: 1-35.

Underwood, E. J. 1940. The significance of trace elements in nutrition. *Nutr. Abstr. and Rev.* **9**: 515.

van Wagenen, G. 1948. Vitamin A deficiency in pregnancy. *Federation Proceedings* **7**: 127.

Warkany, J. 1945. Manifestations of prenatal nutritional deficiency. *Vitamins and Hormones* **3**: 73.

Warkany, J., and Roth, C. B. 1948. Congenital malformations induced in rats by maternal vitamin A deficiency. *Jour. Nutrition* **35**: 1.

Williams, H. L., and Watson, E. M. 1944. The role of arginine in the reproduction and growth of rats. *Rev. Canad. de Biol.* **3**: 426; 1944. The effect of arginine deficiency on the testes of rats. *Urol. and Cutan. Rev.* **49**: 739.

Wilson, J. G., and Warkany, J. 1947. Epithelial keratinization as evidence of fetal vitamin A deficiency. *Proc. Soc. Exptl. Biol. and Med.* **64**: 419.

Wilson, J. G., and Warkany, J. 1948. Malformations in the genito-urinary tract induced by maternal vitamin A deficiency in the rat. *Amer. J. Anat.* **83**: 357.

Wilson, J. G., and Warkany, J. 1949. Aortic-arch and cardiac anomalies in the offspring of vitamin A deficient rats. *Amer. J. Anat.*, in press.

Wolbach, S. B., and Bessey, O. A. 1942. Tissue changes in vitamin deficiencies. *Physiol. Rev.* **22**: 233.

Growth and Development

BY DONALD PAUL COSTELLO

Zoology Department, University of North Carolina, Chapel Hill, North Carolina, and the Marine Biological Laboratory, Woods Hole, Massachusetts

SYNOPSIS

Modern embryology had its beginnings in two great movements which were initiated between 1878 and 1887. The first was the study of cell-lineage, tracing the history of the cleavage blastomeres through to their ultimate fates in producing the parts of the larva or adult. This was developed under the tutelage of Whitman, and carried on by Wilson, Conklin, Lillie and several others. At about the same time, Wilhelm Roux founded "Entwicklungsmechanik," the experimental approach to problems of development and growth. Before this time embryology had been the handmaiden of the new Darwinian evolution—useful chiefly in elucidating the recapitulation theory.

During the last decade of the nineteenth century, embryologists were concerned largely with the problem of mosaic versus regulative development. They approached this problem from the standpoints of (1) descriptions of normal embryological events; (2) the development of egg-fragments and isolated blastomeres; (3) defect experiments. Other more physiologically-minded investigators began to study the role played by the external environment in differentiation. The effect of gravity on the development of the frog's egg was investigated by Pflüger, Schultze, Roux, etc. Herbst (and later, Loeb) studied the effects of altering the inorganic content of sea water, with the remarkable discovery (Herbst, 1892) of lithium-induced exogastrulation. The later demonstration of the non-specificity of this action does not lessen the biological significance of the phenomenon. These studies on salt solutions led to the discovery of artificial parthenogenesis, usually attributed to Loeb, 1899. A second important outcome of such investigations was the description of differentiation without cleavage, by Lillie, 1902. Later the effects of other environmental factors such as temperature, osmotic pressure, pH, etc., were investigated.

An outgrowth of the attempts to investigate the possible effects of gravity in determining the polarity of eggs was the extended series of experiments on magnified gravity (centrifugal force) by Morgan, Lyon, Lillie, Conklin and others, which demonstrated the importance of the ground substance as the seat of polarity, bilaterality and localization in the egg (see Section II). The morphology of fertilization in relation to the new chromosome theory of heredity was described. Meanwhile the relative roles of nucleus and cytoplasm in differentiation were being elucidated. It became clear from Wilson's polar lobe extirpations on the eggs of *Dentalium,* Spemann's constriction experiments on urodele eggs and the pressure experiments of Wilson, Driesch, Morgan, and Pflüger, that the nuclei of all cleavage blastomeres must be the same, and that such localizations as exist are cytoplasmic differentiations. The problem of nucleus versus cytoplasm in development is still being investigated by means of hybridization and transplantation, merogony, parthenogenesis, and heteroploidy (Section IX).

By combining the use of Herbst's calcium-free sea water and Spemann's glass needles with an excellent operative technique, Hörstadius, in 1928, inaugurated a new era of experimental work. His observations, plus results by Lindahl in the field of developmental physiology, afford evidence for Runnström's theory of a two-gradient interacting system in the Echinoderm egg. Although not generally acknowledged as such, this theory is undoubtedly a special example of one of the few comprehensive theories of development that have ever been enunciated—the axial gradient theory of C. M. Child. By means of the generalizations of this theory, which covers regeneration as a developmental process as well as embryonic development, it is possible to interpret many facts which might otherwise be unrelated (see Section II, 2).

Because of its ready availability and its adaptability to operative procedures, the amphibian egg soon became the chief object of embryological investigation. In a brilliant series of experiments (Spemann and others, 1901-1907, etc.) it was demonstrated that a diffusible substance released by the eye vesicle in contact with the overlying epidermis acts in certain species to induce lens formation. In other species an independent differentiation of lens from epidermis of this region is also possible. This work established the principles of induction, competence and double assurance.

The classical constriction experiments of Spemann, 1902 and 1903, had shown that some factor in the region of the prospective blastopore was essential for differentiation. This factor was later shown (Spemann and H. Mangold, 1924) to be released to the overlying ectoderm by invaginated (or implanted) chorda mesoderm and to "organize" the formation of a neural axis. By study of the properties of living, dissociated, crushed, killed and extracted "organizer" material, it was shown by Bautzmann, Holtfreter and Wehmeier that the neural inductor is a moderately heat-stable chemical substance which is capable of diffusing into an agar block; it does not depend for its action on the integrity of the living tissue. It was subsequently shown to be a common constituent of many dead tissues, and not limited to the dorsal-lip region of the amphibian gastrula. A rapidly succeeding series of studies attempting to ascertain the chemical nature of the neural inductor, carried out by Holtfreter in Germany, Needham and collaborators in England, Woerdeman in Holland, by Barth in the United States, and by many others, constituted an important chapter in the new field of chemical embryology.

The early results appeared to point to several different compounds as "organizer." It became apparent that there was little specificity involved. Another difficulty arose from the fact that in the living gastrula only chorda mesodermal cells normally release the inductor. But *killed* cells from any portion of the gastrula, or indeed, from practically any animal tissue, produced an effect. Thus when a given substance was implanted into an amphibian gastrula, it was impossible to distinguish between a *direct action* of the introduced substance, inducing a secondary neural plate, and an indirect action of the substance in killing neighboring host gastrula cells and thus releasing bound organizer.

This, in brief, constitutes the background on which the present review is based.

With a shift of interest from the inductor to the competence of the reacting tissue (Sections VI and VII) came the realization that there are, after all, relatively few phenomena in development which may be attributed to diffusible substances. The great majority of developmental events apparently involve substances of such molecular properties that they are, for all practical purposes, nondiffusible (Section XII).

A union between genetics and embryology has been made through the transplantation techniques used for the study of gene hormones (Section XII). A stronger union is now being welded between embryology and biochemistry, due largely to the attempts to trace morphogenetic processes back to their biochemical precursors (Section V).

The major problem of embryology today is still the problem of differentiation—i.e., the origin of diversity during development. The various approaches to this fundamental problem include (1) the manner of origin of cytoplasmic localizations, especially in the unsegmented egg (Section II); (2) the time and mode of action of genes during development (Section XII); (3) the mechanisms of morphogenetic cellular movements, in relation to developmental patterns (Section VIII); (4) the origin and characteristics of the differential metabolism of the parts (Section V, 2 and 3), with elucidation of the enzyme systems involved.

I. General Concepts of Growth

Growth of an organism may be defined as an increase in the total protoplasmic mass. This definition excludes from the category of growth fluctuations in the quantity of water or reserve materials stored in the organism.

Development is the concatenation of processes making up the gradual changes in the individual organism. These developmental changes may be of a progressive or of a retrogressive nature. Certain developmental processes (regeneration, replacement and repair) continue after the adult stage is reached, so the study of development extends throughout the life cycle of the organism. The primary problem of development is the problem of differentiation, or the origin of diversity of the parts of living things. Differentiation becomes manifest, in part at least, through differential growth.

Hammett (1946) discusses the multiple manifestations of growth, considering the latter to be the direct summation of integrated developmental and incremental processes. He classifies the components of growth as initiation, proliferation, differentiation, organization and constructive substance increase. By initiation, he means the transformation of lifeless into living substance. By proliferation, he means cell division or increase in cell number. By differentiation, he means the processes which make one cell differ from another. This should be extended, of course, to differences within a given cell, making one part of the cell different from other parts. Organization is segregation of differentiating cells into paths of specialization. Constructive substance increase is increase in the living protoplasm, which may proceed independently of proliferation, differentiation and organization, but which appears to the present writer to be identical with initiation.

II. Polarity and Symmetry

It is common knowledge that the ovum itself, before maturation, fertilization or cleavage, often shows structural differentiations which foreshadow certain features of the future embryo, larva or adult organism. The most fundamental of these is egg polarity, which, if it does not directly predelineate, normally bears some definite relation to the polarity of the embryo, and of the future adult. In the bilaterally symmetrical embryos of many forms, the two secondary axes (dorso-ventral and right-left) may be determined later than the primary axis. Embryos of certain other forms, at least in their early stages, possess radial symmetry around the polar axis. Still others are asymmetrical, and may or may not pass through a transition into the bilateral form. In the forms possessing bilateral symmetry in which the median plane is not laid down during egg-growth (as it is in the eggs of cephalopods and insects, and perhaps in some others), some subsequent event, such as fertilization, or the path taken by the sperm nucleus in moving toward the egg nucleus, may inaugurate a series of events which condition the localization of the median plane. The work of a large number of investigators over a period of some 50 years, however, has shown that this relation is not so simple as was first supposed, and that factors other than sperm path influence the position of the median plane. It was shown by Brachet (1911) that when a frog's egg is activated parthenogenetically with a needle, the point of pricking bears no fixed relation to the median plane. Such parthenogenetic embryos may nevertheless develop with normal symmetry; the median plane is therefore assumed to be predelineated. The influence of the sperm path in normal development may therefore be to shift the predelineated but not irrevocably determined plane of symmetry.

This problem of bilateral determination has been re-investigated by Ancel and Vintemberger (1943a, 1943b, 1943c, and 1944). Rotation of the eggs of the frogs *Rana fusca* and *Rana esculenta,* augmented by the specific gravity of the medium, acts so that it may oppose the effect of the sperm entrance point in determining the axis of symmetry. They have studied the speed of the initial rotation-orientation of the eggs in several different media, and report that the speed of swelling of the jelly matrix is an important factor in determining the resistance to egg rotation provided by the jelly matrix surrounding the eggs.

The whole problem of the relations of symmetry of the developing embryo has been admirably discussed by Harrison (1945), using as specific examples a number of previously unpublished observations on the developing amphibian ear. The problem of symmetry relations in this developing organ is basically similar to the problem of origin of the embryonic axes of the whole animal.

1. The Growth of the Ovum

During the growth period of the primary oöcyte, a large quantity of material is added, laid down in the form of inclusions as well as ground substance (hyaline protoplasm), and there is also a disproportionately great growth of the nucleus to produce the large germinal vesicle. Materials are extruded from this germinal vesicle in the form of nucleoli or as nuclear fluid released at the time of formation of the maturation spindle. This residual substance from the germinal vesicle conditions the cytoplasm for fertilization, and presumably adds nuclear organic materials to the cytoplasm for use in differentiation. In certain forms nurse cells synthesize yolk spheres which are later added to the oöcyte in some pattern in relation to existing polarity. Worley (1944a, 1944b), using vital staining methods for Golgi bodies, studied yolk formation in oöcytes of the mussel, *Mytilus,* and reports that the primary oöcyte stage lacks formed protein yolk, but is filled with fat droplets elaborated by the Golgi bodies. He attributes (1943a,

1943b) to the multiplying Golgi elements in the developing eggs of the molluscs *Navanax* and *Mytilus* the function of a protein and fat elaborating system.

Investigations of the nucleic acid content of developing oöcytes have been stimulated by the early work of Caspersson (1936) and Brachet (1941). Bretschneider (1942) reports that oöcyte stages of the snail *Limnaea* are devoid of thymonucleic acid protein which is present only in the chromosomes of the oögonia. The role of the nucleic acids in differentiation is not yet clear, but Brachet attributes to them a possible primary significance. The function of the germinal vesicle in differentiation has long been a subject for interesting conjecture. In the amphibian oöcyte, the germinal vesicle contains the "lamp-brush" chromosomes. Products given off by these chromosomes may be the "gene-products" added to the nuclear sap which condition the initial cytoplasmic differentiation. At each successive cleavage additional nuclear products are added to the cytoplasm as the nuclear membrane disappears during the formation of the cleavage spindle. Ris (1945) interprets the "lamp-brush" chromosomes of the germinal vesicle not as devices for sloughing off heterochromatin, but as typical diplotene chromosomes with a great longitudinal growth of chromonemata, with loops representing the main coils of the laterally-separated strands.

It has long been accepted that embryonic differentiation is largely cytoplasmic, the nuclei of all cleavage blastomeres being the same. Mather (1948) states that there is a growing body of evidence that differentiation is at times, though by no means always, accompanied by changes in the nucleus.

The recent work of Sonneborn (1945, 1946, 1947) and others on the interaction of chromosomal and cytoplasmic factors in the production of the "killer" phenotype is of interest with respect to the problem of the origin of diversity in genetically uniform cells. It has been shown that the chromosomal factor *K* and the cytoplasmic factor kappa must interact to produce the typical phenotype, *K* alone producing no detectable effect.

2. *Gradients*

The axial gradient theory of Child (1911, 1928) was the first comprehensive theory attempting to account for the pattern of development in terms of localized regional differences along one or more axes of the developing ovum. Child considered physiological differences in metabolism as the basic cause of the regional differences which, according to his earlier views, initially were impressed upon the egg from outside. A contrasting view is that the physiological and morphological bases of differences in different parts are due to a common cause inherent in the cell itself. Actually, external and internal stimuli both appear to exert their influences on the developing or regenerating organism. From its earliest stages, the animal oöcyte typically reveals some visible regional differences, such as those reflected by the position of the centrosome at one side of the nucleus, and later by differences in quantity of hyaline protoplasm as compared with inclusions along the main (polar) axis of the egg. Even where the polar differences of animal eggs are not visibly apparent, there is every reason to assume that polar differentiation is an inherent quality of the egg from some early developmental period, and is not impressed upon the egg from the outside environment at a late stage.

One of the best examples of a developmental system which appears to fulfill many of the requirements of Child's theory is the egg of the alga, *Fucus,* which has been thoroughly explored in the work of Whitaker and his students, supplementing and completing the observations of earlier workers. Initially, the fertilized egg is apparently universally symmetrical. A number of different inequalities in the environment may upset this egg symmetry. If it rests on the bottom of a dish containing the sea water in which it develops, a gradient is established from top to bottom by differential diffusion of oxygen into (and of carbon dioxide away from) the cell at the free surfaces, as compared with the surface in contact. In some manner not completely understood, but possibly involving a gradient of amount or activity of growth hormone (indole-3-acetic acid) in the egg, a rhizoid (root-like protuberance) is formed on the side of the egg in contact with the bottom of the glass dish. Cell division occurs with the division wall established at right angles to the vertical axis, i.e., cutting off the rhizoid protuberance in one cell. This initial gradient can be established along any egg diameter. Subsequently the axial gradients become more and more complex. The initial minor environmental difference between the upper and lower part of the egg sets off a chain series of reactions that leads eventually to the fully differentiated seaweed. A most significant property of the *Fucus* egg is that the initial determination of polarity can be brought about by differential environmental agents, such as mechanical elongation, stratification of egg contents by centrifuging, temperature gradients across the egg, hydrogen ion concentration differences, an electrical potential across the egg and unilateral differences in illumination with either visible or ultraviolet light. Whitaker (1942a, 1942b) and Reed and Whitaker (1941), in an analysis of the action of ultraviolet radiation in determining the polarity of the *Fucus* egg, suggest that the radiation effect is not mediated through the activation of an auxin. An increase in viscosity due to the irradiation is demonstrable on the irradiated side as the earliest detectable indication of an effect.

A variation of the axial gradient idea is the double gradient system proposed for the sea-urchin egg by Runnström, and experimentally demonstrated by Hörstadius and Lindahl. This double gradient is supposed to have as its basis a gradient of carbohydrate metabolism extending downward from the animal polar region, and a gradient of protein metabolism extending upward from the vegetal polar region (Lindahl, 1936).

Since there is much evidence that susceptibility gradients, yolk gradients, visible protoplasmic gradients, etc., do exist in eggs, our primary interest should be in the origin of these gradients. Most investigators in this field, including Child, seem to agree that a purely quantitative difference in metabolic rate between the regions of the egg is inadequate. The origin of a qualitative difference from this initial quantitative difference appears to be a necessary part of the axial gradient theory. Some quantitative factors may persist, however.

There have been various experimental attempts to alter the axes of the egg by imposed chemical gradients. Primary egg polarity usually is not affected by such superimposed gradients, the exceptions being the *Fucus* egg and certain experiments indicating reversal of polarity in part of the sea-urchin egg after treatment with thiocyanate (Lindahl, 1933, 1936) or certain operative recombinations (Hörstadius, 1939).

Whitaker and Berg (1942) described a method for creating a steep concentration gradient of chemical substances across eggs. It makes use of a gelatin or agar partition in which eggs are embedded, separating the two chambers of a container.

Whitaker and Berg (1944) embedded eggs of the alga, *Fucus,* in a thin agar membrane, and reared them with sea water on one side and 3 to 5×10^{-5} M. dinitrophenol in sea water on the other side. In this concentration gradient, the majority of the developing eggs (74% to 99%) form rhizoids on the side toward the higher concentration of dinitrophenol.

Pease (1941, 1942a, 1942b) has attempted to modify bilateral determi nation in the egg of the sanddollar, *Dendraster,* by exposing the eggs to concentration gradients of a variety of substances, including some inhibitors of respiratory enzymes. He made use of a device in which a flow of substance was maintained past eggs on a sintered glass disc. Enzyme poisons were found to be effective in shifting the plane of bilaterality, the regions of greatest inhibition becoming dorsal, those least inhibited becoming ventral. Apparently the enzymes concerned in the cyanide-sensitive part of the oxidative mechanism, possibly cytochrome oxidase, play a role in determining bilaterality. The data reveal that bilaterality is affected only by a certain rate of flow of the substances. This rate is apparently not the same for different inhibitors, and it would be gratifying to have some of the observations repeated, using the gelatine embedding technique, which would eliminate the possibility of movement and re-orientation of the eggs during treatment.

Child (1942, 1943) has devised a simple method for demonstrating "respiratory" gradients in eggs by means of certain oxidation-reduction indicators, such as paraphenylenediamine. The simplicity of the method, and the reproducibility of the results stand in striking contrast to the elaborate ultramicromanometer methods which for some years have been yielding such diverse and controversial sets of data in the hands of several groups of investigators. It is not clear, however, that these indicator methods measure the same physiological characteristics as do the microrespirometer methods. Using such indicators as indophenol and Janus green, he has studied (1945) the oxidation-reduction gradients during the development of the fish, *Brachydanio rerio.*

Child (1942) suggests that polarity of the egg of *Drosophila hydei* is correlated with respiratory gradients in the ovary.

Miller (1946) studied the differential reduction of Janus green in the early development of *Tubularia crocea.* Rapid reduction is indicative of an actively growing region. The results show a step-by-step activation of new growing regions preceding visible changes in development. The endoderm appears to initiate these changes.

In the comparison of the metabolic characteristics of the dorsal lip or organizer region, as compared with indifferent ectoderm of other regions of the amphibian gastrula, a wide diversity of results has been obtained. If one lists the ratios of the respiratory rates of the dorsal lip as compared with ventral ectoderm of various species of amphibian gastrulae, as recorded (Boell, 1942) by Brachet (1934, 1936), Waddington, Needham and Brachet (1936), Brachet and Shapiro (1937), Fisher and Hartwig (1938), Boell and Needham (1939), Boell, Koch and Needham (1939), Brachet (1939), Needham, Rogers and Shen (1939), the values range from 0.98 to 1.47. Correcting for yolk content and basing the calculations on "active material" leads to the conclusion (Barth, 1942) that there is a gradient in oxygen consumption from 35 at the animal pole to 8 at the vegetal pole. The dorsal lip consumes oxygen at a higher rate than the corresponding region on the opposite side of the gastrula, where the same relative yolk content obtains. The size of the pieces taken for comparison determines in part the magnitude of the absolute values obtained.

3. *Fields*

In his studies of amphibian development, Spemann as early as 1921 used the term "field," but made little effort to discover its physico-chemical basis. The field concept has been widely used, but, although carefully delimited by Weiss (1939) as being a symbolic rather than a physical term, is still hazy for the very reason that it has not been properly defined in the fundamental terms of space, time and energy.

Lund (1947) believes (as did Burr and Northrop, 1935) that the inherent electric fields of cells, tissues and organisms play an important role in the spatial organization of metabolic processes. He suggests that there is the possibility of using the data on electric fields to define more exactly the term "field" as it is now employed by embryologists. The method of approach to the problem of the role of bioelectric potentials in vital phenomena is the distortion of the inherent electric field by superposition of another field, by changing the electrical resistance of the environment, or by changing the "electrodes" in the field by chemical agents such as oxygen, cyanide, and anesthetics. Lund suggests that the electric field affects growth and other functions by a movement and redistribution of materials such as growth hormones and ionic substances, and by orientation of structural polar molecules.

However, there are difficulties in interpreting either cell migrations or the movement of oöplasmic substances in terms of a migration of materials, essentially similar to an electrophoretic migration in an electric field. Current distribution within most living cells cannot easily be studied, and in a medium of high salt content, such as the sea water in which many living things develop, superimposed electric potentials from outside cannot be very effective. Practically all the current flow would be around, rather than through the living tissue. An alternative hypothesis which attempts to explain the phenomenon of the segregation of oöplasmic constituents in animal egg cells has been proposed by Costello (1945a) in terms of a Teorell "diffusion effect." This is a modified Donnan effect (Teorell, 1935, 1937; Meyer and Sievers, 1936) which may bring about an exchange of charged particles in response to a mobility difference between the ions of a diffusing substance. There is as yet no physical evidence that such a phenomenon is effective in moving substances within living cells.

All these attempts to arrive at a physico-chemical basis for the origin of polar differences are at present inadequately supported by crucial evidence, but they are indicative of two important trends: (1) the realization that the study of embryonic differentiation must go back beyond the study of the gastrula to the earliest stages in the formation of the oöcyte, and (2) that physical as well as chemical and biological methods will eventually contribute to the elucidation of the problems of early differentiation.

III. The Spermatozoon and Fertilization

1. *General*

In anisogametic animals, the role of the sperm in development must not be neglected. It is obvious that in most cases the sperm contributes a haploid set of paternal chromosomes and an activating influence which initiates resumption of development by the egg. There is a possibility that the sperm has other material contributions as well, but the chief object of numerous investigations has been to elucidate the maintenance of the fertilizability of the sperm, and the role of the sperm in egg activation. Hayashi (1945) has described a factor (probably protein) present in the seminal fluid of the sea-urchin, *Arbacia,* which prolongs the fertilizing capacity of the sperm. This factor is not present in the perivisceral fluid. In equivalent concentration of fresh suspension, the fertilizing capacity of the sperm is much greater in seminal fluid than in sea water.

MacLeod (1947) studied the motility of human spermatozoa under various experimental conditions. His results suggest that motility is dependent upon the integrity and lability of the sulfydryl groups in certain enzyme systems. Lithium destroys the motility. Lithium, copper and arsenicals produce a marked depression of glycolysis.

2. *Precocious Sperm Entrance*

One of the most interesting aspects of the problem of fertilization is the contribution of the sperm in removing the block to development which is present in the unfertilized eggs of almost all animals. One aspect of this is the question as to whether the sperm contributes some active principle which speeds up the metabolism (and hence, development) of the egg, or merely releases a checked mechanism to enable the egg to proceed at a rate determined by its own metabolic system. We know, for example, that parthenogenetically activated eggs usually develop more slowly than fertilized eggs, but we do not know whether this is due to the fact that the parthenogenetic treatment is sub-optimal. One approach to the problem is provided by the work of Lovelace (1947) in treating the eggs of *Nereis* with an agent (alkaline sodium chloride) that causes the sperm to enter considerably earlier than it does in normal, untreated material. Normally, the attachment of the sperm to the egg surface initiates the maturation divisions, and the sperm enters some forty-five minutes after attachment, forms a sperm aster and eventually gives rise to the cleavage spindle. In the eggs treated with alkaline sodium chloride five minutes after insemination, the precocious sperm entrance takes place during the first maturation division. This speeds up the maturation divisions and produces a definite acceleration of the first cleavage. As a control for the effect of the alkaline sodium chloride itself, Lovelace subjected some eggs to treatment twenty minutes after insemination. This produces a delay in sperm entrance and first cleavage. Correcting for this retardation of cleavage by the alkaline sodium chloride, Lovelace concludes that precocious sperm entrance ought to have an even more marked effect in accelerating the early developmental changes than that observed.

There have been numerous electron microscope studies of spermatozoa. Schmitt, Hall and Jakus (1943) describe a fairly definite number of fibrils (nine or ten) in the tail of squid sperm. The presence of a number of fibrils in the tail filament of bull sperm has also been suggested by the brush-like tip described by Baylor, Nalbandov and Clark (1943). A protoplasmic cap around the head is also described by these authors. Harvey and Anderson (1943) find about ten fibrils, each circa fifty millimicra in diameter, in *Arbacia* sperm.

Pollister and Lavin (1944) observed degeneration of chromosomes during the atypical spermiogenesis of *Viviparus maletus,* which was followed by the appearance of eosinophilic granules in the cytoplasm of the larger spermatids. They suggest a possible conversion of desoxyribose nucleic (chromonucleic) acid into ribose (plasmonucleic) nucleic acid in the granules.

3. *Hyaluronidase*

A special enzyme, hyaluronidase, secreted or liberated by spermatozoa, is responsible for freeing mammalian ova from the surrounding follicle cells. Its properties are being extensively studied (McClean and Rowlands, 1942; Fekete and Duran-Reynals, 1943; etc.). When produced by certain bacteria, this enzyme favors the spread of infection in tissues by dissolving the hyaluronic acid components.

Simpson and Ayengar (1947) report that local injection of hyaluronidase into malignant epithelial tumors produces marked enhancement and metastasis of the tumors.

Rowlands (1944) finds that hyaluronidase increases the fertilizing power of sperm, so that experimental rabbits require only about one-sixth as high a sperm concentration as the controls, to obtain 50% fertilization. Swyer describes assay methods for hyaluronidase (1947a), the hyaluronidase content of semen of various vertebrates (1947b), and its release from rabbit spermatozoa (1947c).

4. *Activation*

Scheer and Scheer (1947) suggest some interrelations between drug and ion action in the artificial activation of *Urechis* eggs. Activation of *Urechis* eggs was obtained in solutions of sea water containing an excess of sodium ions, nicotine, and by exposing eggs to ultraviolet radiations. The results are discussed in relation to the suggestion that calcium, potassium, adenosinetriphosphatase and acetylcholine are important in excitation generally, but no general theory of parthenogenesis is evolved. Addition of a low concentration of acetylcholine increased the effectiveness of the ultraviolet, and a high concentration inhibited the effectiveness. Adrenaline, pilocarpine, atropine, arecoline, histamine or choline inhibited ultraviolet activation.

Mann (1945) found cytochrome a, b and c present in bull and ram sperm. Under both aerobic and anaerobic conditions, a decrease of ATP concentration of surviving sperm was found to coincide with the time of loss of motility. Lardy and Phillips (1945) suggest that the energy source for motility of mammalian sperm is via the isocitric acid cycle, metabolizing fats as well as carbohydrates.

Connors and Scheer (1947) have demonstrated adenosinetriphosphatase in the egg of the sea-urchin, *Strongylocentrotus purpuratus*. There is some evidence that the activity of this enzyme increases on fertilization of these eggs.

5. *Birefringence*

The use of polarization optics as a tool in elucidating the changes of molecular orientation in cell structure has been popularized by the work of W. J. Schmidt and F. O. Schmitt.

A complete re-investigation of the chemical and physical properties of the surface layers and cytoplasm of the sea-urchin egg is now in progress (Runnström and Monné, 1945a, 1945b; Runnström, Monné and Broman, 1944; and Monné, 1945a, 1945b). Monné suggests (1945a) that the ground substance (hyaline protoplasm) is fibrillar. Runnström and Monné (1945a) studied the changes in the properties of the surface layers of immature and mature sea-urchin eggs which temporally accompany nuclear and cytoplasmic maturation. They recognize four distinct layers—the gelatinous coat, the vitelline membrane, the plasma membrane, and the cortical gel, the latter two being termed also the cortical layer. The vitelline membrane before elevation shows no sign of birefringence, but this increases to a maximum as it is fully elevated to form the fertilization membrane (Runnström, Monné and Broman, 1944). The cortical layer shows a positive birefringence in the radial direction with no change on insemination. The birefringence of the cortex is lowered by treating the egg with lipoid-liquefying agents, which suggests that the birefringence is due largely to oriented lipoid layers. For a later view of this topic, see Monné (1948).

Monroy (1947) reports further observations on the molecular structure of the cortical layer of unfertilized and fertilized sea-urchin eggs by means of polarization microscopy. A protein component is demonstrated in the cortex, both before and after fertilization. The evidence suggests that the proteins are arranged parallel to the egg surface, whereas the lipids are radially arranged.

Monroy and Montalenti (1947) describe a cyclical variation in the birefringence of the cortex of fertilized and parthenogenetically (hypertonic sea-water) activated sea-urchin eggs. The important changes occur fifteen to twenty minutes after fertilization or activation, and from the end of the metaphase to the telophase of the first cleavage. Treating the eggs with colchicine did not alter this cycle.

Chambers (1942) finds that fragments of the elevating fertilization membranes of *Arbacia* and *Asterias* eggs continue to expand after removal from the egg, indicating that membrane elevation is not due to osmotic forces, but to intrinsic molecular rearrangements in the membrane itself.

IV. Cell Division

Cell division, the basis of proliferation and cleavage of the embryo, has received a full share of the attention of research workers during the past five years. Schrader's (1944) book, *Mitosis,* has presented a careful, critical and somewhat pessimistic view of our present knowledge of theories of karyokinesis. Actually, there has been little advance in working out a practicable theory of karyokinesis, although there have been some additions of factual data, including an interesting discussion by Schrader (1947) on metaphase mechanics.

From the standpoint of the study of cytokinesis, the data on the local changes of surface area during the passage of the cleavage furrow constitute an invaluable basis for considerations of the mechanism of cleavage. These data were obtained by the kaolin particle method, for the eggs of several echinoderms, a mollusc and a coelenterate by Dan and his coworkers (1937, 1938, 1942, 1947). Additional descriptions of the behavior of the cleaving cells containing artificial perforations (1943) and of the formation of new surface along the furrow region (1940) provide more factual data. The several sources of evidence constitute the basis of Dan's (1943) theory which attempts to explain astral cleavage in terms of autonomous spindle elongation, acting through astral radiations which are attached to the cell cortex and cross in the furrow region. It appears that this hypothesis may not reasonably be extended to forms like the *Crepidula* egg, or to those showing anastral cleavage. Chambers (1946) also emphasizes the role of mitotic elongation in bringing about cytokinesis. Bonnevie

(1947) stresses the stoppage of spindle elongation just before metaphase and the change of spindle shape before resumption of elongation as evidence for her theory that two groups of automatic processes coöperate in order to bring about mitosis. These processes are (1) rhythmical activity of sister centrosomes in concentrating hyaloplasm around themselves, and (2) a rhythmical process causing longitudinal division of the chromosomes combined with a rise and fall of their electrical (?) potential. This descriptive morphological theory is not, as yet, adequately supported by physicochemical or quantitative data.

Another approach to the problem of cell division is the study of the action of antimitotic agents, such as colchicine. The voluminous literature references on this subject have been assembled by Eigsti (1947). In general, colchicine stops mitosis at the metaphase, by interfering with some achromatic part of the spindle mechanism. Other antimitotic drugs include stilbestrol (used by Lüscher, 1945), phenanthrenequinone and naphthoquinone (used on *Tubifex* eggs by Huber, 1945), 1,4-benzoquinone (employed by Lehmann, 1945) and podophyllin (Cornman, 1947).

V. Biochemical Embryology

1. *General*

A characteristic feature of the period covered by the present review is the increasing interest in the biochemical aspects of developmental processes. This is exemplified in the publication of such books as Brachet's *Embryologie Chimique* (1944), written in occupied Belgium, without access to much of the literature, or to Needham's *Biochemistry and Morphogenesis* (1942), which covers encyclopedically the same general field.

The detection of enzyme systems by microchemical or micromanometer methods constitutes an interesting and important series of attempts to trace gradients or differences of embryonic potency back to their individual biochemical causes. There is no doubt that there are different concentrations of certain enzymes in different cleavage blastomeres, or in different embryonic areas having different prospective embryonic fates. Whether or not this difference of concentration is of any more significance than the visible differences of content of yolk or hyaline protoplasm in the several cleavage blastomeres is a question to be settled by the embryologist rather than by the biochemist. The enzymes adsorbed on the surfaces of cytoplasmic granules or other inclusions would be expected to follow the distribution of these granules. The enzymes present in the fluid hyaline portion of the protoplasm likewise would be distributed with this material. What must be ascertained is whether experimental alteration of enzyme distribution in itself will bring about altered morphogenesis. Modifications in the distribution of yolk and hyaline protoplasm such as that brought about by centrifuging does not ordinarily produce any morphogenetic effect, as is well known from the classic experiments of Morgan, Conklin, Lillie and others.

In view of the great importance of phosphorus compounds in carbohydrate metabolism, it is not surprising that they are receiving their share of attention from chemical embryologists. Barth and Jaeger (1947) report that the ATP concentration is about the same from early cleavage to the early neurula stage in the frog's egg. The relative amount of ATP breakdown at various stages in response to nitrogen-produced anaerobiosis paralleled the amount of inhibition of development. In arrested hybrid gastrulae, the lower respiration rate and lower rate of glycolysis is accompanied by a decreased ability to keep the ATP in a phosphorylated condition.

Harris (1944) describes a new enzyme, phosphoprotein phosphatase, from the frog's egg. This enzyme, which is bound at least in part to the yolk platelets, is thought to liberate inorganic phosphate, as needed in carbohydrate metabolism.

2. *Nucleic Acids in Development*

Bodenstein and Kondritzer (1948) report an effect of nitrogen mustards on nucleic acids present during early amphibian development. Normally, the nucleic acid content of the embryo (for both desoxyribose and ribose nucleic acids) rises with increase in age, reaching a peak at the period of yolk resorption. Embryos treated with nitrogen mustards showed a rise only in ribonucleic acid, synthesis of desoxyribonucleic acid being prevented. The effects of nitrogen mustards on the ectoderm (Bodenstein, 1947) include an antimitotic effect. All the mitotic activity is at a standstill two days after exposure, with the nuclei at interphase. Continued growth of these interphase nuclei to a giant size takes place. The nuclei of cells exposed early in development enlarge more than those exposed later. There is apparently no recovery to a normal resumption of mitosis. Bodenstein assumes that these giant nuclei are not heteroploid, since the presence of only two nucleoli suggests that they have remained diploid.

Painter (1940) proposes the theory that the rapid reduplication of chromosomes by the dividing zygote nuclei during cleavage in the egg of *Drosophila* is due to the contribution of materials from the highly polyploid nurse cells, which are engulfed by the egg during oögenesis, providing chromatin material in a readily usable form. He suggests also (1945a) that the form of chromosome diminution occurring in the growth of the germinal vesicle of the oöcyte, in which heterochromatin is detached from the chromosomes in the form of small granules of desoxyribonucleic acid, and appears in the cytoplasm in the form of ribonucleic acid, is a device to provide an adequate supply of ribonucleic acid in the cytoplasm, where it may play a role in the elaboration of yolk for rapid development. This is further correlated with endomitosis (Painter, 1945b), since the occurrence of this phenomenon in gland cells may be a mechanism by which heterochromatic centers and nucleolar organizers are increased, to permit secretion of large quantities of substances. The heterochromatin is used up during secretion.

Brachet is attempting to correlate the presence and synthesis of the pentose nucleic acids with such developmental phenomena as gastrulation and induction (1941, 1943; Brachet and Chantrenne, 1942). By histochemical methods, he demonstrates (1940) a definite synthesis of pentose-nucleoproteins in amphibian development, and finds them in higher concentration in the dorsal than in the ventral lip. Brachet and Jeener (1946) discuss micromethods for the detection of thymonucleic acid, and some of the physical properties of nucleic acids.

3. *Metabolism*

The nitrogen metabolism of *Rana pipiens* during embryonic development was studied by Gregg and Ballentine (1946). They find an apparent stability of the principal nitrogen compounds during development, indicating that very little combustion of protein occurs in the embryo as a whole during this period. Local changes are not easily detectable by the methods employed.

Lindahl and Holter (1941) measured the oxygen consumption of the primary oöcytes of the sea urchin *Paracentrotus,* and found it to be as high as that of the unfertilized egg, though oxygen consumption decreases temporarily during the maturation divisions. The *Chaetopterus* egg after fertilization shows an increase in permeability to water, although the rate of oxygen consumption decreases independently (Shapiro, 1941).

Collier (1947) studied the relation between metabolism and morphogenesis during the regeneration of *Tubifex tubifex.* During the first week of regeneration, oxygen consumption is nearly normal, while localization and early differentiation are proceeding; during the second week a marked increase occurs. No cyanide-sensitive respiration fraction was noted.

Bodine and Fitzgerald (1947) studied by means of fluorescence microscopy riboflavin and other fluorescent compounds in the developing orthopteran egg. The total fluorescence of the egg at pH 4.5 is fairly constant throughout development as is the riboflavin content. The compounds produced late in development are thought to be pterines.

Sawyer (1947a, 1947b) reports cholinergic stimulation of the release of melanophore hormone by the hypophysis in salamander larvae. Before the hypophysis is functional, dermal melanophores attain their maximum expansion directly in response to cholinergic drugs, and atropine induces contraction. After the pituitary is functional, there is almost no direct response to drugs in hypophysectomized animals.

Poulson and Boell (1946) have been comparing the choline-esterase activity of normal and genetically deficient strains of *Drosophila melanogaster*. In the "Notch" deficiency, they find that the enzyme concentration is normal, the activity reaching a peak at about forty hours.

Jaeger (1945) made determinations by the Heatley ultra-micromethod for glycogen on excised fragments of the embryo during invagination and induction. It was found that glycogen is used not only by the invaginating "organizer" region of the dorsal lip, but also by the non-inductive material that turns in at the ventral blastoporal lip. Jaeger states that this new fact renders untenable the earlier hypothesis of the Cambridge workers (see Needham, 1942) that the "masked evocator" is liberated by glycolysis. There is no glycogen disappearance in the dorsal lip unless gastrulation movements take place. The suggestion has been made (Barth, 1942) that disappearance of glycogen is correlated with the condition of partial anaerobiosis (Pasteur Effect) of the invaginated materials. Jaeger discusses some of the disadvantages of this interpretation and suggests other possible explanations. Further experiments must be done to demonstrate the morphogenetic significance of this localized glycolysis.

VI. Gastrulation

One of the more interesting contributions to our knowledge of the structure of the egg during its early stages is Holtfreter's (1943) description of the morphological properties of the surface coat of the amphibian egg and early embryo. It originates as an integral covering of the ovarian egg and during cleavage holds the surface cells together by its supercellular elastic properties. Holtfreter believes that these intercellular connections account in part for the unification of cell behavior during the progress of gastrulation. As a detailed description of a structure of a particular type of egg, the observations are unparalleled. However, it is difficult to accept the surface coat as being of general significance in morphogenetic cell movements and in all types of gastrulation until its counterpart has been discovered and described in many other types of eggs. Possibly the elastic coat of the egg of the zebra fish, *Brachydanio* (Roosen-Runge, 1938) is a similar structure. It is doubtful if the hyaline plasma layer of the echinoderm egg is analogous. Holtfreter's 1943 and 1944 studies of gastrulation attempt to trace the movements of the several regions of the embryo in gastrulation to basic properties of certain cell groups, and to their response to specific stimuli emanating from their environment. He invokes local surface tension changes in the membranes of certain flask-shaped cells, brought about by a greater alkalinity of the blastocoel fluid, as the primary cause of gastrulation.

Modern cell physiology, however, has discarded surface tension changes as being of any great physiological significance to cells, since all actual measurements of the magnitude of the tension at the surfaces of cells have indicated an almost infinitesimally small value. If the surface tension is low, agents producing slight changes in it cannot have much effect. The "zipper" hypothesis of Brown *et al.* (1941) seems a more fruitful point of departure for an attack on the problem.

Schechtman (1942) has also studied the mechanism of amphibian gastrulation. He emphasizes the correlative movements bringing about gastrulation, in contrast to some earlier views on the intricate mosaic arrangement of various autonomous movements. The method used was the study of the behavior of various portions of the blastula subjected to various types of explantation, transplantation and isolation *in situ.* He finds that the presumptive chorda region of the dorsal lip of the blastopore possesses an inherent capacity for extension, but not for invagination. The presumptive pharyngeal endoderm and head mesoderm of the circumblastoporal region have an inherent capacity for invagination. The presumptive somites, lateral plate mesoderm, and tail mesoderm of the lateral portion of the marginal zone have inherent capacities for stretching, involution and invagination, but these are incapable of dorsal convergence and of constriction over the yolk mass. They are, therefore, correlative movements, which take place only if there is continuity between the lateral marginal zones and the dorsal lip materials.

Lewis (1947) attempts to explain invagination and neurulation in terms of a single essential factor. This factor is an increase or decrease of contractile tension of the superficial gel layers on one side of a group of adherent epithelial cells that offer some resistance to distortion. The explanation is somewhat formal, since we must seek the causes of the increase or decrease in contractile tension, and the chemical mechanics by which these causes make their effects manifest.

Hybrids between certain species of anuran amphibia develop as far as the blastula stage, when a block to further development takes place (Moore, 1946). Barth (1946a) studied the nature of the block to gastrulation in *Rana pipiens* × *Rana sylvatica* hybrids. The results suggest that a block in the phosphorylation process is operative.

VII. Neurulation

The basic problem of cell layer folding in neurulation must be essentially similar to that of gastrulation. However, in the former process, in amphibia, the "organizer" plays a role. The older view that the folding of the neural plate is due either to cell proliferation, local cell enlargement, or a combination of the two derives no support from recent investigations (Burt, 1943; Gillette, 1944; Hutchinson, 1944). Nor is the differential swelling of the neural plate due to imbibition of water to be regarded as the effective cause, if the density measurements on amphibian embryos during gastrulation of Brown *et al.* (1941) are regarded as decisive. The "zipper" hypothesis of these authors replaces the older views with a theory based upon surface attractive forces exerted by re-arrangements of surface molecules, or of a binding substance between the cells.

The folding process in chick embryos is inhibited by irradiation with monochromatic ultraviolet light, between the primitive streak and 8-somite stages (Davis, 1944), whereas cell division and volume changes are not obviously affected. It is suggested that the effect may become manifest through action of the ultraviolet on sterols which may be taking part in the formation of the internal membrane of the neural tube.

Induction in Amphibia

Spofford (1947, 1948) investigated the inductive effect of the intact posterior chorda-mesodermal axis on competent prospective ectoderm in *Amblystoma.* This was accomplished by removing the posterior neural plate and replacing it with competent prospective ectoderm from stage 11. These grafts formed tail somites. Replacement of more plate gives rise to spinal cord in the anterior portion of the graft, and to somites in the posterior portion. This sharp break is indicative of differences of inductive capacity along the chorda-mesodermal axis.

Van Cleave (1947) tested neuralization induction by denatured optic cup, hindbrain and larval liver in isolated gastrula ectoderm explants. The first two denatured organs produce qualitatively and quantitatively similar neuralization. Denatured larval liver was almost ineffective.

Pasteels (1947) reports that following centrifuging of amphibian eggs in the blastula or gastrula stages, various complexes of ectoblastic and mesoblastic organs appear in the ectoblast. *In vitro* studies suggest that these are very abnormal secondary embryos, which are formed without action of the normal organizer. The ectoblast in these cases is characterized by a very high ribonucleic acid content.

VIII. Differentiation

1. *Invertebrates*

Clement (1947) repeated the early defect experiments of Crampton on the eggs of *Ilyanassa obsoleta* (removal of polar lobe, destruction of certain cleavage blastomeres), and by an improved semi-sterile technique, raised the defective embryos to considerably later stages than had hitherto been possible. He concludes that the polar lobe material is essential to normal development, because if the lobe is removed at the trefoil stage of first cleavage, a partial larva results. The polar lobe passes into the *D* quadrant at the second cleavage. If the 4*D* macromere is destroyed after it has given off the *D* quadrant ectomeres of the first three quartets and the 4*d* cell (mesentomere), the resultant larva, though small, is almost normal. This suggests an allocation or segregation of the essential polar lobe materials during the early cleavages.

Costello (1945b) isolated various blastomeres and combinations of blastomeres of the cleaving eggs of the annelid, *Nereis*. From the two through the thirty-two cell stage, and probably later, each isolated cleavage blastomere develops as a partial embryo, with little or no tendency toward regulation. The "determinative" cleavage of isolated trochoblasts, which divide only twice and then differentiate prototrochal cilia from three of the four products, is particularly striking. The results, in general, are reminiscent of those obtained by E. B. Wilson for the eggs of *Dentalium* and *Patella,* and add another example to the forms which appear to develop without benefit of induction.

Barth (1946b) describes a control of differentiation in the hydroid, *Tubularia,* brought about by a natural inhibitor which diffuses from the cut ends of the stem, but which is retained by the perisarc. This inhibitor prevents differentiation of hydranths from the coenosarc during regeneration.

Rulon (1946a) studied the effects of lithium chloride and of sodium thiocyanate on the process of reconstitution in planarians. Treatment with lithium chloride before amputation of the piece gave increased head frequency in the regeneration of short posterior pieces. Treatment after amputation gave decreased head frequency. Treatment with sodium thiocyanate at corresponding times gave exactly opposite effects. A combination of lithium chloride and sodium thiocyanate gave the highest head frequencies.

Moment (1946) has studied growth limitation in the regeneration of posterior segments of the earthworm. He finds that the number of segments regenerated posteriorly from the 94th to the end is independent of the original number of segments in the worm; it is a linear function of the distance in segments (but not in millimeters) of the cut from the anterior end. Moment proposes a theory of limitation of normal growth and regeneration in terms of the addition of new cells until "a critical inhibitory voltage is thereby built up, thus stopping proliferation at the growing end."

2. *Teleosts*

The goldfish egg has been used by Tung *et al.* (1945) as material for studying the developmental potencies of teleost blastoderms, and their latitudinal fragments. Equatorial separation of the egg at the one- or two-cell stage leads to the formation of hyperblastulae; at the four- to sixteen-cell stages, almost perfect embryos result. The existence in the periblast of an organizing substance which flows up from below the equator to enter the blastoderm during the four-cell stage is suggested as an explanation of the results.

The work on the organization of the teleost blastoderm has been reviewed by Oppenheimer (1947b). She concludes that during cleavage, blastula and gastrula stages, the fundamental dynamics of development in the teleost are comparable to those operative in amphibian development, as evidenced by the nature of the regulative processes which follow appropriate experimental manipulation. The organization of the blastoderm differs during gastrulation in the embryos of *Salmo* and *Fundulus*. Isolation, defect and transplantation experiments on gastrulae of *Salmo* suggest the existence of a physiological gradient field in the blastoderm of this form.

Oppenheimer (1947a) finds that the central nervous system of *Fundulus heteroclitus* tends to regulate functionally to an orderly whole if more than the usual amount of material is incorporated into it at a very early stage by operative methods.

3. *Amphibia*

a. During Embryonic Development. Nieuwkoop (1947) investigated the origin of the germ cells and the development of the lateral plates and germ ridges in urodeles. He finds that the ectoderm determines the behavior of the outer layer of the lateral plate in forming the somatopleure, and the endoderm conditions the inner layer in forming the splanchnopleure. Both the lateral plate and nephrogenous cord have a role in the formation of the germ cells, the endoderm having an inductive action on the mesoderm. The determination of the germ cells, which form in the presumptive lateral plate, occurs very rapidly. The germ ridges develop from peritoneal epithelium.

By operative techniques on the larvae of *Hyla regilla,* Eakin (1946) rotated the presumptive retina of the eye, reversing the positions of the vitreal and tapetal surfaces. If the operation is performed before Stage 21, regulation takes place; otherwise, the parts develop in their inverted positions. He concludes that the determination of polarity of the retina occurs relatively late in development, during the swimming stage after hatching of the larva.

Detwiler (1946) reports on the regeneration of midbrain in *Amblystoma*. Unilateral excision of the mesencephalon at stage 20-21 (neurula with closed folds) is followed by gradual restoration, from material of the opposite side.

Humphrey (1945) studied the progeny of amblystomid salamander females experimentally converted into males, to ascertain the mechanism of sex determination in these forms. The findings (percentages of males and females produced in the different crosses) are approximately what would be expected if the male is the homogametic (*ZZ*) sex, and the female normally the heterogametic (*WZ*) sex. Unusual females of the type (*WW*) are also possible. It is probable that the *W* chromosome is identical with the *Z* chromosome, except for the absence of a male-determining gene or genes. Mintz (1947) failed to reverse sex or produce intersexes by treating female amblystomid larvae with testosterone propionate.

b. Limb Regeneration. For the regeneration of limbs, a certain minimum number of nerve fibers must be present. This is in contrast to the fact that an embryonic limb bud can undergo its original differentiation and growth without a nerve supply. An adequate supply of either sensory (Singer, 1943) or regenerated motor fibers (Singer, 1946) will permit regeneration. Each amputation level in the adult *Triturus* forelimb requires the presence of an adequate quantity of nerve fibers for regeneration to proceed, this quantity differing for the different levels. Singer (1947) has shown that the quantity of nerve fibers required at the different levels is actually the same per unit area of amputation surface, except in the hand region.

When a larval urodele limb is amputated, a regular sequence of cellular dedifferentiation, blastema formation, cessation of dedifferentiation, morphogenesis and organogenesis occurs. If the limb is denervated, the equilibrium of these factors is destroyed, so that dedifferentiation gains ascendancy and proceeds to the end unchecked by blastema formation. In denervated adult salamander limbs, the growth of connective tissue seals the amputated region before much dedifferentiation has occurred.

Adult salamander limbs with the threshold number of nerve fibers normally undergo regeneration; those of adult frogs and other anura do not. Treatment of the stump of a frog's limb with a strong sodium chloride solution following amputation (Rose, 1942, 1944, 1945) stimulates internal dedifferentiation and, in some cases, limb regeneration. Rose views this salt stimulation as equivalent to one of the stimulatory effects of nerves in regeneration.

A new method has been devised (Rose and Rose, 1947) of subjecting the stump 24 hours after amputation of a frog's limb to a temperature shock of 55°C., for 1 minute. This produces the same sort of stimulatory effect on regeneration as does the salt solution.

Another effect of the nerves in regeneration of urodeles is to produce more rapid growth of the cells of the regeneration blastema. In denervated limbs the cells grow more slowly and differentiate prematurely. Schotté and Butler (1941) suggested that a chemical secretion of nerve cells is a controlling factor in the dedifferentiation-differentiation equilibrium. A young blastema transplanted to a freshly amputated limb is capable, by its presence, of actually suppressing the dedifferentiation phase of regeneration.

4. *Chick Differentiation*

Spratt (1942) has studied the location of germinal areas in the pregastrular (unincubated) blastoderm of the hen's egg by means of transverse cuts across the blastoderm, and by a marking method using carbon particles (1946). He finds that almost the entire posterior half of the epiblast layer of the pregastrula enters the primitive streak and later gives rise largely to mesoderm. The medullary plate originates entirely in the anterior half of the germinal disc, and is altered by the end of gastrulation through the movements of the adjacent posterior and lateral material into a pear-shaped area surrounding the anterior end of the primitive streak. It is subsequently completed by very unequal growth during the period of regression of the primitive streak. Spratt (1947a) studied the process of regression and shortening of the primitive streak of the chick blastoderm by explantation methods. He concludes that the primitive streak is apparently pushed from the scene of action by the growing embryo in front of it. As it shortens, the posterior end of the streak is progressively transformed into embryonic and extra-embryonic ectoderm and endoderm. The node and a small portion of the streak behind it become the end-bud, and later form the remainder of the embryo behind the twenty-seventh somite level. Explantation media suitable for continued development of chick blastoderms were investigated by Spratt (1947b). When a blastoderm was placed in a medium composed of a saline extract of the whole egg contents plus a saline-agar base, it continued growth and differentiation throughout the period of development studied. A non-nutrient saline-agar medium was found to be inadequate to support development.

Rudnick (1944) reviews the early history and mechanics of the chick blastoderm, and presents two admirable summary figures of (1) the distribution of potencies in the definitive primitive streak blastoderm, tested under various experimental conditions, and (2) of the prospective embryonic areas. The latter is based largely on the work and assumptions of Pasteels. Rudnick comments on the current biochemical-physiological approach to the study of the unique properties of the primitive streak (chiefly micro-respiration determinations) by suggesting that embryologists might well remember that the morphodynamic relations in the primitive streak need much clarification before the problem can be handed over in one neat package to the biochemist.

Rawles and Straus (1948) performed an experimental analysis of the development of the trunk musculature and ribs in the chick. This was done by marking with carbon the lateral plate and somites at the 27 to 30 somite stage. Tracing these carbon marks, they find that the somites form only the dorsal part of the trunk musculature and skeleton, the lateral and ventral portions being produced from the lateral plate material.

Rudnick (1945) studied limb-forming potencies of the chick blastoderm by removing measured pieces of right and left prospective trunk regions from primitive streak to 15-somite stages, and growing them as coelomic grafts. From these, the tissue content obtained was the same as in chorio-allantoic grafts. An appreciable percentage formed wings or legs, with recognizable skeletal parts. A wing was obtained from a graft as young as the late head-fold (presomite) stage. The youngest donor yielding a leg was in the 6-somite stage. The limbs form as polarized buds, in which the skeletal parts are better developed than the other limb parts.

Rawles (1947) made further observations on the developmental properties of the presumptive hind-limb area of the chick. Well-developed hind limbs were obtained in coelomic grafts of isolated lateral plate material including, at most, only the anterior margin of the normal hind limb material in the 27 to 29 somite chick. This is taken as evidence that the limb area at this stage is a regulatory system rather than a regionally determined system.

Saunders (1947) studied the origin of wing parts in the chick. His observations indicate that these parts originate in proximo-distal sequence under control of apical ectoderm. This supersedes the older idea of apico-basal order and passivity of the ectoderm.

5. *Other Forms*

The curious streaming-migration of myxamoebae to form the complex cell aggregates of slime molds such as *Dictyostelium* is well known from the work of Raper (1940, 1941). Bonner (1947) presents evidence that this aggregation occurs by chemotaxis, after ruling out various possible physical causes. A diffusion of substance out from a central mass of myxamoebae is described. For this substance, Bonner proposes the name "acrasin."

Stentor is a large ciliate protozoon with a long nucleus resembling a string of beads. It has long been a favorite object for studies of the behavior of cell fragments, since it may be cut easily, and shows considerable regenerative ability. Weisz (1948) has reinvestigated the behavior of cut fragments in relation to original polarity of the organism, and nuclear content of the piece. He finds that neither the "Kern-plasma relation" nor physiological gradients can play a role in determining regeneration. If a representative mass of cytoplasm is present along with a representative bit of macronucleus, regeneration will occur.

6. *Pigment*

The recent work of Holtfreter has stressed the importance of a knowledge of the behavior of explanted embryonic cells under a variety of experimental environments as a prelude to the interpretation of cell behavior in the developing organism. For some years Twitty has been analyzing the behavior of embryonic chromatophores under various conditions of tissue culture. The detailed observations are given in a number of comprehensive papers (Twitty, 1944, 1945; Twitty and Bodenstein, 1939). A recent general conclusion (Twitty, 1947) is that the dispersal of chromatophores is activated by chemical influences mutually exerted by the cells themselves.

Rawles (1947b), using the mouse as experimental material, demonstrated that the pigment cells of mammals originate from the neural crest, just as do the pigment cells of amphibia (DuShane, 1934, 1935; Twitty, 1936; Raven, 1936) and birds (Dorris, 1936; Rawles, 1939; Eastlick, 1939; Ris, 1941; and others). Rawles isolated various axial levels of 8-12 day black mouse embryos in the coelom of White Leghorn chicks, and found that only tissues containing presumptive neural crest, histologically recognizable neural crest, or cells migrating from the neural crest can produce melanophores.

Niu (1947) studied the axial organization of the amphibian neural crest, with special reference to the origin of the pigment cells. He divided the neural crest of *Triturus torosus* into five segments and explanted these portions. The posterior trunk fold portion produced the largest number of chromatophores. After complete extirpation of the cranial folds, the remainder of the embryo produced more head chromatophores than it would normally have produced. Niu suggests that there may be a reservoir of potential melanophores in the head region, normally suppressed by the influence of the intact folds.

DuShane (1948) reviews the present knowledge of the development of pigment cells in vertebrates, supplementing his earlier discussions (1943, 1944) of this problem.

Willier (1948) summarizes the data on hormonal control of feather pigmentation in the fowl. The melanin pigmentation pattern arises through the interaction of migratory melanoblasts and the feather papilla. As restated by Willier, "The hormones merely serve as regulators of the expression of the inherent potentialities of the diverse interacting tissue components of the feather germ."

IX. Heteroploidy

Böök (1941, 1943) investigated the effects of low temperatures (1 to 2 degrees C.) on cleavage of the eggs of *Triton taeniatus,* with special reference to the mechanism of production of haploids, triploids, and chromosomal mosaics of this species. This method of producing heteroploids was originally suggested by the work of Rostand (1933, 1934) on hybrid gynogenesis of *Anura,* and applied to *Triturus viridescens* by Fankhauser and Griffiths (1939). Treating the eggs within half an hour after insemination produces a large number of triploids. Eggs treated later than this showed a high mortality and the survivors were chromosomal mosaics. It is interesting to note that in spite of widely varying chromosome numbers within the cells of different regions of these embryos, the individuals were not macroscopically abnormal.

Results similar to those obtained by Böök for treatments shortly after insemination were obtained by Fankhauser and Griffiths (1939), but they did not obtain mosaics by later treatment. The entire subject of the effects of changes of chromosome number on amphibian development has been reviewed by Fankhauser (1945a). In general, the larger size of nuclei and cells in polyploid individuals is compensated by a reduction in the number of cells in a given organ, so that body size is approximately normal (Fankhauser, 1945b). Fankhauser and Humphrey (1943) have established a relation between the number of nucleoli and the number of chromosome sets in axolotl tail-fin cells, so that euploid heteroploids may be recognized on the basis of nucleolar counts.

Fischberg (1944) applied the Fankhauser cold treatment technique to the eggs of *Triton alpestris.* He obtained a wide variety of heteroploid and mosaic heteroploid individuals, describing nine types in all. One haploid salamander lived 289 days, and died after beginning metamorphosis. This is the oldest haploid thus far described (in age, though not in stage of development), and points to the fact that haploidy as such does not necessarily produce abnormalities of structure or low viability.

Costello and Henley (1947) observed an unusually high frequency of mosaics (43% of a sample of 126 individuals) in tail-tip preparations of *Triturus torosus,* from animals that had been shipped in the usual thermos jug for embryological materials. Numerous mitotic abnormalities were observed, including multipolar spindles, lagging or lost chromosomes or chromosome fragments, and similar cytological variations, which may be conducive to production of aneuploidy.

Fischberg (1948) obtained a large number of heteroploid individuals of *Triton alpestris*, principally by applying a temperature shock cold treatment to the eggs within 30 minutes after insemination. Haploid, triploid, tetraploid, euploid and aneuploid mosaics are described, and the origin of the various types discussed. He stresses the fact that the addition or subtraction of one or two chromosomes of a set is not necessarily fatal or productive of abnormal embryos.

Stauffer (1945) produced haploid merogones of the axolotl by the familiar Baltzer technique of removing the second maturation spindle after insemination. These haploids lived for varying periods of time, but none attained an age approaching that of the *Triton alpestris* haploid.

Michalski (1948) reports an unusually high incidence (5.1%) of spontaneous heteroploidy in the salamander, *Eurycea bislineata*.

By heat treatment of *Rana pipiens* eggs (four minutes at 37°C.) beginning twenty minutes after insemination, following the method devised by Fankhauser and Watson (1942) for eggs of newts, Briggs (1947) produced triploids in 38% of the eggs treated. Some mosaics were also obtained. Artificial production of triploids is of importance in determining the effects of whole sets of chromosomes on development, relations of cell size to organ size and body size, and of interest in providing experimental approaches to the problem of heterogamety. For example, Briggs (1946), using a combination of irradiation of *Rana catesbiana* spermatozoa and subsequent heat treatment of *Rana pipiens* eggs activated by these injured spermatozoa, produced gynogenetic diploids of *Rana pipiens*. The heat-treated controls (*Rana pipiens* sperms and non-irradiated eggs) became triploid. Since both males and females were obtained among the gynogenetic diploids, Briggs suggests that the female is heterogametic, and that the first maturation division is reductional for the sex-determining factors.

Following up some of the developmental effects of triploidy, Humphrey and Fankhauser (1946) studied the formation, structure and functional capacity of the ovaries of triploid axolotls. They found little difference between early diploid and triploid ovaries, though later the triploid ovaries are smaller, because of the degeneration of many of the oöcytes. Those that escape degeneration attain maturity. The degeneration is apparently due to the extra set of chromosomes present rather than to a hormonal or nutritional deficiency in the animal, but why all oöcytes do not degenerate is unexplained.

X. Effects of Radiations on Development

There have been many studies of the effects of x-rays on cells, with the view of ascertaining whether nuclei or cytoplasm are more directly influenced. Duryee (1947) adds to the voluminous literature the observation that high dosages affect the ovarian eggs of the salamander, *Triturus pyrrhogaster,* by producing immediate fragmentation of egg chromosomes, loss of lateral chromonemata loops, and vacuolization of nucleoli, when the entire cell is irradiated. The fact that isolated nuclei and chromosomes do not react markedly when irradiated directly suggests to Duryee that the damage is an indirect effect, caused by chemical changes induced in the cytoplasm. However, there appears to be no real criterion for deciding whether or not the nuclei remain alive after isolation. The usual test for viability of gametes, fertilizability, is obviously not practicable here.

Much more critical evidence of the locus of effects of x-rays is provided by the work of Whiting (1946) who obtained haploid androgenetic males of *Habrobracon* by heavily x-raying the eggs (in the females) and then fertilizing by mating. The results suggest that x-ray injury at least up to the lethal dose is directly chromosomal, since the untreated paternal chromosomes can function normally in the heavily treated cytoplasm of an egg whose own chromosomes are so seriously injured as to be unable to function.

Giese (1946) studied the comparative sensitivity to ultraviolet radiations of the sperm and eggs of several marine invertebrate animals, including the echinoderms *Strongylocentrotus purpuratus, Strongylocentrotus franciscanus, Arbacia punctulata, Dendraster excentricus,* and *Patiria miniata,* the annelids *Nereis limbata* and *Chaetopterus pergamentaceus,* the echiuroid *Urechis,* and the clam, *Mactra.* He finds that the absolute amount of energy required to affect the retardation of cell division of the zygote to the same extent by irradiating the sperm was very much less than that required when the egg was irradiated. The most striking difference was found in the case of the echinoderms, less in the case of the annelids and mollusc. Giese points out that the action spectrum for the retardation of division of eggs fertilized with irradiated sperm resembles the absorption of ultraviolet light by proteins.

Spikes (1944) irradiated fertilized *Lytechinus* eggs unilaterally with ultraviolet light and obtained excentric elevation of the fertilization membrane. If the wavelength of the radiations is around 2537 A the membrane remains applied to the egg surface on the irradiated side. Wavelengths longer than 3000 A produce no noticeable effect. Irradiation apparently determines the position of the first cleavage plane, which almost invariably passes through the center of the irradiated region.

XI. Effects of Chemicals on Development

Sodium azide has been found by Hall and Moog (1947) to have the property of suppressing development of amphibian eggs for considerable periods without preventing normal development after the exposure to treatment is terminated. It is thought to act as a specific enzyme poison on some phase of the phosphorylative breakdown of glycogen.

Child (1948) obtained exogastrulae of *Strongylocentrotus purpuratus* by means of inhibition with sodium azide, similar to those produced with lithium. Rulon (1948) treated both unfertilized and fertilized eggs of *Arbacia* with malonic acid. The former developed, upon subsequent fertilization, into abnormal blastulae, the latter into inhibited late gastrulae or early plutei. Rulon (1946b) produced typical modifications of development of the sand-dollar by exposure of the eggs to lithium chloride and to sodium thiocyanate. The former has an endodermizing effect, the latter ectodermizes. A double treatment produces predominately endodermal effects. The effect of lithium in inducing exogastrulation in echinoderm eggs has been known since the experiments of Herbst (1892), and extensively reinvestigated by the Scandinavian school of embryologists. Nevertheless, there is still no really adequate explanation of the effects of this ion.

Marvel and Fisher (1948) subjected squid embryos to cyanide and found the early embryos to be much more resistant to its effects than the later embryos or adults. The change in sensitivity was found to be a gradual process, which suggested to these authors the possibility that the site of this change was in the central nervous system.

Smith and Gray (1948) studied the distribution of copper in early chick embryos by the use of Cu^{64} as a radioactive tracer. Cu^{64} was injected at early stages, and the distribution in the embryos studied by a radioautograph technique. Relatively impressive concentrations of Cu^{64} were noted in rapidly developing structures, usually appearing as the structure starts its development.

Nowinski and Pandra (1947) injected thiocyanate into chick embryos, and studied the malformation produced. They list such effects as omphalocephaly, non-formation of tube from neural plate and superposition of two neural folds, among the numerous abnormalities resulting.

Van Dyke and Ritchey (1947) studied the influence of colchicine during the embryonic development of rats. Their results indicate that the drug retards the development of advanced embryos, but is lethal to the younger ones. The cephalic end of the embryo seems more resistant to the effects than the remainder of the body, which is a curious exception to the usual susceptibility differences.

Antithyroxine Compounds

Harnley and Goldsmith (1946) studied the effects of thiourea on the development of *Drosophila melanogaster.* The effects described include suppression of eversion of imaginal discs in some cases, eversion of thoracic disc complex only, or of both thoracic and abdominal disc complexes in other cases. Normal pupation and absence of any effect on pigmentation were reported.

Lynn (1947) treated early limb-bud stages of *Plethodon cinereus* with thiourea and phenylthiourea, inducing this terrestrial form to undergo the transition into the form of aquatic larvae, even though these are not normally developed in the life history of this species. He suggests that the effects may be due to an inhibition of the thyroid. The phenylthiourea produced colorless embryos. These same agents (thiourea and phenylthiourea) were used (Lynn, 1948) on the developing embryos of a toad, *Eleutherodactylus ricordii,* which has no aquatic larval stage. The treated embryos retained their larval tails and failed to complete differentiation of their limbs. The phenylthiourea animals were pigment-free.

Lynn performed these experiments, because these thyroid-inhibiting drugs effectively block the production of thyroid hormone and hence are useful in attempting to elucidate the role of the thyroid in metamorphosis. Some of these drugs secondarily produce a depigmentation of the animals. Richter and Clisby (1941) had noted a graying of the hair of black rats to which phenylthiourea had been administered. Dieke (1947) found alpha-naphthylthiourea similarly effective. Lynn and Sister Alfred de Marie (1946) were the first to report the effects of thiourea derivatives on the pigmentation of amphibia. They obtained a depigmentation of tadpoles of *Rana pipiens* with 0.05% thiouracil. Somewhat similar depigmentation effects were obtained with allylthiourea, phenylthiourea, aminobenzoic acid, and sulfanilamide. Figge, as early as 1938 (a, b) had observed an inhibition of tyrosinase melanin production in amphibian larvae raised in solutions of sodium benzenone indophenol and phenol indophenol. It does not destroy or dissolve the pigment granules after they are once formed. It is not known whether the thiourea derivatives affect the tyrosinase system in the same manner as do the indophenol dyes.

Markert (1947) studied the *in vitro* effects of thyroxine and antithyroxine compounds on chick melanoblasts in tissue cultures. He finds that thyroxine does not increase pigment production as it does *in vivo.* Thiourea derivatives with a phenyl group are quite effective in preventing pigment production, but there appears to be no correlation between this capacity and their effect as antithyroxine compounds.

XII. Induction, Gene Hormones, and Genetic Control of Morphogenesis

The study of development has reached a point at which there are several divergent pathways of knowledge that might be followed. The older concept of specific organ-forming substances in a mosaic pattern in the cytoplasm of eggs has long since been abandoned. The newer attempt to explain all development in terms of organizers, evocators, or other diffusible substances has been followed into several apparently insoluble dilemmas. One of these dilemmas results from the fact that the competences of tissues (i.e., their ability to react to a developmental stimulus) are at least as important in the inductive system as the inductor. The origin of these competences is therefore more significant for an understanding of development than is the fact that a diffusible substance can spread throughout an embryo to condition the formation of an embryonic structure. Another difficulty arises from the fact that diffusible substances acting during development must be limited, *per se,* to compounds of relatively small molecular size, i.e., small enough and of a composition such that they may pass through cell membranes to make their action manifest (Costello, 1945b).

We know from genetic studies that there must be many gene products produced in different mutant stocks that are incapable of diffusing throughout an embryo to affect the embryonic processes. Nevertheless, many of these genes may have an effect on development, through the products which they produce within cells acting in those cells according to the substrate present. In fact, of all the gene-controlled substances that may be involved in the production of eye color in *Drosophila,* only two (the v^+ and the cn^+ substances) have been demonstrated to be capable of diffusing through the tissues of a differentiating larva or pupa (Ephrussi, 1942).

A third difficulty is a methodological one. It has become apparent that it is impossible to test directly to ascertain the chemical nature of an inductor, because it is apparently impossible to distinguish between a direct action of an applied chemical and an indirect action of this chemical in causing adjacent cells to release some product which will bring about the resulting action. A fourth difficulty is the fact that inductors are apparently non-specific. This non-specificity may be due, however, to the situation described above, i.e., non-specific substances may call forth from the living cells the release of a specific substance with inductive action.

Other comments, including the suggestion that organizers must be considered from the viewpoint of reconstitutional studies as well as from the standpoint of embryonic development, are made in Child's (1946) critical review of the organizer concept.

There are relatively few well-elucidated cases correlating biochemical mutations with morphogenetic processes during development. There is, of course, no dearth of genes, both newly described and previously known, which make their action morphologically manifest in the developing embryo, but most of these have not been studied biochemically (See the reviews by Wright, 1945; Danforth, 1946; and Irwin, 1947). The eye-color hormones (v^+, cn^+) of *Drosophila* intervene in the biochemical synthesis of pigment, rather than in a morphogenetic process. There has been a report on the use of insulin in producing rumplessness in fowl (Landauer and Bliss, 1946), but this phenotypic effect can be produced also by shaking normal eggs, or by incising the backs of young embryos (Zwilling, 1945).

The outstanding contribution in this field in recent years is that of Chevais (1943), who has studied the intervention of diffusible substances effective in increasing the facet number in the eyes of the mutant Bar of *Drosophila*. Extracts of pupae of *Calliphora* (a blowfly), fed to *Drosophila* larvae at a certain sensitive period of development produce an increase in facet number. If exposed before this sensitive period, the larvae are capable also of converting a portion of the *Calliphora* extract into an "insensitizing" substance, which prevents increase in facet number. In a careful study of the growth of the imaginal discs giving rise to the eyes of Bar and of wild-type *Drosophila,* Chevais found that the imaginal optic discs of the Bar flies are initially smaller than those of the wild-type, but during later larval life grow at the same rate. Chevais visualizes a scheme as follows: *Drosophila* carrying the Bar gene (1) have smaller imaginal optic discs, and (2) lack the quantity of B^+ substance present in wild-type flies. The first is brought about by an early effect of the Bar gene on disc development, which either reduces the initial number of cells or decreases the rate of growth. If the latter, this effect is temporary, since later the discs (Bar and wild-type) grow at the same rate, although they are of different sizes. Much later, during the larval period, the second effect is manifested, i.e., suppression, in part, of the production of B^+ substance.

Pursuing the problem further, Khouvine *et al.* (1943) tested various derivatives of imidazole for B^+ activity. Substances showing B^+ activity should increase the number of facets of the eyes of Bar mutants of *Drosophila,* provided an appropriate dosage is injected into the larvae at the proper time, and is not too toxic. Among the compounds tested, l-methyl-hydantoine produced the greatest effect. The experimental procedure for trying to identify the B^+ substance is similar to that which was employed in elucidating the nature of the v^+ substance, shown to be kynurenine by Butenandt, Weidel and Becker (1940), and by Tatum and Haagen-Smit (1941).

References

Ancel, P., and Vintemberger, P. 1943a. *Compt. Rend. Soc. Biol.* **137**: 223.
Ancel, P., and Vintemberger, P. 1943b. *Compt. Rend. Soc. Biol.* **137**: 183-184.
Ancel, P., and Vintemberger, P. 1943c. *Compt. Rend. Soc. Biol.* **137**: 387.
Ancel, P., and Vintemberger, P. 1944. *Compt. Rend. Soc. Biol.* **138**: 84-87.
Barth, L. G. 1942. *Physiol. Zool.* **15**: 30-46.
Barth, L. G. 1946a. *Anat. Rec.* **94**: 401.
Barth, L. G. 1946b. *Anat. Rec.* **94**: 403.
Barth, L. G., and Jaeger, L. 1947. *Physiol. Zool.* **20**: 133-146.
Baylor, M. R. B., Nalbandov, A., and Clark, G. L. 1943. *Proc. Soc. Exptl. Biol. and Med.* **54**: 229-232.
Bodenstein, D. 1947. *Jour. Exptl. Zool.* **104**: 311-341.
Bodenstein, D., and Kondritzer, A. A. 1948. *Jour. Exptl. Zool.* **107**: 109-121.
Bodine, J. H., and Fitzgerald, L. R. 1947. *Physiol. Zool.* **20**: 146-160.
Boell, E. J. 1942. *Growth,* Suppl. **7**: 37-54.
Boell, E. J., and Needham, J. 1939. *Proc. Roy. Soc. Lond.* **B127**: 363-373.
Boell, E. J., Koch, H., and Needham, J. 1939. *Proc. Roy. Soc. Lond.* **B127**: 374-387.
Bonner, J. T. 1947. *Jour. Exptl. Zool.* **106**: 1-26.
Bonnevie, K. 1947. *Jour. Morph.* **81**: 399-423.
Böök, J. 1941. *Kung. Fysiogr. Sällsk. i. Lund. Forh.* **11**: Nr. 12 1-16.
Böök, J. 1943. *Hereditas* **29**: 195-197.
Brachet, A. 1911. *Arch. d. Biol.* **26**: 337-363.
Brachet, J. 1934. *Arch. d. Biol.* **46**: 25-45.
Brachet, J. 1936. *Compt. Rend. Soc. Biol.* **122**: 108-110.
Brachet, J. 1939. *Arch. d. Biol.* **50**: 223-267.
Brachet, J. 1940. *Enzymologia* **10**: 87-96.
Brachet, J. 1941. *Arch. d. Biol.* **53**: 207-257.
Brachet, J. 1943. *Bull. de l'Acad. roy. de Belg.* 5 Ser. **29**: 707-718.
Brachet, J. 1944. Embryologie Chimique. Masson et Cie, Paris.
Brachet, J., and Chantrenne, H. 1942. *Acta Biol. Belg.* **2**: 451-454.
Brachet, J., and Jeener, R. 1946. *Arch. Med. Belg.* **1**: 168-177.
Brachet, J., and Shapiro, H. 1937. *Jour. Cell. and Comp. Physiol.* **10**: 133-146.
Bretschneider, L. H. 1942. *Arch. néerl. Zool.* **6**: 471-472.
Briggs, R. 1946. *Anat. Rec.* **96**: 510.
Briggs, R. 1947. *Jour. Exptl. Zool.* **106**: 237-266.
Brown, M. G., Hamburger, V., and Schmitt, F. O. 1941. *Jour. Exptl. Zool.* **88**: 353-372.
Burr, H. S., and Northrop, F. S. C. 1935. *Quart. Rev. Biol.* **10**: 322-333.
Burt, A. S. 1943. *Biol. Bull.* **85**: 103-115.
Butenandt, A., Weidel, W., and Becker, E. 1940. *Naturwiss.* **28**: 447-448.
Caspersson, T. 1936. *Skand. Arch. Physiol.* **73**: Suppl. 8, 1-151.
Chambers, R. 1942. *Jour. Cell. and Comp. Physiol.* **19**: 145-150.
Chambers, R. 1946. *Anat. Rec.* **94**: 31.
Chevais, S. 1943. *Bull. Biol. de la Fr. et de la Belg.* **77**: 1-108.
Child, C. M. 1911. *Jour. Exptl. Zool.* **10**: 265-320.
Child, C. M. 1928. *Protoplasma.* **5**: 447-476.
Child, C. M. 1942. *Physiol. Zool.* **15**: 13-29.
Child, C. M. 1943. *Physiol. Zool.* **16**: 141-161.
Child, C. M. 1945. *Jour. Exptl. Zool.* **100**: 577-589.

Child, C. M. 1946. *Physiol. Zool.* **19**: 89-148.
Child, C. M. 1948. *Jour. Exptl. Zool.* **107**: 1-38.
Clement, A. C. 1947. *Biol. Bull.* **93**: 191-192.
Collier, Jane G. 1947. *Biol. Bull.* **92**: 167-177.
Connors, W. M., and Scheer, B. T. 1947. *Jour. Cell. and Comp. Physiol.* **30**: 271-283.
Cornman, I. 1947. *Biol. Bull.* **93**: 214.
Costello, D. P. 1945a. *Jour. Elisha Mitchell Sci. Soc.* **61**: 277-289.
Costello, D. P. 1945b. *Jour. Exptl. Zool.* **100**: 19-66.
Costello, D. P., and Henley, C. 1947. *Anat. Rec.* **99**: Suppl. 26.
Dan, K. 1943. *Jour. Fac. Sci. Tokyo Imp. Univ. Ser. IV.* **6**: 297-321.
Dan, K., and Dan, J. C. 1940. *Biol. Bull.* **78**: 486-501.
Dan, K., and Dan, J. C. 1942. *Cytologia* **12**: 246-261.
Dan, K., and Dan, J. C. 1947. *Biol. Bull.* **93**: 163-188.
Dan, K., Dan, J. C., and Yanagita, T. 1938. *Cytologia* **8**: 521-531.
Dan, K., Yanagita, T., and Sugiyama, M. 1937. *Protoplasma* **28**: 66-81.
Danforth, C. H 1946. *Ann. Rev. Physiol.* **8**: 17-42.
Davis, J. O. 1944. *Biol. Bull.* **87**: 73-95.
Detwiler, S. R. 1946. *Anat. Rec.* **94**: 229-237.
Dieke, S. H. 1947. *Endocrinology* **40**: 123-136.
Dorris, F. 1936. *Proc. Soc. Exptl. Biol. and Med.* **34**: 448-449.
Duryee, W. R. 1947. *Biol. Bull.* **93**: 206-207.
DuShane, G. P. 1934. *Science* **80**: 620-621.
DuShane, G. P. 1935. *Jour. Exptl. Zool.* **72**: 1-31.
DuShane, G. P. 1943. *Quart. Rev. Biol.* **18**: 109-127.
DuShane, G. P. 1944. *Quart. Rev. Biol.* **19**: 98-117.
DuShane, G. P. 1948. *Spec. Publ. N. Y. Acad. Sci.* **4**: 1-14.
Eakin, R. M. 1946. *Anat. Rec.* **96**: 509-510.
Eastlick, H. L. 1939. *Jour. Exptl. Zool.* **82**: 131-157.
Eigsti, O. J. 1947. *Lloydia.* **10**: 65-105.
Ephrussi, B. 1942. *Cold Spring Harbor Symposia on Quantitative Biology* **10**: 40-48.
Fankhauser, G. 1945a. *Quart. Rev. Biol.* **20**: 20-78.
Fankhauser, G. 1945b. *Jour. Exptl. Zool.* **100**: 445-455.
Fankhauser, G., and Griffiths, R. B. 1939. *Proc. Nation. Acad. Sci. U. S.* **25**: 233-238.
Fankhauser, G., and Humphrey, R. R. 1943. *Proc. Nation. Acad. Sci. U. S.* **29**: 344-350.
Fankhauser, G., and Watson, R. C. 1942. *Proc. Nation. Acad. Sci. U. S.* **28**: 436-440.
Fekete, E., and Duran-Reynals, F. 1943. *Proc. Soc. Exptl. Biol. and Med.* **52**: 119-121.
Figge, F. H. J. 1938a. *Proc. Soc. Exptl. Biol. and Med.* **39**: 569-571.
Figge, F. H. J. 1938b. *Jour. Exptl. Zool.* **78**: 471-481.
Fischberg, M. 1944. *Rev. Suisse de Zool.* **51**: 430-436.
Fischberg M. 1945. *Rev. Suisse de Zool.* **52**: 407-414.
Fischberg, M. 1948. *Genetica* **24**: 213-329.
Fisher, F. G., and Hartwig, H. 1938. *Biol. Zentr.* **58**: 567-589.
Giese, A. C. 1946. *Biol. Bull.* **91**: 81-87.
Gillette, R. 1944. *Jour. Exptl. Zool.* **96**: 201-222.
Gregg, John R., and Ballentine, R. 1946. *Jour. Exptl. Zool.* **103**: 143-168.
Hall, T. S., and Moog, F. 1947. *Biol. Bull.* **93**: 213.
Hammett, F. S. 1946. *Scientia.* **5**[e] Ser. 93-98.
Harnley, M. H., and Goldsmith, E. D. 1946. *Anat. Rec.* **96**: 566.
Harris, D. L. 1944. *Biol. Bull.* **87**: 164.

Harrison, R. G. 1945. *Trans. Conn. Acad. Arts and Sci.* **36**: 277-330.
Harvey, E. B., and Anderson, T. F. 1943. *Biol. Bull.* **85**: 151-156.
Hayashi, T. 1945. *Biol. Bull.* **89**: 162-179.
Herbst, C. 1892. *Ztschr. f. wiss. Zool.* **55**: 446-518.
Holtfreter, J. 1943. *Jour. Exptl. Zool.* **93**: 251-323.
Holtfreter, J. 1944. *Jour. Exptl. Zool.* **95**: 171-212.
Holtfreter, J. 1945. *Anat. Rec.* **93**: 59-74.
Holtfreter, J. 1946a. *Jour. Exptl. Zool.* **101**: 355-405.
Holtfreter, J. 1946b. *Jour. Exptl. Zool.* **102**: 51-108.
Holtfreter, J. 1946c. *Jour. Morph.* **79**: 27-62.
Holtfreter, J. 1946d. *Jour. Exptl. Zool.* **103**: 81-112.
Holtfreter, J. 1947a. *Jour. Morph.* **80**: 25-55.
Holtfreter, J. 1947b. *Jour. Morph.* **80**: 57-91.
Holtfreter, J. 1947c. *Jour. Morph.* **80**: 345-368.
Holtfreter, J. 1947d. *Jour. Exptl. Zool.* **106**: 197-222.
Hörstadius, S. 1939. *Biol. Rev.* **14**: 132-179.
Huber, W. 1945. *Rev. Suisse de Zool.* **52**: 354-360.
Humphrey, R. R. 1945. *Amer. Jour. Anat.* **76**: 33-66.
Humphrey, R. R., and Fankhauser, G. 1946. *Jour. Morph.* **79**: 467-510.
Hutchinson, C. 1944. *Anat. Rec.* **88**: 439.
Irwin, M. R. 1947. *Ann. Rev. Physiol.* **9**: 605-628.
Jaeger, L. 1945. *Jour. Cell. and Comp. Physiol.* **25**: 97-120.
Khouvine, Y., Chevais, S., and Grégoire, J. 1943. *Compt. Rend. Acad. Sci.* (Paris) **217**: 161-163.
Landauer, W., and Bliss, C. T. 1946. *Jour. Exptl. Zool.* **102**: 1-22.
Lardy, H. A., and Phillips, P. H. 1945. *Arch. Biochem.* **6**: 53-61.
Lehmann, F. E. 1945. *Rev. Suisse de Zool.* **52**: 342-348.
Lewis, W. H. 1947. *Anat. Rec.* **97**: 139-156.
Lindahl, P. E. 1933. *Arch. Entw. Mech. Org.* **128**: 661-664.
Lindahl, P. E. 1936. *Acta Zool., Stockh.* **17**: 179-365.
Lindahl, P. E., and Holter, H. 1941. *Compt. Rend. Trav. Lab. Carlsberg, Sér. Chim.* **24**: 49-57.
Lovelace, R. 1947. *Anat. Rec.* **99**: 655.
Lund, E. J. and collaborators. 1947. Bioelectric Fields and Growth. Univ. of Texas Press, Austin, Texas.
Lüscher, M. 1945. *Rev. Suisse de Zool.* **52**: 349-354.
Lynn, W. G. 1947. *Biol. Bull.* **93**: 199.
Lynn, W. G. 1948. *Biol. Bull.* **94**: 1-15.
Lynn, W. G., and Sister Alfred de Marie. 1946. *Science* **104**: 31.
McClean, D., and Rowlands, L. W. 1942. *Nature* **150**: 627-628.
McLeod, J. 1947. *Anat. Rec.* **97**: 354-355.
Mann, T. 1945. *Biochem. Jour.* **39**: 451-457.
Markert, C. L. 1947. *Anat. Rec.* **99**: 588.
Marvel, R. M., and Fisher, K. C. 1948. *Biol. Bull.* **94**: 45-54.
Mather, K. 1948. *Nature* **161**: 872-874.
Meyer, K. H., and Sievers, J. F. 1936. *Helv. Chim. Acta* **19**: 649-664.
Michalski, J. 1948. *Anat. Rec.* **100**: 696.
Miller, J. A. 1946. *Anat. Rec.* **94**: 359.
Mintz, B. 1947. *Physiol. Zool.* **20**: 355-373.

Moment, G. B. 1946. *Jour. Exptl. Zool.* **103**: 487-506.
Monné, L. 1945a. *Ark. f. Zool.* **36** (A) #10: 1-26.
Monné, L. 1945b. *Ark. f. Zool.* **36** (A) #23: 1-29.
Monné, L. 1948. *Advances in Enzymology* **8**: 1-69.
Monroy, A. 1947. *Jour. Cell and Comp. Physiol.* **30**: 105-109.
Monroy, A., and Montalenti, G. 1947. *Biol. Bull.* **92**: 151-161.
Moore, J. A. 1946. *Jour. Exptl. Zool.* **101**: 173-219.
Needham, J. 1942. Biochemistry and Morphogenesis. Cambridge Univ. Press, Cambridge, England.
Needham, J., Rogers, V., and Shen, S. C. 1939. *Proc. Roy. Soc. Lond.* **B127**: 576-583.
Nieuwkoop, P. D. 1947. *Arch. néer. Zool.* **8**: 1-205.
Niu, M. C. 1947. *Jour. Exptl. Zool.* **105**: 79-113.
Nowinski, W. W., and Pandra, J. 1947. *Anat. Rec.* **97**: 400.
Oppenheimer, J. 1947a. *Anat. Rec.* **99**: 565-566.
Oppenheimer, J. 1947b. *Quart. Rev. Biol.* **22**: 105-118.
Painter, T. S. 1940. *Proc. Nation. Acad. Sci. U. S.* **26**: 95-100.
Painter, T. S. 1945a. *Trans. Conn. Acad. Arts and Sci.* **36**: 443-448.
Painter, T. S. 1945b. *Jour. Exptl. Zool.* **100**: 523-547.
Pasteels, J. 1947. *Experientia* **3**: 30-32.
Pease, D. C. 1941. *Jour. Exptl. Zool.* **86**: 381-404.
Pease, D. C. 1942a. *Jour. Exptl. Zool.* **89**: 329-345.
Pease, D. C. 1942b. *Jour. Exptl. Zool.* **89**: 347-356.
Pollister, A. W., and Lavin, G. I. 1944. *Anat. Rec.* **89**: 557-558.
Poulson, D. F., and Boell, E. J. 1946. *Anat. Rec.* **96**: 508.
Raper, K. B. 1940. *Amer. Jour. Bot.* **27**: 436-448.
Raper, K. B. 1941. *Growth,* Suppl. **5**: 41-76.
Raven, C. P. 1936. *Arch. Entw. Mech. Org.* **134**: 122-146.
Rawles, M. E. 1939. *Jour. Genet.* **38**: 517-532.
Rawles, M. E. 1947a. *Anat. Rec.* **99**: 648-649.
Rawles, M. E. 1947b. *Physiol. Zool.* **20**: 248-266.
Rawles, M. E., and Straus, W. L., Jr. 1948. *Anat. Rec.* **100**: 755.
Reed, E. A., and Whitaker, D. M. 1941. *Jour. Cell. and Comp. Physiol.* **18**: 329-338.
Richter, C. P., and Clisby, K. H. 1941. *Proc. Soc. Exptl. Biol. and Med.* **48**: 684-687.
Ris, H. 1941. *Physiol. Zool.* **14**: 48-66.
Ris, H. 1945. *Biol. Bull.* **89**: 242-257.
Roosen-Runge, E. C. 1938. *Biol. Bull.* **75**: 119-133.
Rose, S. M. 1942. *Proc. Soc. Exptl. Biol. and Med.* **49**: 408-410.
Rose, S. M. 1944. *Jour. Exptl. Zool.* **95**: 149-170.
Rose, S. M. 1945. *Jour. Morph.* **77**: 119-139.
Rose, F. C., and Rose, S. M. 1947. *Anat. Rec.* **99**: 653.
Rostand, J. 1933. *Compt. Rend. Soc. Biol.* **113**: 346-347.
Rostand, J. 1934. *Compt. Rend. Soc. Biol.* **115**: 1680-1681.
Rowlands, L. W. 1944. *Nature* **154**: 332-333.
Rudnick, D. 1944. *Quart. Rev. Biol.* **19**: 187-212.
Rudnick, D. 1945. *Trans. Conn. Acad. Arts and Sci.* **36**: 353-377.
Rudnick, D. 1945. *Jour. Exptl. Zool.* **100**: 1-17.
Rulon, O. 1946a. *Anat. Rec.* **94**: 358-359.
Rulon, O. 1946b. *Physiol. Zool.* **19**: 58-66.
Rulon, O. 1948. *Physiol. Zool.* **21**: 100-105.

Runnström, J., and Monné, L. 1945a. *Ark. f. Zool.* **36** (A) #18 1-27.
Runnström, J., and Monné, L. 1945b. *Ark. f. Zool.* **36** (A) #20 1-23.
Runnström, J., Monné, L., and Broman, L. 1944. *Ark. f. Zool.* **35** (A) #3 1-32.
Saunders, J. W., Jr. 1947. *Anat. Rec.* **99**: 567.
Sawyer, C. H. 1947a. *Anat. Rec.* **97**: 366-367.
Sawyer, C. H. 1947b. *Jour. Exptl. Zool.* **106**: 145-179.
Schechtman, M. 1942. *Univ. Calif. Publ. Zool.* **51**: 1-35.
Scheer, B. T., and Scheer, M. A. R. 1947. *Physiol. Zool.* **20**: 15-32.
Schmitt, F. O., Hall, C. E. and Jakus, M. A. 1943. *Biological Symposia* **10**: 261-276.
Schotté, O. E., and Butler, E. G. 1941. *Jour. Exptl. Zool.* **87**: 279-322.
Schotté, O. E., and Harland, M. 1943. *Anat. Rec.* **87**: 165-180.
Schrader, F. 1944. Mitosis. Columbia Univ. Press, New York.
Schrader, F. 1947. *Chromosoma,* **3**: 22-47.
Shapiro, H. 1941. *Jour. Cell. and Comp. Physiol.* **18**: 143-149.
Simpson, W. L., and Ayengar, A. R. G. 1947. *Anat. Rec.* **97**: 369.
Singer, M. 1943. *Jour. Exptl. Zool.* **92**: 297-315.
Singer, M. 1946. *Jour. Exptl. Zool.* **101**: 221-239.
Singer, M. 1947. *Jour. Exptl. Zool.* **104**: 251-265.
Smith, E. E., and Gray, P. 1948. *Jour. Exptl. Zool.* **107**: 183-206.
Sonneborn, T. M. 1945. *Ann. Missouri Bot. Gard.* **32**: 213-221.
Sonneborn, T. M. 1946. *Cold Spring Harbor Symposia on Quantitative Biology* **11**: 236-255.
Sonneborn, T. M. 1947. *Advances in Genetics* **1**: 263-358.
Spikes, J. D. 1944. *Jour. Exptl. Zool.* **95**: 89-104.
Spofford, W. R. 1947. *Anat. Rec.* **97**: 372-373.
Spofford, W. R. 1948. *Jour. Exptl. Zool.* **107**: 123-163.
Spratt, N. T., Jr. 1942. *Jour. Exptl. Zool.* **89**: 69-101.
Spratt, N. T., Jr. 1946. *Jour. Exptl. Zool.* **103**: 259-304.
Spratt, N. T., Jr. 1947a. *Jour. Exptl. Zool.* **104**: 69-100.
Spratt, N. T., Jr. 1947b. *Jour. Exptl. Zool.* **106**: 345-366.
Stauffer, E. 1945. *Rev. Suisse de Zool.* **52**: 231-327.
Swyer, G. I. M. 1947a. *Biochem. Jour.* **41**: 29-34.
Swyer, G. I. M. 1947b. *Biochem. Jour.* **41**: 409-413.
Swyer, G. I. M. 1947c. *Biochem. Jour.* **41**: 413-417.
Tatum, E. L., and Haagen-Smit, A. J. 1941. *Jour. Biol. Chem.* **140**: 575-580.
Teorell, T. 1935. *Proc. Nation. Acad. Sci. U. S.* **21**: 152-161.
Teorell, T. 1937. *Jour. Gen. Physiol.* **21**: 107-122.
Tung, T. C., Chang, C. Y., and Tung, Y. F. Y. 1945. *Proc. Zool. Soc. Lond.* **115**: 175-188.
Twitty, V. C. 1936. *Jour. Exptl. Zool.* **74**: 239-302.
Twitty, V. C. 1944. *Jour. Exptl. Zool.* **95**: 259-290.
Twitty, V. C. 1945. *Jour. Exptl. Zool.* **100**: 141-178.
Twitty, V. C. 1947. *Anat. Rec.* **99**: 587.
Twitty, V. C., and Bodenstein, D. 1939. *Jour. Exptl. Zool.* **81**: 357-398.
Van Cleave, C. D. 1947. *Physiol. Zool.* **20**: 32-45.
Van Dyke, J. H., and Ritchey, M. G. 1947. *Anat. Rec.* **97**: 375.
Waddington, C. H., Needham, J., and Brachet, J. 1936. *Proc. Roy. Soc. Lond.* **B120**: 173-198.
Weiss, P. 1939. Principles of Development. Henry Holt & Co., New York.

Weisz, P. B. 1948. *Jour. Exptl. Zool.* **107**: 269-287.
Whitaker, D. M. 1942a. *Jour. Gen. Physiol.* **25**: 391-397.
Whitaker, D. M. 1942b. *Biol. Bull.* **82**: 127-137.
Whitaker, D. M., and Berg, W. E. 1942. *Anat. Rec.* **84**: 500.
Whitaker, D. M., and Berg, W. E. 1944. *Biol. Bull.* **86**: 125-129.
Whiting, A. R. 1946. *Science* **103**: 219-220.
Willier, B. H. 1948. *Spec. Publ. N. Y. Acad. Sci.* **4**: 321-340.
Worley, L. G. 1943a. *Proc. Nation. Acad. Sci. U. S.* **29**: 225-228.
Worley, L. G. 1943b. *Proc. Nation. Acad. Sci. U. S.* **29**: 228-231.
Worley, L. G. 1944a. *Jour. Morph.* **75**: 77-101.
Worley, L. G. 1944b. *Jour. Morph.* **75**: 261-289.
Wright, S. 1945. *Ann. Rev. Physiol.* **7**: 75-101.
Zwilling, E. 1945. *Jour. Exptl. Zool.* **98**: 237-247.

Virus Tumors

BY L. M. BLACK

Brooklyn Botanic Garden, Brooklyn, N. Y.

I. INTRODUCTION

Relatively few virus tumor diseases are known in plants and animals today and in some of these it has been difficult to demonstrate the involvement of the virus. Ever since viruses were shown to cause certain cancers in chickens there has been a keen interest in the possible importance of these agents to the tumor problem in general.

The task of reviewing information now available on virus tumors in plants and animals has been undertaken in the hope that it will be of value to others. Presentation of the material from the viewpoint of a plant virologist may not be without virtues to compensate for deficiencies perhaps all too apparent to specialists working with animals. However, the principal aim of this review is to bring the virus tumor problem to the attention of biologists generally.

Much help has been derived from earlier reviews on particular phases of the subject or on related subjects and these are cited in the bibliographies along with the original literature consulted.

The diseases reviewed here are the relatively few tumor maladies caused by viruses which have been extensively studied. They include a virus tumor disease of plants, kidney cancer of the leopard frog, the fowl leucosis complex (a disease of the white blood cells), the Rous sarcoma (a cancer of chickens), rabbit myxoma and fibroma (diseases of connective tissue cells), infectious warts of rabbits, and mammary cancer of the mouse.

I am much indebted to Dr. Wendell M. Stanley and to Dr. Edward W. Shrigley who have read the manuscript critically for errors of fact, to Dr. Balduin Lucké for valuable assistance with the section on frog kidney carcinoma and to Dr. Joseph W. Beard for a critical review of the section on infectious papillomatosis of rabbits. Responsibility for interpretations and speculations rests solely with the author.

There are a number of other virus infections which might well yield results similar to those discussed here if they were the subject of intensive study. The Fiji disease of sugar cane, caused by the virus *Galla fijiensis* H.[1]

[1]Wherever possible in the text, Holmes' (Holmes, 1948) use of the binomial system of naming viruses has been employed even though it is realized that any classification of viruses advanced today will probably be subject to radical revision in the future. The binomials provide a key by means of which the general reader will have access to many additional selected references to original literature.

and clubroot of tobacco (Valleau, 1947), are examples among the plant diseases. Very little is known about club root of tobacco but although Fiji disease is known only on sugar cane, the specific insects which carry the causal virus are known and the inclusion bodies and pathological histology have been studied. Among the viruses causing growths of animals that have not been so thoroughly investigated are those inducing common warts of man (*Molitor verrucae* H.), *Condyloma acuminatum* of man, cattle-warts (*M. bovis* H.), canine oral-papillomatosis (*M. buccalis* H.) and rabbit oral-papillomatosis (*M. gingivalis* H.) (Holmes, 1948).

There are a number of viruses in plants and animals which have a predominantly necrotizing or inhibiting action on cells but which also cause some cell proliferation in a slight degree or under special circumstances. Tobacco mosaic ordinarily causes a dwarfing of cells, but on certain hosts it may regularly cause leafy outgrowths from the undersides of the veins. In animals there is cell proliferation in the various pox diseases, but the viruses are largely killing in their action. These diseases serve to emphasize that there is no sharp boundary between the viruses causing cell death and those causing cell growth. Such diseases have not, however, been dealt with in this review.

1. *Viruses*

Before embarking upon a discussion of virus tumors, it is essential that the reader have an understanding of the basic facts about viruses. To provide such orientation, some of the important elementary knowledge of these interesting particles will be presented briefly. The principles summarized are common knowledge to virologists and will usually be found in more extended discussions in one or another of the excellent books now available on the subject (Bawden, 1943; Doerr und Hallauer, 1938 and 1939; Holmes, 1948; Rivers, 1928; Smith, 1934 and 1937; van Rooyen and Rhodes, 1948).

A. GENERAL PROPERTIES

Viruses are disease-producing agents so small that they pass through filters that will hold back ordinary bacteria. The small size of most viruses makes it impossible to see them with the ordinary microscope. Although they increase in their living hosts, they have not been cultivated in media free of living cells. These criteria of reproduction in living host cells but not in cell-free media, filterability and invisibility, are arbitrary rather than natural and cannot be expected to fit all the agents known. For example, the organism causing contagious bovine pleuropneumonia (*Asterococcus mycoides* Borrel *et al.*, Dienes, 1948) has a filterable form that is smaller than the largest viruses. This organism may be seen with the ordinary light microscope and if its exacting requirements are met, may be grown in cell-free media. Despite such border-line exceptions, the minute size of viruses that confers invisibility and filterability, tends to be associated with inability to grow on cell-free media. These characters have been of great importance in the recognition of viruses, and still have a general validity and usefulness. In this article an agent having these properties will be called a virus.

B. MORPHOLOGY

Before the advent of the electron microscope, the size and shape of virus particles were estimated indirectly from various physical measurements employed in calculations based on physical laws and theories. The electron microscope has made the determinations of size of many of these viruses easier. The diameters of different species of virus particles vary between about 10 mμ (millimicrons) in the case of the bacterial virus, *Phagus minimus* Holmes and about 300 mμ for some of the pox viruses of animals. Some plant viruses have the shape of rods. In the case of tobacco mosaic virus, there is some variation in particle length but the most common particle measures 15×280 mμ (Oster and Stanley, 1946). The vaccinia virus is shaped like a small bacillus and electron micrographs show an internal structure. Some bacterial viruses have a spherical head-like portion showing internal structure and a tail-like appendage (Anderson, 1946). Electron micrographs sometimes show what appear to be the surface membranes of viruses from which the contents have disappeared (Green, Anderson and Smadel, 1942).

C. HOSTS

Viruses cause disease in bacteria, the higher plants, insects, fish, frogs, birds and mammals, including man. There are at present great gaps in the known host range of viruses. One of the most striking of these is the absence of known virus infections in all plants between the bacteria and the angiosperms or flowering plants. It would be most interesting to know if this is an illusion caused by our ignorance or if the algae, fungi, mosses, liverworts, ferns, and gymnosperms really are free from virus attack.

D. SYMPTOMS

In bacteria, virus (bacteriophage, phage) infection usually causes the disintegration (lysis) of bacterial cells. Thus liquid cultures, turbid because of the presence of multitudes of growing bacterial cells, become clear. In confluent masses of bacteria growing on the surface of solid media, clear circular spots (plaques) may develop at each center of virus infection.

The cells of higher plants may be stunted, stimulated to enlargement or division or killed by viruses. The most common macroscopic evidence of infection in plants consists of a mosaic of light and dark green areas on the leaf as in the mosaic diseases. A general yellowing of the leaves combined with an excessive production of slender shoots is the usual manifestation of plant virus disease of the "yellows" type. Less common are dead spots, ring and line patterns, curling and a considerable variety of other alterations in leaves, stems, roots, flowers and fruits.

Caterpillars infected with virus may be reduced to a semi-fluid mass inside the skin. In the higher animals fever and changes in the cellular composition of the blood are usual but not invariable accompaniments of virus infection. In these hosts the viruses may exhibit a narrow specialization in the tissue cells they attack. They may destroy nerve cells as in rabies or the epithelial cells of the lung as in influenza. They may induce local enlargement and multiplication of the cells of the skin as in the various wart diseases. On the other hand, the virus can be general in its action as in hog cholera. The disease processes result in a legion of unhappy manifestations: nasal discharges, rashes, vesicular eruptions, glandular swelling, diarrhea, anemia, weakness, pain and many others.

E. INCLUSION BODIES

In both plants and animals, abnormal bodies within the cells are characteristic of some virus infections. Cytoplasmic inclusions are not uncommon in plant virus maladies. In tobacco mosaic, two distinct types occur: one is protoplasmic in appearance, may have vacuoles and appears to be enclosed by a membrane; the other is crystalline and on treatment with acid breaks up into needle-like crystals very similar to those formed by purified virus. Crystalline intranuclear inclusions have been described for a few plant viruses.

In animals, cytoplasmic and intranuclear inclusions are associated with many virus diseases (Findlay in Doerr und Hallauer, 1938). In the case of fowl pox, it has been demonstrated that the inclusions contain the elementary virus particles. In the psittacosis-lymphogranuloma group of diseases, the inclusion bodies represent part of the life cycle.

F. RECOVERY FROM VIRUS INFECTION

Cultures of bacteria attacked by virus frequently recover because of the appearance in the culture of a mutant resistant to the virus. In plant virus infections, recovery is rare. Sometimes the virus, being an obligate parasite, is localized by the death of the cells it invades as in tobacco mosaic virus in *Nicotiana glutinosa* L. (Holmes, 1929). The infected leaf may be dropped from the plant before the virus enters the stalk as is the case with pepper plants resistant to tobacco mosaic virus (Holmes, 1937). Such plants are then free of virus but susceptible to re-inoculation. In other instances, the virus causes a severe acute stage followed by a chronic stage with lowered virus content and very mild symptoms. The plant in this case is not susceptible to re-inoculation with the same virus (Price, 1940).

In animals it is common to have recovery from virus infection accompanied by the development of antibodies to the virus in the blood. The subsequent immunity to the same virus may last for life and it has been suggested that such immunity is due to the hidden presence of the virus somewhere in the animal body. At the other extreme are viruses like the common cold virus of man, *Tarpeia premens* H., in which the immunity following recovery only lasts for a few weeks. This may be due to the loss of the virus from the body. Animals may develop immunity to a virus without having demonstrable neutralizing antibodies in the blood as in the case of the mouse and lymphocytic choriomeningitis virus, *Legio erebea* H. (Traub, 1936). Animals may also recover from symptoms of virus infection and still contain demonstrable virus years afterwards as happens in the case of the horse and infectious anemia virus, *Trifur equorum* H. (Stein, 1942). Usually, however, after mammals or birds recover from a virus infection, the virus is not demonstrable in their bodies and their blood carries specific antibodies to the virus.

G. SEROLOGY

Animal viruses and some plant and bacterial viruses when injected into mammals and birds induce the formation of antibodies in their blood. Such antibodies when mixed with virus *in vitro* may be detected in a number of ways. If they are demonstrated to render the virus noninfective, they are called neutralizing antibodies; if shown to precipitate the virus, they are called precipitins or precipitating antibodies; and if, in the presence of the virus, they remove from fresh blood a substance called complement, they are called complement-fixing antibodies. Because of the specificity of the reaction between the virus and the antibody it induces, serological reactions are useful in the identification of viruses and in a number of other ways.

During some animal virus infections, a specific soluble substance is produced that can be separated from the virus and will give a specific antibody reaction with the serum from immune animals.

H. LATENT INFECTION

Viruses may occur in apparently healthy bacteria, higher plants and animals. Filtrates of some cultures of bacteria have the ability to infect (lyse) certain other cultures. This is due to the fact that they harbor a virus without themselves showing symptoms of disease. They are, in effect, carriers (lysogenic bacteria). In plants inapparent infections are not at all uncommon and sometimes a plant harboring a virus in this way is an important reservoir from which other kinds of plants are infected and seriously damaged or killed. A special case of a similar sort occurs in the insect vectors of some plant viruses which grow in the carrier insects yet in no detectable way affect their health. In the higher animals too, virus may lurk in the body of an individual that has at one time shown disease but later appears healthy.

I. TRANSMISSION

It is desirable to dwell at greater length on the transmission of viruses because in some of the virus tumor diseases, the means by which virus gets from one animal to another is devious or obscure. The transmission of viruses from one host to another is of intriguing variety and great importance.

In bacteria large numbers of virus particles are released into the fluid environment upon the disintegration of the host cell. When a particle makes contact with a healthy bacterium, it sticks to the bacterial cell, new virus particles are quickly produced and the process repeated.

The most important artificial means of transmitting viruses in plants is by rubbing the leaves of healthy plants with juice from diseased ones or by grafting diseased and healthy plants together. Natural dissemination occurs in a variety of ways. Some plant viruses reach a high concentration, can survive for considerable periods outside their host and can readily gain entrance to a new plant when they come in contact with wounded cells. Some of these viruses are spread by the wind blowing the leaves of diseased and healthy plants together so that they are both injured, as in the case of the latent virus of potatoes. They may be spread by man handling the plants in cultural operations, as in tobacco mosaic virus. A few plant viruses are harbored in the soil and infect plants growing in it.

However, the most important means for dispersal is by insects, chiefly the sucking insects of the order Hemiptera. In one type of transmission, the insect acquires the virus in about 2 minutes' feeding on a diseased plant, is capable of transmitting it immediately thereafter to a new plant and then loses the virus within about an hour's feeding on a healthy host (Watson and Roberts, 1940). Transmission of this sort is the common type in aphids, the most important vectors of plant viruses.

In another type of transmission, the insect is not able to inoculate healthy plants immediately after acquiring the virus from diseased ones. Instead, an interval of hours, days, or even weeks must first elapse. In some cases, the virus is known to increase in the insect during this period. Once the interval is over, the insect may transmit the virus to plants daily or at irregular intervals for a considerable time or even until it dies from old age. Such transmission is common in leafhoppers. Frequently transmission of a particular virus is accomplished only by species of insects closely related to each other. Sometimes a vector species varies genetically in its ability to transmit. With few exceptions, there is no transmission from parent insect to progeny. Other plant viruses are transmitted by insects other than the leafhoppers and aphids.

Although some plant viruses pass through the seed, the rarity of such transmission is an important fact in plant virology. Most plants grown from seed start life free of virus. On the other hand, because of the usual systemic nature of plant viruses, the danger of perpetuating virus infections in crops reproduced vegetatively (that is, by means of cuttings, scions, bulbs, tubers, roots, runners, etc.) is of paramount importance to agriculture.

Many animal viruses are spread by more than one method. The most common artificial methods of inoculation are by injection of the virus into some part of the animal body or rubbing it on some wounded tissue. Perhaps the commonest means of natural dispersal in animals is by the infected animal coughing or sneezing contaminated droplets of mucus into the air. Some of these are taken into healthy animals through the nostrils or mouth and the virus they contain begins new infections. The virus of the common cold is admirably adapted to such dispersal. The habits of animals also lead to the spread of many viruses from one to another by contact of the nostrils, mouth, or other parts of the body, as in distemper. A virus disease of sheep is transmitted venereally. The virus of rabies is adapted to dispersal by its occurrence in the saliva of its victims and by the fact that infected canines tend to bite other hosts. Presumably the various wart viruses are naturally transferred by gaining entrance to abrasions of the skin. Virus may be excreted in the faeces as in poliomyelitis or in the urine as in hog cholera. From such sources, there is always the danger that the virus in one way or another will reach the nostrils or mouth. Infection through the ingestion of food contaminated with virus occurs in both insects and higher animals.

Although arthropods do not play such an important role as vectors of animal viruses as they do in the case of plant viruses, they are none the less important. Mosquitoes, ticks, triatoma, lice and flies have been shown to transmit viruses from one animal to another. Mosquitoes are probably the most serious pests in this respect. In equine encephalitis, the virus cannot be transmitted by the mosquito until several days have elapsed after its acquisition. Moreover, the virus multiplies in the insect. Ticks and triatoma will also transfer this virus. In spite of this the eastern strain of the virus cannot be naturally transmitted by the mosquito *Aedes aegypti* L., a species that will transmit the western strain.

A very interesting case is that of a mouse virus (lymphocytic choriomeningitis) which may pass from the mother mice to the young while they are still in the uterus (Traub, 1939).

The involved cycle which the virus of swine influenza undergoes deserves special mention. Although the virus passes from one mammal to another by droplet transmission, it is also able to enter the lungworms, *Metastrongylus elongatus* and *Choerostrongylus pudendotectus,* parasitic in infected pigs. It can remain viable in them as long as 2 years while the lungworms undergo parts of their life history in earthworms. Such earthworms eaten and digested by swine permit the lungworms and the virus to gain entrance again to the lungs. If the swine then undergo some unfavorable nonspecific stimulus during autumn, winter, or spring, and if the bacterium, *Haemophilus influenzae suis,* is present, they will develop typical swine influenza (Shope, 1941).

Although only the more important aspects of virus transmission have been dealt with, it should be clear that the route taken by the virus between one host and another may be quite involved and in some cases very difficult to discover. In the absence of knowledge of such a route, the hypothesis of *de novo* origin of a virus has sometimes been suggested, perhaps more frequently in the case of tumor viruses than in others. Although there is no reason to doubt the evolutionary origin of a virus from some pre-existing non-virus unit or units, its generation *de novo* frequently enough to explain repeated cases of disease is a very different matter. The possible vagaries of transmission (not to mention latency, reservoir hosts, long incubation period, etc.) should make one wary of accepting this hypothesis as more than a possibility to be put to the test by research workers when opportunity affords. Thus far such tests have failed to demonstrate *de novo* origin of viruses.

J. VARIATION

Viruses frequently occur in a number of strains in nature. There is little doubt that the basis for this variety is mutation, for the fact that viruses mutate has been amply demonstrated. With both plant viruses (Jensen, 1933) and bacterial viruses (Luria, 1945), it has been possible to start with a single virus particle and derive from it a number of variant strains produced by mutation during the multiplication of the virus.

The demonstration that infectious myxoma virus can be reconstituted from the heat inactivated virus plus infectious fibroma virus (Berry and

Dedrick, 1936a) and the recent work with bacterial viruses (Hershey, 1946; Delbrück and Bailey, 1946; Luria, 1947; Hershey and Rotman, 1948) showing that a transfer of characters may occur from one bacterial virus to another and that the characters may be governed by some mechanism of linkage is of the utmost importance for virology in general. The work with the bacterial viruses has shown that even among the viruses, a mechanism with the evolutionary value of the sexual process exists.

K. A GENERAL CONCEPTION OF THE NATURE OF VIRUSES

Research on viruses has been particularly vigorous during the past two decades and much has been learned about their nature. The hypothesis advanced by Green (1935) that they represent various stages in a retrograde evolution of parasites fits the known facts about viruses and may serve as a point of orientation for the reader. According to this hypothesis as the parasites lost various physiological functions provided by the host, they also underwent simplification in structure. As an ultimate result of the process, Green postulated a molecule having the power to reproduce itself in a suitable host. Although proposed shortly after Stanley crystallized the first virus (Stanley, 1935) and although tremendous strides have been made in virus research since then, this hypothesis is still attractive to many virologists. It is, for example, in harmony with one of the outstanding chemical facts about viruses: that all so far isolated in pure form contain nucleoprotein, the proteins characteristic of the nucleus.

Although this account of the nature of viruses and virus diseases is not exhaustive, it should provide the uninitiated reader with sufficient background for profitable consideration of the various virus tumor diseases that will now be discussed.

II. Wound-Tumor Disease

1. *Introduction*

This is a plant disease caused by the wound-tumor virus (*Aureogenus magnivena* Black). The virus was discovered in leafhoppers being tested on plants for the possible presence of viruses related to the potato yellow-dwarf viruses (Black, 1944). Because of the rarity of recognized plant virus tumors it is of considerable scientific interest (Black, 1947).

2. *Host Range*

In general, plant viruses have a much wider host range than animal viruses and the wound-tumor virus is no exception in this respect. In a survey it was found capable of infecting 43 species of plants in 20 different families. There is every reason for expecting that more extensive tests would reveal additional susceptible species in these and in other families (Black, 1945).

3. Description of the Disease

Although tumors on the stem and on the root are usually the only symptoms of disease in sweetclover (*Melilotus alba* Desr.), in most species there are other manifestations of the infection. In fact, in some hosts tumors may be quite inconspicuous and the symptoms may consist principally of irregular enlargement of leaf veins. This enlargement is always on the underside of the leaf. It usually consists of overgrowth all along the veins accompanied by localized protuberances such as nodules, papillae, leafy growths or even small vein tumors. These localized growths vary considerably depending upon the species affected. There may be other symptoms too, such as leaf curling, shortening of the internodes, thickening of the stem, suppression of flowering and stunting of the plant.

On many different kinds of plants the virus causes tumors on the roots and in a few, notably sweetclover, tumors on the stems as well (Fig. 1). Depending on the species, root tumors vary from mere pustule-like growths in some, to tumors about 1 cm. or more in diameter in others. There may be one or a few of these growths on an extensive root system or there may be so many that they practically cover the root. The tumors tend to be spherical in shape and usually are firm or woody in texture. They have a striking tendency to be located adjacent to lateral roots.

Old root tumors rot, so that on badly affected old roots there may be very little of the root system left.

When growing on the plant, the tumors are limited in size. They have a poor connection with the vascular system of the host plant and their own vascular system lacks organization. The tumors will grow indefinitely as tumors if small pieces are grafted to healthy plants in successive transplants or if they are grown aseptically on a suitable synthetic medium.

In most species the disease becomes general throughout the plant but in some the disease has been observed to remain localized in a part of the plant for many months.

A histological study of the young tumors of sweet clover (Kelly and Black, 1949) revealed that most of the tumors on roots originate by tangential divisions of a group of cells in the pericycle. (In the young root, the pericycle is a single layer of cells lying beneath the outer tissues.) The pericycle normally gives rise to lateral roots. Early in the development of the tumor abnormal phloem differentiates at its base, or inner surface. Shortly thereafter irregularly shaped xylem cells differentiate from the

FIG. 1

Large tumors on stems of sweet clover infected with the wound-tumor virus. Tumors reach this size under optimum conditions. (×1.0) (Photograph by J. A. Carlile)

outermost or "apical" cells of the tumor. Xylem differentiation occurs in successive cells in an internal direction to form erratic, radiating finger-like extensions from the outer surface. In these early stages, certain resemblances to normal processes of tissue differentiation are discernible. Cell multiplication continues from the meristematic, immature cells between the xylem and phloem and between the xylem extensions. This consistent pattern of early development soon degenerates into a system of growth from irregular zones of immature cells distributed among groups of distorted xylem, phloem and parenchyma cells. By its growth, the tumor forces its way through overlying tissues and reaches the surface.

In the stems of sweet clover, tumors also developed from the pericyclic region. However, not all tumors arise from the pericycle. Some tumors in sorrel, *Rumex acetosa* L. were found to start from the cork cambium, a layer of immature cells near the surface of the root. There is no evidence of metastasis in the sense in which this term is generally used in tumor literature, that is, where tumor cells become detached, are transferred to a new location and become implanted there without the intervention of man. In fact, there is no real evidence of metastasis in any plant tumor disease.

Tumor cells in sorrel often show inclusions in the cytoplasm which are spherical, non-granular bodies staining intensely with safranin. In their staining properties with the Feulgen and Unna techniques, the bodies resemble nucleolar material (Littau and Black, 1949).

All tumor cells have a tendency to an irregular shape and an irregular orientation one with another. The non-tumorous cells of a virus infected plant appear normal.

4. *Wounds*

The fact that tumors on the roots tend to be located in immediate juxtaposition to lateral roots has already been mentioned. The lateral roots of flowering plants arise from the pericycle and grow out through several overlying layers of cells. The wounding of cells is inevitable in this process, and it is thought that such wounding accounts for the frequent location of the tumors at points where lateral roots emerge. The comparative rarity of stem tumors may be due in part to the fact that the leaves, branches and other lateral appendages of the stem arise without wounding, from superficial groups of immature cells left behind by the growing point. Certain it is that tumors can be induced by artificial wounds such as pin pricks in infected sweet clover stems and have been observed to arise at the site of accidental injuries (Black, 1946a). The younger the wounded infected tissue the more likely it is to produce a tumor. Environmental conditions have a marked effect on this disease but these factors have not as yet been systematically studied.

5. *Differences in Host Susceptibility*

It has been demonstrated (Black, 1946b) that the different heredities of individual sweet clover plants account for a wide variation in the size, number, and location of tumors that develop on infected plants. Some plants are very severely affected and develop many large root tumors; others, though infected, develop very small tumors and are not much damaged; still others occupy an intermediate position. The heredity of the plant also influences the morphology of the tumor. To account for the hereditary diversity of tumor responses in sweet clover, it seems necessary to assume that many genes may influence the outcome.

6. *The Virus*

There is at present no method of detecting the agent of this disease in cell-free suspensions and it has therefore not been possible to test its ability to pass through bacteria-proof filters. Accordingly, it seems desirable to present the evidence for considering the agent to be a virus. That it perpetuates itself in its plant hosts is clear because it can be transmitted from one plant to another indefinitely by grafts. In spite of this fact, no organisms are visible in the tumor tissue. Tumor tissue from sorrel roots may be grown on a synthetic medium indefinitely and although this tissue is readily subject to cultural tests for microorganisms, none can be grown from it. Nevertheless, if it is grafted back to healthy plants, they develop the systemic disease, showing that the agent has been perpetuated in the cultured tissue. The symptoms of the disease other than the tumors are of a sort generally recognized by plant virologists as being due to virus infection. Moreover, the natural means of transmission is typical of a group of plant viruses most of which have not been demonstrated to be filterable because no method of assaying them in cell-free extracts has been discovered.

7. *Insect Transmission*

The wound-tumor disease is transmitted by certain leafhoppers (Black, 1944) and like most plant viruses so transmitted it cannot be transferred from one plant to another by rubbing juice from sick plants on the leaves or cut stems of healthy ones. Diseased and healthy plants may be grown in close proximity without any danger of spread. Transfer of the virus is accomplished by the leafhopper *Agalliopsis novella* (Say) in which the virus was first collected in nature. Certain other related leafhoppers (*Agallia constricta* Van Duzee and *Agallia quadripunctata* Provancher) will also transmit the virus, while another (*Aceratagallia sanguinolenta* Provancher) will not transmit it at all. After virus-free insects have fed on diseased plants, 2 weeks or more must elapse before they are able to inoculate healthy plants (Maramorosch, 1949). Another 3 weeks or more elapses before the inoculated plants show the first symptoms of disease. The virus does not pass from parent insect to young through the egg or sperm. Therefore in nature the virus must alternate between plant and insect to survive.

III. Cancer of the Kidney in Leopard Frogs

1. *Introduction*

This interesting disease is relatively common in leopard frogs (*Rana pipiens*) of New England and adjacent Canada (Lucké, 1934); in other regions the tumor is less frequently encountered. About 2.7% of 10,317 frogs that were examined had the disease (Lucké, 1938b). Males and females were equally affected.

2. *The Tumor*

The growths occur in one or both kidneys as solitary or multiple, white, solid or partially cystic tumors. They vary in size from tiny nodules to masses several times the size of the tissues which they replace. Such large tumors bring about considerable distention of the body cavity and displacement of the viscera (Fig. 2); one of the largest encountered measured $42 \times 25 \times 25$ mm. (Lucké, 1938a). None of the carcinomas are encapsulated. The larger and more rapidly growing tumors not uncommonly metastasize. The secondary tumors occur chiefly in the liver and pancreas but occasionally they lodge in the intestine, peritoneum, mesentery, ovary, retroperitoneal tissue, urinary bladder, lung and orbit. The liver and pancreas receive blood from the kidney through the renal portal veins and tumor cell emboli are often found in these veins. These facts strongly suggest dissemination of the tumor by means of tumor cells carried in the blood stream. It is possible that secondary tumors may also arise by implantation of fragments from the primary tumor, as for example, in the urinary bladder or the peritoneum. The fact that the primary tumors always occur in the kidney (Lucké, 1938b) is additional evidence for interpreting the tumors that occur elsewhere later as metastases rather than independent neoplasms started by the virus in these locations. As in human tumors, the metastasized tumor closely resembles the parent growth.

Histologically, the majority of the neoplasms have the appearance of adenocarcinoma or cancer of a glandular structure. The component cells are atypical in appearance and much larger and more basophilic than

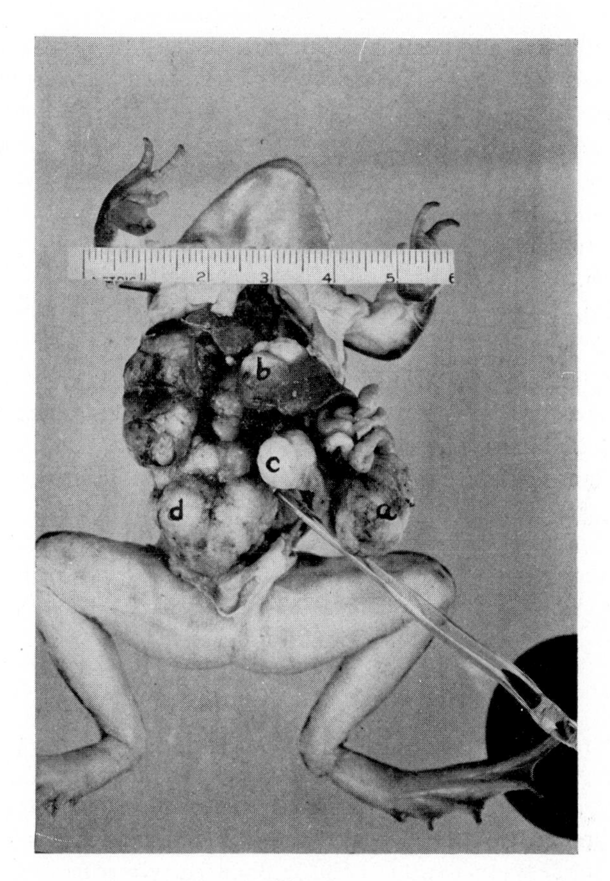

FIG. 2
A frog with a large primary growth in the kidney (a) and extensive secondary metastases in the liver (b) pancreas (c) and mesentery (d). (Courtesy of Dr. Balduin Lucké)

normal kidney cells; usually they are crowded in disorderly multiple layers around irregularly shaped acini (the smallest lobules of the gland). The glandular spaces are often dilated, forming small cysts into which papillary projections extend from the margins. The stroma or supporting connective tissue is scanty and poorly vascular. Tumors of this type infiltrate and destroy the adjacent kidney. A minority of tumors, nearly all of them of small size, have a more regular glandular structure; the tumor tubules are single layered and more regularly arranged; although these growths are not encapsulated, infiltration of adjacent tissue is less evident. Such smaller tumors probably represent earlier stages in the development of the carcinoma. All gradations are found between the apparently benign and the frankly malignant invasive and destructive tumors. The disease, once established, is progressive, for tumors with evidence of regression, such as atrophy, extensive necrosis and marked overgrowth of stroma, are uncommon.

The cancer takes its origin from renal epithelium. The tumor cells are considerably larger than normal kidney cells; they vary in size and shape, but are generally cylindrical. Their nuclei are prominent. Mitoses are commonly observed and often are very numerous, denoting active proliferation.

One of the main characteristics of the frog carcinoma is the frequent presence of acidophilic intranuclear inclusions, such as are typical of a number of virus infections. These do not stain by the Feulgen technique. The inclusions are invariably confined to the tumor cells, and have never been observed in the adjacent normal renal epithelium, nor in the stroma, nor in the wandering cells. The nuclei which contain inclusions are swollen, their chromatin is reduced in amount and condensed at the nuclear periphery; the nucleoli usually disappear. Eventually badly affected cells disintegrate, their places being taken by new tumor cells. When fully developed the inclusion bodies are conspicuous; but they cannot be demonstrated in all tumors.

3. *The Virus*

It is very probable that the frog carcinoma is caused by a virus. The cancers may be frozen at —80°C., dessicated by high vacuum distillation in the frozen state, stored in vacuum at refrigerator temperature for 2 or 3 weeks, ground to a fine powder and still prove infectious when resuspended in sterile water (Lucké, 1938b). Similarly, glycerinated tumors prove to be infectious. When either dessicated or glycerinated material is injected into the body cavity, kidney tumors develop in somewhat over 20% of animals surviving more than 6 months. When living tumor cells are inoculated at various sites they disintegrate, and no significant local growths result. Subsequently, however, tumors develop in the kidney in approximately 20% of the frogs, probably because of liberated virus. No microorganisms have ever been observed in the tumors (Lucké, 1934) and the fact that the tumor can be grown in tissue culture for as long as 6 months attests to the absence of cultivable microorganisms (Lucké, 1939). Failure to infect *Rana clamitans, R. catesbiana* and a subspecies of *R. pipiens* occurring in New Jersey indicates that the causal virus may be quite specific in its host relationships as well as its tissue affinities.

4. *Morphogenetic Studies of the Tumor*

The frog carcinoma is readily transplantable to the anterior chamber of the eye, not only of the homologous species, *Rana pipiens,* but equally well to alien species of frogs, *R. clamitans* and *R. catesbiana.* In the toad, *Bufo americanus,* which belongs to a different family, intraocular transplants become established in a somewhat smaller proportion of animals (Lucké and Schlumberger, 1939, 1940a), but when established grow well.

In the anterior chamber the manner of growth of the living tumors may be observed through the transparent cornea by means of the microscope. Through such observations it has been learned that growth of the cancer is not entirely lawless, but that the transplanted tumors develop according to definite and well-defined structural patterns, their type depending on the immediate physical environment (Fig. 3) (Lucké, 1940). Three such morphogenetic patterns may be observed. Where the tumor grows out in the midst of the aqueous humor, surrounded by fluid and unimpeded by solid tissue, its habit of growth is always tubular or papillary. If, however, the tumor or its buds come in contact with a firm surface such as lens or cornea, broad membranous sheets form which spread over the surface. If contact is made with a loose distensible tissue, a third structural pattern is assumed; the tumor extends inward and forms glandular spaces or acini within the invaded tissue.

Similar growth patterns may be observed in tissue culture. When explanted in plasma media, the outgrowths are tubular so long as they remain completely surrounded by plasma. When, however, contact is made with the surface of the glass, the part in contact becomes flattened out, and the cells now grow no longer as tubules but as membranes (Lucké and Schlumberger, 1939).

Recent studies have shown that the characteristic growth patterns remain unchanged when the tumor is transplanted for 14 serial generations over a period of more than 2 years (Schlumberger and Lucké, 1949).

The frog carcinoma can be grown in tissue culture or in the anterior chamber of the eye over a wide range of temperatures (Lucké and Schlumberger, 1940b). Just as in normal tissue, it has been found that temperature affects growth and development of the cancer both quantitatively and qualitatively. The most striking effect is acceleration in the rate of growth of the tumor at higher temperatures and retardation at lower. This effect is equally well demonstrable in explants and transplants. In explants kept at higher temperatures, the cells exhibit a tendency to become detached at the margin and wander away, their rate of locomotion being directly proportional to the environmental temperature. Intraocular transplants, at

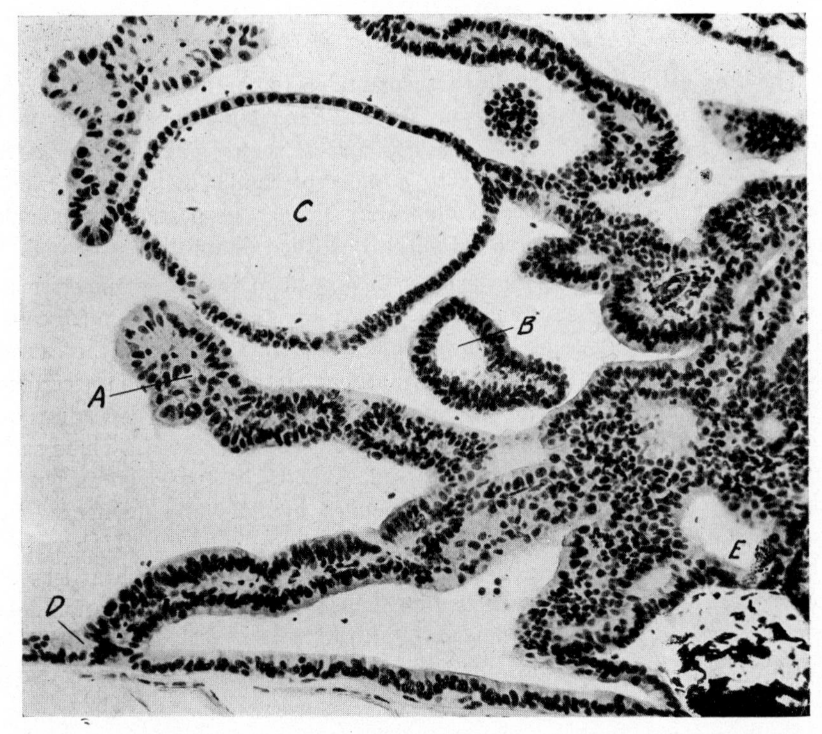

FIG. 3

Section of frog kidney tumor transplanted into the eye. It shows several patterns of growth. At A is a solid cylindrical outgrowth. At B a tubule has formed through accumulation of fluid between the cells, and at C excessive accumulation of fluid has led to the formation of a cyst. At D the tip of a cylindrical outgrowth upon making contact with the solid surface of the lens has become adherent and has continued its growth in the form of a membrane. At E the tumor is invading the iris and forming a glandular type of growth. (Courtesy of the *Journal of Urology*.)

higher temperatures (28°C.) are more efficiently vascularized than at lower temperatures (7° and 18°). The outgrowths at higher temperatures are long, branching, and often cystic, whereas at lower temperatures they tend to be short, stubby and rarely cystic.

Lately, it has been demonstrated that temperature exerts a profound effect on the process of metastasis (Lucké and Schlumberger, 1949), greatly influencing the frequency of its occurrence and the extent of its dissemination. When tumor-bearing frogs are maintained for several months at 7° or 18°C., only 6% of the animals develop secondary tumors, whereas metastases occur in over 50% of animals maintained for several weeks at 28°. Moreover, at the higher temperature the extent of dissemination is far greater than occurs in frogs existing in a state of nature or kept at lower temperatures under laboratory conditions. The mechanism which induces metastasis is complex; it is probable that temperature affects the adhesiveness of cells, their locomotion, their invasiveness and the rate with which the tumor obtains vascular stroma from host tissue. All these experiments indicate that cancer is not a wholly autonomous growth, but that its rate and structural pattern is greatly influenced by various environmental factors.

Tumor fragments from adult frogs have been transplanted into tadpoles at various sites (Briggs, 1942) where they grow but usually later regress. In the dorsal mesenchyme of the anterior third of the tails of young tadpoles, the tumor fragments grow well until the tadpoles approach metamorphosis when rapid regression of the transplant usually occurs. However, in tadpoles from which the thyroid or hypophysis is removed so that they remain as permanent tadpoles, the same growth-regression sequence occurs. If any regressive changes in the transplants are due to metamorphic influences, these influences must precede morphological metamorphosis and be independent of the thyroid or hypophysis. It seems more likely that tumor regression in these experiments is due to the development of individual specificity in the later larval stages (Briggs and Grant, 1943).

Rose and Wallingford (1948) made subcutaneous transplants of frog renal carcinoma to the forelimbs of the salamander *Triturus viridescens*. After the transplants were growing and invading the salamander limbs, the limbs were amputated through the cancer. After dedifferentiation and regeneration, patches of frog muscle, cartilage and fibrous connective tissue were found in the regenerated limb, interspersed and blended with corresponding salamander tissue. Most patches of normally differentiated frog tissue were adjacent to unchanged tumor remaining in the old part of the limb proximal to the level of dedifferentiation. The frog cells were distinguishable because their nuclei are much smaller than those of the salamander cells. To be certain that cancerous frog cells had been converted to normal cells in these experiments, one would have to be sure that the normal frog cells in the regenerated salamander limb did not arise from the stroma of the tumor.

IV. Fowl Leucosis Complex

1. *Introduction*

In the following account, the general treatises of Brandly, Waters and Hall (1942) and of Jungherr (1943) have been drawn upon. These sources have been supplemented by recourse to original literature.

This disease, first described by Marek in 1907 (Jungherr, 1943), is prevalent in many parts of the world. It causes many deaths in birds between 6 weeks and 18 months of age. In the United States, it is believed to cause greater loss than any other disease and is considered responsible for about 40% of the high mortality of growing stock. It is estimated to cause an annual loss in excess of $50,000,000 (Brandly, Waters and Hall, 1942; Hutt and Cole, 1947).

A confusing variety of disease expressions is included under the term, "avian leucosis complex." However, all of them have an important feature in common, namely, an uncontrolled multiplication of the precursors of blood cells, usually the white blood cells. Ordinarily, these cells would stop dividing, would differentiate and mature in the blood-forming tissues such as the bone marrow before being released into the blood stream. However, in this disease multiplication continues after release and the cells lodge and grow in almost any tissue or organ of the body. They thereby cause a plethora of disease symptoms.

2. *Description of the Disease*

The most common type of the disease complex is the visceral (visceral lymphomatosis). It tends to occur in adults rather than in young birds. Outward symptoms are indefinite. The birds may lose appetite and weight. They may assume unnatural postures. The comb becomes pale and shrivelled. Diarrhea may be an accompaniment of the disease. The animal may die after prolonged illness or suddenly, without previous indication of poor health. At autopsy almost any organ may show nodular growths, tumor-like masses or a general enlargement without tumors. The great variety of gross symptoms is in striking contrast to the comparatively uniform cellular pathology which consists of massive accumulations of multiplying white blood cells. The latter are comprised of small round cell lymphocytes, large lymphoblast-like cells and intergrading forms. These diseased cells may infiltrate surrounding tissues or may form coherent tumorous masses. The cells tend to accumulate in organs with normal lymphoid tissue. The liver, kidney and ovary are most commonly affected. The external expression of the disease varies according to the part or parts attacked. Varying abnormal increases in the white cell count of the blood may be present or the blood may appear normal.

The nerve type of the disease (neural lymphomatosis, fowl paralysis, etc.) may cause paralysis of one or both legs or wings, sour crop, wry neck, difficult breathing or a general incoordination of the entire body depending on where the infiltrating diseased blood cells become located in the nerves. The majority of the pathologic blood cells are mononuclear white blood cells indistinguishable from lymphocytes designated as small round cells. However, other blood cell types are represented. The affected nerve may show local or diffuse, soft grayish swellings. Usually there are no significant blood changes. This form of the disease attacks principally young birds between 2-5 months of age.

An eye type (ocular lymphomatosis) is associated with neural lymphomatosis and occurs most commonly in young adults. The iris loses its pigment and the pupil becomes irregular in outline and reduced in size. This is due to the infiltration of the iris with the diseased mononuclear white blood cells. The optic nerve may also be affected. Partial or complete blindness results and the bird has difficulty getting food.

Birds afflicted with the blood types (leucoses) become thin, weak and pale. The wattles, comb and skin may become intensely yellow. Parts of the bone marrow may be swollen and may vary in color from dark to white or chalky. The blood is often pale and watery. These types are largely limited to changes within the blood vessel system, although immature blood cells often accumulate in the smaller blood vessels of the various organs and cause an enlargement resembling that in the other forms. In the leucoses, the blood cells affected may be of different sorts. In some it is the precursors of the erythrocytes that multiply in excess, in others the precursors of certain of the white blood cells. The other types seldom show such progressive changes within the blood system.

A hardening and thickening of the long bones, without increase in length (osteopetrosis), has been associated with certain outbreaks of the disease. The symptoms develop in the long bones of the wings and legs, in the pelvis and shoulder girdle and in rare cases in the spine. The space occupied by the bone marrow may be much reduced or obliterated. The phalanges and skull bones seem resistant. Osteopetrosis is relatively rare and is usually accompanied by some form of visceral lymphomatosis.

A single bird may exhibit symptoms of any combination of these main types. Readers interested in further details of the various manifestations of this complex disease and the variety of names which they bear should consult more extended treatments (Jungherr, 1943; Feldman and Olson, 1943; Brandly, Waters and Hall, 1942).

3. The Virus (Trifur gallinarum *H.*)

A. HISTORY

In 1908, Ellermann and Bang (Ellermann, 1921) showed that emulsions of the organs of chickens suffering from leucosis could be rendered cell-free by centrifugation followed by filtration through Berkefeld filters and yet still produce the disease when injected intravenously into other chickens. This constituted the first evidence that the disease was caused by a virus. The reproduction of the disease by filtrates free of host cells and cultivable microorganisms has been carried out by various investigators in innumerable experiments.

B. VARIATION

There is evidence that many different virus entities exist in nature because, in spite of disconcerting inconsistencies and the appearance of various forms of the disease when inoculum from one type is employed, there is nevertheless a tendency for a particular source of inoculum to reproduce the type or types of disease from which it came. This is shown in the work of many investigators (Furth, 1936a; Burmester, 1947). The relationships of these entities is not understood. There is not enough evidence at present to eliminate the possibility that these entities are not closely related. However, it seems more likely that there exists in nature a number of closely related mutating viruses that are responsible for the leucosis complex. The possibility of a transfer of properties from units of one strain to those of another in mixed infections must also be considered. If affinity for host cell type, infectivity of filtrates, and contagiousness, were some of the properties subject to mutation and transfer the fowl leucosis complex would be more readily understood.

The possible close relation between the chicken sarcoma viruses, like Rous sarcoma virus, and the fowl leucosis viruses is an unsolved question of the greatest fundamental importance. Sources of inoculum have been discovered that produce symptoms of both types of disease and evidence adduced that a single virus entity is responsible. The experience with Furth's strain 13 virus will serve as a concrete example of some of these points. The strain 13 virus appeared in a chicken inoculated with Furth's strain 1 virus which for years had caused leucosis without sarcoma. Strain 13 produced leucosis, sarcoma in muscle injected with it, and diffuse sarcomatosis of the spleen, bone marrow and several other organs. The disease picture was variable from bird to bird. Small quantities of blood (0.00001 ml.) were sufficient to reproduce the disease. When sarcoma from a chicken inoculated with strain 13 was grown in tissue culture, the diseased blood cells died within a few days. Nevertheless, when the tissue culture was employed to inoculate other birds, it caused both sarcoma and leucosis even after 8 to 10 transfers during 67 days in culture. In contrast to this when strain 1, causing leucosis alone, and strain 11, causing sarcoma alone, were both inoculated into the same bird, they were readily separable. Tissue cultures of sarcoma from a chicken with both diseases produced sarcoma alone upon injection into other birds. When blood from a chicken with both the sarcoma and leucosis was injected into other chickens only leucosis developed. These experiments and others support the idea that strain 13 is a single virus. This in turn indicates this virus, with changed and broader tissue affinities, arose by mutation from strain 1. (Furth and Stubbs, 1934; Stubbs and Furth, 1935; Furth, 1936a,b).

C. PROPERTIES

The different strains of the viruses vary in regard to such properties as infectivity and the length of time they withstand dessication. These differences may reflect different concentrations attained by the different strains in the tissues of the host. Some of the properties determined have been for one strain and others for different strains.

Furth (1932) found that the smallest volume of plasma from diseased birds that would produce leucosis was 0.000001 cc. and of cell suspension was 0.00001 cc. Inoculation with cell suspensions was more successful (33-71% of takes) than inoculation with corresponding amounts of plasma (20-28%). With the smaller amounts of plasma the incubation period was greatly prolonged, but the percentage of takes was approximately the same over a wide range of concentrations.

Furth and Miller (1932) found that the leucosis virus readily passed through all types of silicious filters and experiments with graded collodion filters indicated it was smaller than the bovine pleuro-pneumonia organism (250 mμ). Later, the diameter of Furth's strain 1 of fowl leucosis virus was estimated at about 72 mμ by sedimentation (Stern and Kirschbaum, 1939). It is viable after dessication for at least 54 days; may be stored in glycerine at least 104 days; and may be preserved at -60°C. for at least 6 months. It is destroyed by storage for 14 days at 37.5°C. but not 4°C. It withstands freezing and thawing (Holmes, 1948).

D. TRANSMISSION

There is much evidence showing that the younger the birds when exposed to natural infection the higher the incidence of the disease. In fact some control may be attained by the isolation of young birds from old stock during the first 5 months. The time between exposure and the development of the disease is usually long but varies from several days to many months (Brandly, Waters and Hall, 1942).

The viruses are present in high concentration in the blood and plasma throughout the course of the disease and do not produce a solid immunity (Furth, 1932). Ratcliffe and Stubbs (1935) failed to transmit the virus of chicken leucosis by means of two species of mosquitoes, *Culex pipiens* and *Aedes aegypti,* or the common red mite *Dermanyssus gallinae*. Johnson (1937) reported successful transmission with the same mite. Possibly, blue bugs, *Argas persicus* Oken may be vectors (Brown and Cross, 1941). The work with arthropod vectors is not extensive enough to be conclusive. The virus can be transferred from diseased to healthy birds in the process of vaccination against fowl pox (Johnson, 1937).

However, there is evidence that other and probably more important routes of transmission exist. It has been demonstrated that the virus passes from parent to young through the egg (Durant and McDougle, 1939; Waters, 1945, 1947a, b). The earliest appearance of the disease in a population with egg-transmitted virus as the only source was 40 days after hatching. By strict isolation and quarantine methods, families of susceptible birds can be selected and maintained free of the disease. If mixed with infected birds as many as 44% of the originally virus-free chicks become infected. These pass on the virus to their progeny through the egg. In the United States Regional Poultry Research Laboratory at East Lansing, Michigan, where these experiments have been carried out, the only parasites known to exist have been small infestations of coccidia (sporozoan parasites). In such an environment, it seems unlikely that mites could account for the spread of the disease from bird to bird. A number of investigators (Jungherr, 1943) support transmission of the disease by contact. It has been shown that the faeces of diseased birds contain the virus and such virus could readily gain access to the mouths or nostrils of other birds. That entrance through the mouth or nostrils may be the common route is suggested by recent artificial inoculation studies on resistant and susceptible lines of birds that had been selected under conditions of natural exposure. Subcutaneous inoculation by needle failed to show any correlation in the incidence of disease resulting in the resistant and susceptible lines, with that developing from natural exposure. However, when inoculation consisted of placing 1 cc. of inoculum in the crop, 1 drop in an eye and 1 drop in a nostril, the resulting incidence in the resistant and susceptible lines paralleled that produced by natural exposure (Heisdorf, Brewer and Lamoreux, 1947). The results also suggest that natural resistance resides in the mucous membranes.

4. *Variation in Susceptibility*

Certain forms of the disease have been transmitted to or have been observed in pheasants, turkeys, guinea fowl and various ornamental birds. All breeds of chickens are susceptible (Brandly, Waters and Hall, 1942; Jungherr, 1943). The incidence of the different disease types apparently varies in the different breeds of chickens. Evidence from well over 13,000 post mortem diagnoses indicated that the incidence of the visceral type tended to be higher in Barred Plymouth Rocks than in White Plymouth Rocks, White Leghorns or Rhode Island Reds. On the other hand, the incidence of neural and ocular leucosis was highest in White Leghorns and least in Barred Plymouth Rocks (Davis, Doyle, Walkey and Cenker, 1947). Inbred lines of White Leghorns also show a different incidence of the different forms of the disease (Waters and Prickett, 1946). These observations indicate a genetic influence on the cell specificity of the disease.

Visceral lymphomatosis occurs with greater frequency in females than in males (Jungherr, 1943; Burmester, 1945) whereas in the bone type of the disease, the reverse appears to be true (Jungherr, 1943). Work on the influence of sex hormones on the incidence of lymphomatosis is somewhat confusing because castrated male birds had a higher incidence than such birds treated with either male or female sex hormones. Castrated animals of either sex had a higher incidence than normal birds (Burmester and Nelson, 1945).

Many workers have demonstrated that by selective breeding under conditions of natural exposure to the disease, lines of chickens differing widely in their susceptibility may be obtained (Asmundson and Biely, 1932; Taylor, Lerner, De Ome and Beach, 1943; Waters and Prickett, 1946; Hutt and Cole, 1947). For example, in line 10 of Waters and Prickett, the disease was almost completely absent, whereas in lines 4 and 9, there was over 50%. Hybrids of resistant and susceptible lines are intermediate in their disease incidence (Taylor, Lerner, De Ome and Beach, 1943) and it seems probable that many genetic factors affect susceptibility (De Ome, 1943). There is some evidence that some birds may carry the virus yet not develop the disease (Durant and McDougle, 1939).

The discovery of an artificial method of inoculation which simulates the results obtained by natural exposure (Heisdorf, Brewer and Lamoreux, 1947) may speed efforts to breed resistant birds. The production of resistant strains of birds is one of the most promising methods for controlling the disease.

Research on this disease has been made difficult because of the confusing complexity of the disease forms, the long incubation period, the difficulty of getting animals known to be free of the virus, especially inbred susceptible birds, and by the isolation and quarantine practices necessary to control experimental work. Now that virus-free susceptible birds have been obtained and tested over a period of years such stocks may be expected to play an important part in future studies not only on fowl leucosis but on chicken tumor work generally.

V. Rous Sarcoma Number 1

1. Introduction

This is a cancer of chickens consisting of cells that resemble those of connective tissue. The disease has been the object of intensive scientific investigations since 1911 when it was demonstrated that it could be produced by injecting into healthy birds tumor extracts that had been passed through Berkefeld filters impenetrable to bacteria (Rous, 1911).

2. The Tumor

The original tumor had developed slowly in the right breast of a pure bred Plymouth Rock chicken without apparent impairment of the bird's health. However, when small fragments of the tumor were implanted into the muscles of the left breast and into the peritoneal cavity of the same bird, it died 35 days later as a result of the tumorous growths (Rous, 1910a). At first, the tumor could be transmitted by such tumor tissue grafts only to birds closely related to the one in which the tumor was discovered. Tumor transplants to birds of mixed breed not only failed but also those to other Plymouth Rock birds not within the same familial stock. Experimentation since the original observation has shown that the virus (*Molitor tumoris* H.) causing the disease possesses much greater potentialities than were revealed in the pioneer studies.

3. Description

According to the original description (Rous, 1910a) the sarcoma consists of loose bundles of spindle-shaped cells running in every direction and separated from the lesser blood vessels only by endothelium. Where such a bundle is cut transversely, the appearance is that of a group of round cells of varying sizes. Intercellular fibrils are demonstrable, though rare in the more cellular portions of the growth. The spindle cells, although in general large, vary much in size and shape, some are short and plump, some continued into long slender processes. The nucleus is, as a rule, large and vesicular with a loose network and several coarse masses of chromatin. Occasionally it is rod-shaped and sometimes shrunken in size and having the chromatin condensed to a structureless mass. Mitosis is fairly frequent and cells with two to five or six nuclei occur. These cells give to the growth here and there a somewhat polymorphous appearance. The multinucleate cells occur most frequently where necrosis is beginning. Necrosis is widespread and generally appears to be due to insufficient vascularization although hemorrhage from the thin walled vessels is also occasionally responsible.

The original tumor appeared clinically to be a benign growth and in no way suggested an extrinsic causative agent. It was encapsulated but the capsule was penetrated here and there by the sarcoma. As the tumor grows, it infiltrates and replaces normal tissues (Fig. 4).

Metastasis by way of the blood stream to the heart, lungs, liver, kidneys and peritoneum is common. The spleen is almost completely immune to

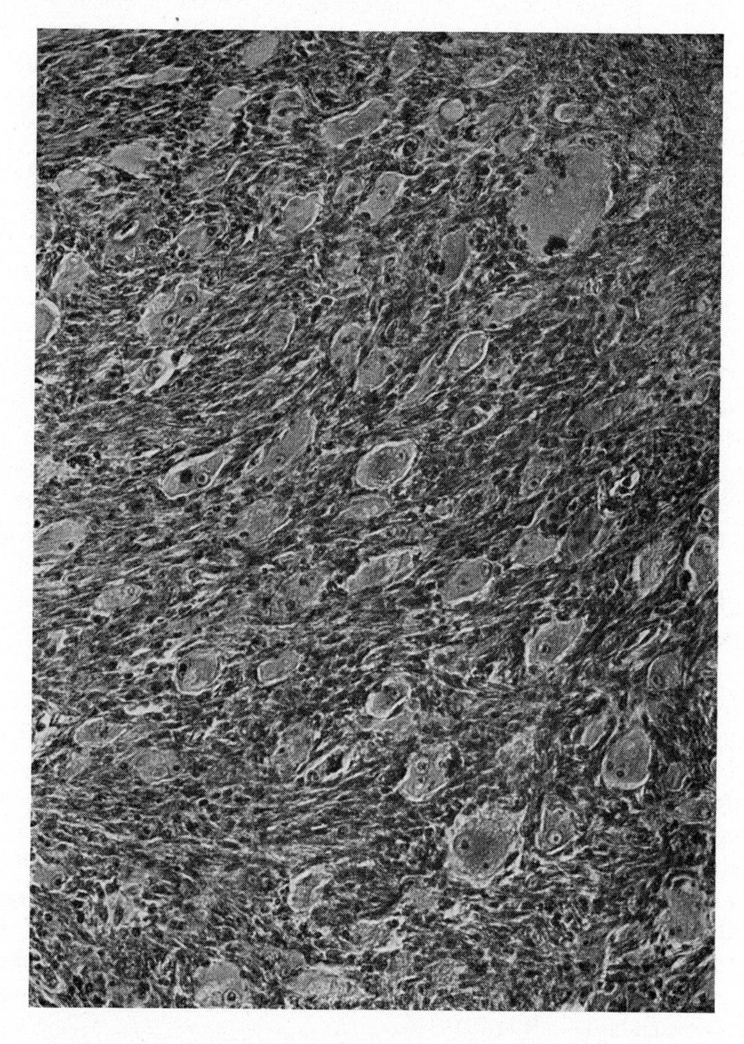

FIG. 4

Invasion of muscle by Chicken Tumor I (the Rous sarcoma). The spindle-shaped sarcoma cells surround the multinucleate muscle fibers which appear round in cross-section. (Courtesy of the *Journal of Experimental Medicine*) metastasis (Rous, 1910b). Dissemination via the lymphatic system is not as frequent. The secondary tumors appear to arise by metastasis and not by spread of the virus from the primary lesion. The cells neighboring the secondary tumors do not appear histologically to participate in secondary tumor growth although one might expect them to do so because of the virus nature of the disease. This interpretation of the histological picture was strengthened by experiments showing that intravenous injection of small fragments of the sarcoma into susceptible chickens gave many lung tumors, whereas similar inoculation with the virus alone gave very few. (Rous, Murphy and Tytler, 1912b).

The first experiments (Rous and Murphy, 1911) on the injection of the virus into chicken embryos resulted in tumor growths from the mesoderm. The tumor cells were strikingly different from normal connective tissue cells adjacent to them. Tumors never developed from wounds in the ectoderm and endoderm with which the virus must have come in contact. However, numerous small ectodermal tumors developed under conditions where only the ectoderm of the incubating fertile egg was exposed to virus that had been propagated for thirty passages on the yolk sac of chicken embryos (Keogh, 1938).

More recently (Duran-Reynals, 1940b; Milford and Duran-Reynals, 1943) it has been demonstrated that if the virus is injected intravenously into chicken embryos or newborn chicks a hemorrhagic disease without tumors may be produced. The virus multiplies in the young host, weakens the cells of the blood vessels and adjacent connective tissue, blebs are formed and the rupture and hemorrhage of these cause death.

4. The Virus

Early work on the Rous sarcoma soon established that no microorganism could be demonstrated in the tumor by study with the light microscope or by attempt to isolate any by culture methods. The passage of an agent through Berkefeld filters that was able to perpetuate itself in susceptible birds indicated that it was a virus. The virus was found to withstand being dried in the tumor tissue for 7 months, to remain active after freezing and thawing or, heating to 53°C. for 15 minutes. A temperature of 55°C. for 15 minutes destroyed the virus as did treatment with a number of chemicals (Rous and Murphy, 1912). The virus does not pass through a dializing membrane (Rous, 1912).

Considerably later a number of workers attempted purification and characterization of the virus with methods that had slowly developed for virus work. Filtration experiments through membranes with ascertainable average pore diameter indicated that the virus had a diameter of about 100 mμ (Elford and Andrewes, 1935) and later studies with high speed centrifugation indicated a particle diameter of about 60-70 mμ (Elford and Andrewes, 1936). Probably the purest virus preparations were obtained in a series of high speed centrifugation studies in which a preparation was obtained that produced infection with 4×10^{-13} g, in terms of dry weight. It was estimated that there were about 2,000 particles in such a minimal infective dose (Claude, 1939b). It must be remembered that there may be a great hazard involved in the process of virus particles making infective contacts with susceptible cells. The particles were estimated to have a diameter of about 70 mμ. However, similar treatment of extracts of normal tissue such as chick embryo yielded preparations of particles, which though uninfective, could not be satisfactorily distinguished chemically from the infective preparations. Both preparations contained phospholipids and ribose nucleoprotein and had approximately the same elementary analysis (Claude, 1940).

Recently methods have been developed for growing certain cells in tissue culture in such a way that they may subsequently be examined under the electron microscope (Porter, Claude and Fullam, 1945). The method has been applied to the Rous sarcoma and has revealed in the cells spherical virus-like particles ranging in size from 67-80 mμ in diameter (Fig. 5). This 20% range in particle diameter is what one would expect if the bodies divided by fission. The high frequency of paired particles and the occurrence of particles in chains of 5 or 6 also suggest such a process. Similar structures were not found in homologous healthy cells. Under the electron microscope the microsomes which contaminated earlier purified preparations of the virus (Claude, 1940) appeared as hollow spheres or vesicles whereas the virus particles are compact dense bodies. The virus and the microsomes appear to be quite unrelated entities. Virus particles of the same size and type but arranged in colony-like groups were found in another chicken tumor investigated in the same way (Claude, Porter and Pickels, 1947).

5. *Variations of the Virus*

It will be remembered that when the virus of the Rous sarcoma was first recognized great difficulty was experienced in getting it to infect birds not closely related to the hen in which it originally occurred and at first no other species tested proved susceptible. By transplanting bits of tumor tissue in series through young birds the power of the tumor to invade and metastasize increased (Rous, 1910b). Later successful tumor tissue transplants were made to the membranes of the embryos of different chicken

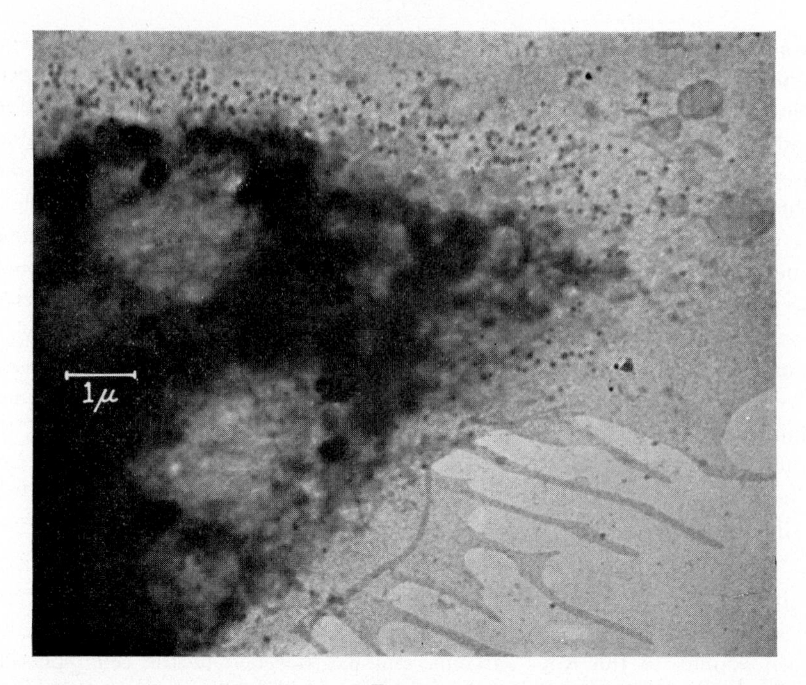

FIG. 5

Margin of a cell from a Rous sarcoma showing the Rous sarcoma virus as it occurs within the cell. The bodies are approximately 70 to 84 mμ in diameter and occur singly, in pairs or in rows up to 6. (Courtesy of *Cancer Research*)

breeds and of pigeons and ducks. However, it could not be transplanted to adult pigeons or ducks (Murphy and Rous, 1912).

Many years later it was demonstrated that the Rous sarcoma virus would infect pheasants (Andrewes, 1932, 1933a). Still later it was found possible to infect newly hatched ducks by injections of large amounts of the Rous sarcoma virus (Duran-Reynals, 1942). The tumors that developed within 9-30 days showed the same characteristics as the original chicken tumor and could readily be propagated through chickens but not through ducks. Other tumors that developed 40-215 days after inoculation showed several new characteristics; a type of tumor rich in collagen (the main albuminoid constituent of connective tissue), affinity for the bones and an ability to be propagated easily through ducks but not through chickens. In other words the variants were different from the original virus in regard to tumor type, tissue affinity and species pathogenicity. It is clear therefore that the Rous sarcoma virus may vary and it is probable that passage in these hosts favors the growth of certain mutants over the original virus. When the process was reversed and the duck variants of the virus were grown again in chickens the first tumors to develop retained the new characteristics that appeared in the tumors developing late in ducks. Other virus variants with regard to tissue affinity and tumor type were secured by successful transfer of the virus to turkeys and to guinea fowls (Duran-Reynals, 1943). It was also shown that the duck variant of the virus had changed markedly from the chicken virus in its antigenicity. Immune antibodies from aging ducks neutralized only duck tumor viruses, as tested on ducks, not as tested on chickens and did not neutralize chicken tumor viruses tested on either ducks or chickens (Duran-Reynals and King, 1947). Additional variants have also been obtained (Duran-Reynals, 1947); in one case by multiplication of the virus in Rous sarcoma (chicken) cells growing in the anterior chamber of the guinea pig eye (Shrigley, Greene and Duran-Reynals, 1945).

6. *Similar Viruses*

The fact that the Rous sarcoma virus mutates in regard to a number of its properties, would lead one to expect that a number of viruses closely related to it would occur in nature. This indeed seems to be the case, because although the virus does not cause a disease of economic importance in chickens, a number of tumor diseases similar to the Rous sarcoma, have been discovered from time to time in various places (Rous, Murphy and Tytler, 1912c; Rous and Murphy, 1914a; Duran-Reynals and Shrigley, 1946). Many of these were treated by Foulds in his review of the subject (Foulds, 1934). These different tumor diseases are characterized by different histological pictures and their distinctness is attested by the reproducibility of the distinctive features of each by the particular virus responsible. A serological study of a number of these viruses (Andrewes, 1933b) showed that although no two of the viruses studied were serologically identical they all have some degree of antigenic relationship and are probably interrelated members of a group.

7. *Resistance to the Virus*

Birds may show a resistance or susceptibility to inoculation with Rous sarcoma cells as distinct from the Rous sarcoma virus. The reaction to the cells probably depends on the degree of their genetic similarity or dissimilarity with the cells of the host and does not concern us here (Rous, 1913). There are two types of resistance to the virus. One depends upon the occurrence of antibodies in the blood; the other upon genetic factors. Although the antibodies may be transmitted from parent to young through the egg-yolk and may confer a resistance for a few weeks (Andrewes, 1939a), young chicks are usually free of these antibodies and they appear in the blood as the chicken grows older, often without obvious contact with the virus (Duran-Reynals, 1940a). As a rule young chicks are more susceptible than adult birds.

Neutralizing antibodies may occur in chickens as long as 1 or 2 years after spontaneous recovery, a fact which may indicate that the virus remains latent in the tissues after tumor regression. Sometimes tumors recur and virus can be demonstrated (Carr, 1943c).

Genetic factors are almost certainly responsible for the resistance or immunity of most species of animals and plants to any particular virus. In the case of the Rous virus genetic influences for resistance also extend into the chicken species. This type of resistance may be present at birth and is not due to serum antibodies. However, such resistance is less at birth and in old age than in young adult birds (Carr, 1943a).

8. *Virus Inhibitors*

Inhibitors have been shown to play an important role in the transmissibility of the virus by artificial means. The case of a slow growing fibrosarcoma, known as chicken tumor 10, is of interest in this connection. Only once or twice during 10 years that the tumor was under observation in the laboratory did the injection of dessicates indicate that a virus might be involved. But when tumor extracts were centrifuged at high speed the sediment contained infectious virus that could be rendered noninfectious by the addition of the supernatant (Claude, 1937). An inhibitor was also found in tumors of the Rous sarcoma (Claude, 1939a). It is not known whether these inhibitors are identical with the serum antibodies or not. They may have a bearing on the finding that the infectiousness of extracts of the Rous sarcoma was inversely proportional to the duration of growth in the host (Carr, 1943b). The virus is not restricted to tumor tissue but may be demonstrated in the spleen, liver, muscle and brain of chickens with a sarcoma. It is believed to enter the cells of these tissues (Mellanby, 1938) and is easiest to demonstrate between the 10th and 18th day after injection.

9. *Environmental Influences*

There appears to be no seasonal effect on susceptibility (Carr, 1942). When diatomaceous earth is injected along with the virus the number of infection foci is greatly increased. The diatomaceous earth causes injury that results in the active proliferation of the connective tissue cells and renders them more susceptible (Rous, Murphy and Tytler, 1912a).

10. *Life History*

Nothing is known about the natural means by which this virus infects chickens. It does not spread from bird to bird in the laboratory and birds cannot be infected by feeding them sarcomatous tissue (Rous, Murphy and Tytler, 1912a).

VI. Infectious Myxoma and Infectious Fibroma of Rabbits

Although the growths caused by these two diseases may not be considered tumors in some interpretations of the word, they are of great interest from a biological viewpoint because of their intermediate position between purely proliferative virus tumor diseases such as the Rous sarcoma and purely necrotizing virus diseases such as hoof and mouth disease.

1. *Infectious Myxoma (Myxomatosis) of Rabbits*

A. HOSTS AND OCCURRENCE

This malady, occurring naturally only in rabbits of the genus *Oryctolagus,* was discovered by Sanarelli in rabbitries around Montevideo, Uruguay, and was first reported in 1898 (Sanarelli, 1898). Since that time outbreaks of the disease have been reported from Central America (Moses, 1940) and from southern California (Kessel, Prouty and Meyer, 1931). The domestic rabbit, *Oryctolagus cuniculus* L., is extremely susceptible. None of its varieties appears to have any resistance whatever. Wild European rabbits of the genus *Oryctolagus* are also susceptible. Rabbits in other genera are resistant and various authors have reported failures in attempts to infect them (Hobbs, 1931; Hyde and Gardner, 1933). However, serial transmission of the virus *Molitor myxomae* (Aragao) H. can be accomplished in the cottontail, *Sylvilagus* sp. by intratesticular inoculation. Intradermal inoculations in cottontails are less successful (Shope, 1936a; Berry, 1937). Serial passage of the virus on the chorioallantoic membrane of the embryonated chicken egg has also been achieved (Lush, 1937; Hoffstadt and Pilcher, 1938). The virus could be transmitted serially through duck eggs only after serial passage in chicken eggs (Hoffstadt, Omundson and Donaldson, 1941).

B. THE DISEASE

(*1*) *Symptoms.* The virus of this disease soon gains access to the blood stream and is distributed to all parts of the body by this route (Swan, 1941). Infectious myxomatosis in the domestic rabbit is characterized by a slight fever and marked swellings at junctions of mucous membranes and skin such as those of the eyelids, nostrils, mouth, anus and genital openings. The swellings are by no means restricted to these regions, however, but occur generally over the body. The subcutaneous swellings about the eyes and nose and at the base of the ears often impart a leonine appearance to the rabbit's face. There is a mucous secretion from the nose, eyes, genitals and from skin nodules that have become ulcerated. Internally the virus induces multiple lesions in the lymph glands, tunica vaginalis, epididymis, testicle, spleen and lungs. Domestic rabbits die 5-15 days after inoculation (Hobbs, 1928; Rivers, 1930; Hyde and Gardner, 1933; Ahlström, 1940a).

(2) *Histology.* Most of the swellings caused by this disease are composed of proliferating and degenerating myxoblast-like cells (mucous connective tissue cells) in a mucinous matrix. Cells characteristic of inflammatory processes also occur in the lesions.

Rivers (1930) described the proliferation of epidermal epithelium overlying the myxomatous swellings followed by necrosis and the formation of vesicles. The epidermal cells were reported to contain cytoplasmic inclusions. He also noted the proliferation of the endothelial cells of capillaries in subcutaneous nodules. Rivers suggested that the virus of infectious myxomatosis bridged the gap between tumor-forming and necrotizing viruses since it combined both actions.

Hurst (1937a) described the changes in the generalized lesions of myxoma in detail. He considered that, although the relative preponderance of destructive and proliferative lesions was determined in part by the virulence of the infecting virus, in general epithelial and some mesodermal structures, such as muscle, tend to degenerate and die when attacked by the virus, whereas other mesodermal structures such as vascular and reticular endothelium, histiocytes and fibroblasts tend to undergo considerable proliferation and develop into myxoma cells. In some situations the proliferating myxoma cells appear to secrete a mucoid substance. Hurst found the same changes in the epithelium of the bronchi as in that of the skin. He described vascular lesions in most parts affected by the virus.

Ahlström (1940a) concluded that the myxoma cells are derived mainly from the reticulo-endothelial system, the specific changes due to the virus being restricted to this system. Marked proliferation of the reticulo-endothelium of the spleen, lymphatic glands and thymus occurs. This condition is found also in the lungs, lymphatic tissue of the intestines and in the skin lesions. In the liver and bone marrow the reticulo-endothelial cells enlarge and assume the character of myxoma cells. He considered hepatic necrosis and cytotoxic changes in the bone marrow, spleen and lymphatic glands to be non-specific features of the disease. Ahlström believed that the virus has a primary affinity for mesenchymal tissues and causes enlargement, proliferation and necrosis of epithelial cells of various tissues only when these are exposed to massively infected mesenchyme. Some affected epithelial cells show very small particles which may be the elementary bodies of the virus.

In the chicken egg the virus causes proliferation of the ectodermal cells of the chorioallantoic membrane and these cells do not show any appearance of being myxoma cells. Later the cells become necrotic; the lesion is invaded by leucocytes and other inflammatory cells and regression takes place (Lush, 1937). Cells of the meso and entodermal layers are also affected and show the presence of very small granular bodies (Hoffstadt and Pilcher, 1938) which may be the virus particles themselves. These results suggest that the virus is not strictly specific in the cells it attacks.

C. THE VIRUS

(*1*) *Morphology.* The virus of infectious myxomatosis is one of the largest. The many observations of small granules in diseased tissues by earlier investigators is reviewed by van Rooyen (1937) who found the elementary bodies measured 0.31 to 0.36 microns when stained by the Paschen method. Occasionally the bodies appeared in short chains of 4 or 5. Because of the large size of this virus, it does not pass through the filters of smaller pore size commonly used in virus research. Purification techniques depending principally on differential centrifugation have provided highly infectious sediments rich in these particles and noninfectious supernatants lacking the bodies (Rivers and Ward, 1937; van Rooyen and Rhodes, 1937). Material from diseased animals is infectious at a dilution of 1:100,000 (Hobbs, 1928). A comparison of experimental dilution curves with curves theoretically calculated for infection produced by 1, 2 or more particles, indicates that a single virus particle will produce the disease when inoculated into the rabbit's skin (Parker, 1940).

(*2*) *Transmission.* Infectious myxomatosis is a highly contagious disease readily transmitted by contact. The virus is present in large amounts in the secretions from the eyes, nose, genitals and ulcerated cutaneous nodules. It does not occur in the urine or faeces (Hobbs, 1928). Rabbits can be infected by dropping the virus into the eye but it seems to gain entrance most commonly through the nose (Hyde and Gardner, 1939). Although transmission by fleas and by flies also occurs, it is probable that these agents are more important for transmission over some distance than at close quarters.

The myxoma virus produces an edematous swelling within a few days after its inoculation into the skin. This rapidly increases in size and becomes hemorrhagic. Secondary myxomatous nodules arise in the vicinity and at about the same time the generalized symptoms appear. Virus can be detected in the blood within 48 hours after inoculation (Ahlström, 1940a). From this channel it invades the whole body, including the nervous system (Swan, 1941).

(*3*) *Variation.* By serial passage of the myxoma virus through the brains of rabbits, Hurst (1937b) was able to select a milder strain. Although this virus was not notably neurotropic, it was called the neuromyxoma virus. The original virus killed all rabbits by the ninth day no matter what the route of inoculation. The neuromyxoma strain when inoculated into the skin caused, in the majority of rabbits, a non-fatal myxomatosis in which recovery began after the ninth to twelfth day. However, it usually killed if it was injected into the testicles. The cells in the swellings resembled fibroblasts rather than myxoblasts.

That Hurst had selected a mutated form of the virus is indicated by the fact that although Rhodes (1938) used the same procedure in attempting to modify the virus, he did not succeed in isolating the same strain, for his killed upon intradermal inoculation. Nevertheless, that Rhodes had isolated a different mutant is indicated by the fact that at the twentieth intracerebral passage a change occurred in the type of lesion induced and was maintained in eight subsequent passages.

Rivers showed that rapid transfer of the virus from rabbit to rabbit in series enhances its virulence so that it kills the rabbit in 5-6 days before large characteristic lesions form. On the other hand, virus stored for a year or more in 50% glycerol at icebox temperature becomes attenuated, causes marked tumor-like growths and takes 3 weeks to kill. In infections with the virulent virus, the degenerative and inflammatory changes are more pronounced, whereas with the attenuated virus proliferative changes are more evident. The attenuated virus causes less sero-mucinous exudate from the lesions (Hyde and Gardner, 1933; Ahlström, 1940a).

D. ENVIRONMENT

Parker and Thompson (1942) showed that rabbits gradually adapted to live at a temperature of 41°C. failed to become infected when given multiple intradermal inoculations with various dilutions of a virus that normally caused 95-97% mortality. That the virus is not destroyed in such animals is shown by the development of the disease if the temperature is lowered too soon, for example, after 17 days at 41°C. At 36-38°C., circumscribed lesions developed that began to regress 6 to 8 days after inoculation and were followed by complete healing. In this temperature range, differences in the individuals of the different breeds of rabbits were revealed. The replicate inoculations on an individual rabbit were consistent but the concentration of virus necessary to cause infection in different individuals varied 1,000 to 10,000 times.

2. *Infectious Fibroma of Rabbits*

A. DESCRIPTION

Infectious fibroma of rabbits was discovered by Shope in 1931 in a wild cottontail rabbit that bore three subcutaneous tumors measuring about 1.5x2 cm. The three tumors were histologically identical and composed of connective tissue cells, sometimes arranged in whorls. Many of the cells resembled fibroblasts, spindle or polygonal in shape with large round or oval nuclei. Most, however, were of the small, thin connective tissue type with scant cytoplasm and thin spindle-shaped nuclei. Mitotic figures were scarce. Intercellular fibrils were quite abundant and largely collagenous in nature. There was a good blood system of small vessels, the walls of which were usually of only endothelial thickness. Lymphocytes and plasma cells surrounded some vessels. Eosinophiles and lymphocytes were not numerous in the tumor substance. However, the base of the tumor was composed of a mass of densely packed lymphocytes. Bulbous masses of epithelial cells projected down from the thickened epidermis into the substance of the tumor. Many of these epidermal cells were greatly enlarged with pale vesicular nuclei and with cytoplasmic eosinophilic inclusions. Shope pointed out that the tumor was not a typical spindle cell fibroma because of its inflammatory features and the odd hyperplasia (abnormal cell multiplication) and degeneration in the overlying epidermis. However, there was no evidence of necrosis preceding the proliferation of the connective tissue. The virus produces similar subcutaneous tumors in domestic rabbits although here epithelial effects are only occasional. In the domestic rabbit the course of the disease is shorter, regression of the tumors, with marked lymphocytic and leucocytic infiltration, usually being completed within 35 days after inoculation. No metastases and no deaths result from the infection. The virus has not produced infection in any animal other than the rabbit (Shope, 1932a).

In general, Shope's description was borne out by the investigations of Hurst (1938) and Ahlström (1938). In the early stages of the disease, the inflammatory reaction is the more marked and later, proliferative activity dominates. Ahlström considered that the virus acted on the undifferentiated mesenchyme in the widest sense, fibroma cells originating not only from fibroblasts but also from perivascular histiocytes and the endothelial cells of young capillaries. A rather pronounced edematous exudation accompanies the early inflammatory stage. He found characteristic basophilic cytoplasmic inclusions in the fibroma cells and eosinophilic granules in the affected cells of overlying epidermis. Necrosis preceded the resorption of the tumor.

Ahlström (1940a) considered fibroma and myxoma anatomically similar. Both attack the undifferentiated mesenchyme. In the early stages both cause proliferation of the endothelial cells of capillaries and venules. The endothelial and adventitial cells migrate into the surrounding tissues and along with adjacent undifferentiated mesenchyme cells form either fibroma or myxoma cells. The fibromas are largely cellular and are more tumor-like than the myxomas where exudate comprises so much of the growth.

Although the virus produces the fibroma only at the site of inoculation, under certain conditions generalized small red papules are produced on the skin of the rabbit (Andrewes, 1936). The virus can be recovered from blood, liver, lung, spleen, kidney, adrenal glands and regional lymph nodes but not from the frontal cortex or lumbar cord during the first week after intratesticular inoculation. Later the virus content in these tissues falls off. In the early stages the disease is therefore a generalized infection like myxoma. It differs from myxoma in not invading the nervous system and in the lower virus titer in all the tissues (Hurst, 1937c).

B. THE VIRUS

The fibroma virus has been classed as a strain of *Molitor myxomae* (Holmes, 1948).

(*1*) *Morphology.* Fibroma virus is filterable through Berkefeld V, N, and W filters (Shope, 1932b). It can be stored for long periods in glycerine. The diameter of the virus causing rabbit fibroma was estimated to be about 125-175 mμ by filtration through graded collodion membranes and to be about 126-141 mμ by centrifugation (Schlesinger and Andrewes, 1937). It is inactivated at 55°C.

(*2*) *Transmission.* The disease does not spread by contact (Shope, 1932a). It may be that in nature the virus is mechanically transmitted by biting arthropods because Philip (1942) obtained transmission of the virus to two rabbits by means of mixtures of three species of triatomid bugs (*Triatoma infestans,* T. *protracta* and *Rhodnius prolixus*). The successful transmissions occurred when the insects were fed for a time on the diseased animals and then transferred at once to healthy ones. When the insects, after feeding on lesions, were held for 12 or 71 days before being placed on healthy animals no transmission occurred. These insects are not known to infest rabbits where the disease occurs naturally.

In artificial inoculations, 6- to 9-day old tumors may be minced, ground with sand, suspended in 0.85% NaCl to give a 5% suspension and the supernatant used as inoculum. Subcutaneous or intratesticular inoculations were successful but intravenous, intraperitoneal or intracerebral inoculations were not. The success of intramuscular inoculations seemed to depend on whether the virus reached connective tissue layers between the muscle bundles (Shope, 1932a).

(*3*) *Variation.* Upon receipt of a sample of Shope's A isolate of the virus, Andrewes discovered that it caused acute inflammatory lesions which were at first similar to those caused by the original virus. However, when those of the latter were still enlarging in size, those of the new strain became necrotic, were massively infiltrated with lymphocytes and regressed. Shope's original A isolate of the virus then became known as the OA strain and the new inflammatory strain as IA. These two strains were shown to be related immunologically.

Shope found that at about the 18th passage of the fibroma virus through the domestic rabbit it lost its ability to produce fibromas and instead caused lesions which were predominantly inflammatory with lymphocytes and mononuclear cells replacing some of the fibroblast-like cells. The partly inflammatory and partly fibromatous character of these lesions was maintained in numerous passages of the "changed" virus through domestic rabbits. Passage through cottontails caused a transient recovery of the ability of the "changed" virus to cause fibromas. This was not true of the IA strain. The "changed" virus reaction could be duplicated by mixing the IA and OA strains and the evidence indicates that IA is a mutation that occurs repeatedly but which does not grow as well in the cottontail as the OA strain does. The strains grow at different relative rates in different domestic rabbits (Andrewes, 1936; Shope, 1936c; Andrewes and Shope, 1936).

3. Relationship Between Infectious Myxoma and Infectious Fibroma

There is abundant evidence derived from studies on the immunology and on the Berry-Dedrick transformation (to be described later) that the viruses of infectious fibroma and infectious myxoma are closely related.

A. IMMUNOLOGY

Domestic rabbits recovered from fibroma possess a high degree of resistance to natural contact infection with myxomatosis, most animals showing no illness whatever (Shope, 1938). When inoculated artificially, fibroma-recovered rabbits may show no reaction, a local lesion at the site of inoculation, a serious illness or even death. Serial intratesticular passage of the myxoma virus is possible in fibroma-recovered domestic rabbits, the lesions produced usually resembling those in the normal resistant cottontail. Intraperitoneal inoculation of fibroma virus does not result in fibroma, does not result in antibody production, and does not induce resistance to either fibroma or myxoma. The resistance to myxoma develops as early as 14 days and persists as long as 100 days after inoculation with fibroma (Shope

1932b, 1936b). Most domestic rabbits survive myxoma infection if the fibroma virus has been injected intradermally just 48 hours earlier (Hyde, 1939). The sera of fibroma-recovered domestic rabbits neutralize myxoma virus, often in high titer (Berry and Lichty, 1936; Lush, 1939).

It is rare that a domestic rabbit survives myxomatosis but when it does it is solidly resistant to infection with fibroma virus. In the cottontail, the myxoma virus causes only a localized fibromatous or myxomatous lesion that later regresses. Such animals are solidly immune to inoculation with the fibroma virus and their sera neutralize both viruses (Shope, 1936a; Berry and Lichty, 1936).

Extensive serological investigations have demonstrated that the antibodies induced in rabbits by each of these viruses not only neutralize both viruses but agglutinate them and fix complement in their presence (Ledingham, 1937; Rivers and Ward, 1937; Lush, 1939; Hyde, 1939; Shaffer, 1941).

Rivers and Ward (1937) showed that virus-free filtrates of emulsions from skin lesions or of serum from animals acutely ill with myxomatosis contain a soluble substance precipitating specifically with anti-myxoma serum and to a lesser extent with anti-fibroma serum. The reaction between this soluble antigen and anti-myxoma serum was shown to fix complement (Lush, 1939). The soluble antigen can be divided into two serologically distinguishable fractions, A and B, by fractional precipitation with $(NH_4)_2SO_4$ (Smadel, Ward and Rivers, 1940). Injection of rabbits with the soluble antigens induces formation of precipitating antibodies to them but does not induce immunity to myxoma, neuromyxoma or fibroma viruses (Rivers, Ward and Smadel, 1939). The soluble antigens occur in infected chorio-allantoic membranes of the chicken egg (Hoffstadt and Pilcher, 1939; Teixeira and Smadel, 1941). Soluble substances fixing complement with anti-fibroma serum were demonstrated in fibroma-infected rabbits and these were shown to be closely related to similar substances in myxoma-infected rabbits (Shaffer, 1941).

B. THE BERRY-DEDRICK TRANSFORMATION

In 1936 Berry and Dedrick (1936a) reported that if domestic rabbits were inoculated with a mixture of fibroma virus and heat-inactivated myxoma virus, some of them developed myxomatosis. Since the myxoma virus is inactivated by a temperature of 55°C. for 10 minutes and the transformation can be accomplished with myxoma virus heated as high as 75°C. (occasionally even 80°C.) for 30 minutes, it is certain that all the myxoma virus used in such transformation experiments has been inactivated. Moreover, adequate controls inoculated with the inactivated myxoma virus fail to become diseased. Shope's A, B, C, D, and E isolates, the IA and OA strains and 2 isolates of the fibroma virus made by Berry and his colleagues have all produced ordinary myxoma virus in transformation experiments. Many inactivated isolates and strains of the myxoma virus have been successfully employed to yield active myxoma virus. When inactivated neuromyxoma or Berry's 80A myxoma virus is used, the resulting disease corresponds respectively with that expected from the neuromyxoma or 80A virus. Myxoma virus inactivated by ultraviolet light may also be used (Berry, 1940). The transformation can be accomplished in the cottontail rabbit but with more difficulty than in the domestic rabbit. Transformation can be accomplished if the inactivated myxoma virus and the fibroma virus are injected separately at different sites and at different times (Berry, 1937). The transformation cannot be effected in fibroma-recovered rabbits (Berry and Dedrick, 1936b) nor in the membranes of the chicken egg (Hoffstadt and Pilcher, 1941), in neither of which does the fibroma virus grow. The production of fibroma virus from inactivated fibroma virus and active myxoma virus has not been reported. The transformation phenomenon has been confirmed by other workers, among them Hurst (1937c) and Gardner and Hyde (1942).

4. *Combined Effect of Tar and Fibroma Virus*

A single intramuscular injection of about 0.2 cc. of tar on the same day that rabbits are inoculated with fibroma virus has a marked effect on the course of the disease. Intravenous injections of the virus are followed by a generalized, sometimes fatal, fibromatosis absent in untarred animals. Intradermal inoculations, following tarring, cause fibromas that do not start to regress until several weeks later than those in untarred rabbits. Sometimes they grow progressively and invasively until they cause the death of the host.

The IA strain of the virus does not have these effects in tarred rabbits. Rabbits receiving tar alone usually look well and maintain or increase their body weight although there may be slight liver damage. Nevertheless, the tar has a generalized effect on the body as revealed by the changed disease. If the rabbits are not inoculated until some months after tarring stops, the rabbits react normally. Inoculated, tarred rabbits develop antibodies to the virus and become immune to re-inoculation. The virus recoverable from tarred rabbits is unchanged fibroma virus. The fibromas in tarred rabbits are more cellular and look more like true neoplasms than the normal growths (Andrewes, Ahlström, Foulds and Gye, 1937; Ahlström and Andrewes, 1938).

In two cases following intravenous injection of the virus, sarcomas developed at the sites of the tar injections. One of these was transplantable, the other not. At first, regression of the transplanted sarcoma was common but later many of the rabbits showed progressive growths. Some showed metastasis. The fibroma virus could not be demonstrated in the sarcoma by inoculation of healthy animals or by the presence of antibodies to the virus in host rabbits. In spite of this it seems probable that the combined effect of the tar and the virus was the cause of the sarcomas because Andrewes and Ahlström (1938) could find no previous report of success in producing sarcomas in rabbits by tarring alone.

Benzpyrene and other carcinogenic chemicals have a similar effect to that of tar (Ahlström and Andrewes, 1938). The administration of 300 to 700 *r* of X-irradiation to the whole body of the rabbit 24 hours before inoculation with fibroma virus also causes effects similar to tarring. The irradiated animals become resistant to re-inoculation more slowly than unirradiated ones (Clemmesen, 1939). Clemmesen thought the increased severity of the disease following irradiation was due to this fact.

5. *Combined Effect of Tar and Myxoma Virus*

The myxoma virus in fibroma-recovered rabbits ordinarily produces a local tumor that regresses after 1-2 weeks. When the myxoma virus was inoculated after an intramuscular injection of tar, the lesions grew larger, regression was delayed as much as 30 days, and the proliferating cells were more closely packed, better preserved and more tumor-like than would otherwise be the case. This result was achieved only with myxoma virus attenuated by long storage and only by injecting it at certain stages in the development of the fibroma immunity. The tarring did not make the rabbits more susceptible to the myxoma virus although it changed the reaction in this manner (Ahlström, 1940b).

VII. Infectious Papillomatosis (Warts) of Rabbits

1. *Introduction*

Cottontail rabbits (*Sylvilagus floridanus* Allen) in the middle western United States (Iowa, Kansas, Oklahoma and Texas) quite commonly bear the wart-like growths of this disease. Since it was first brought to the attention of the scientific world (Shope, 1933), it has been the object of many investigations.

2. *Papillomas of Cottontails*

A. Morphology

In cottontail rabbits the warts ordinarily cause no apparent discomfort or generalized illness. A rabbit may bear one wart, or papilloma, or it may carry so many as to be almost covered by them. Usually the papillomas occur on the inner surface of the thighs, on the abdomen, or about the neck and shoulders.

About 6-30 days after experimental infection occurs, minute, barely visible elevations appear on the skin. The more concentrated the virus in the inoculum the shorter the time before the warts appear and this relationship may be employed to assay virus preparations (Bryan and Beard, 1941). The growths usually become warty 16 to 20 days after they first appear or when they have attained a height and diameter of about 3 mm., although the time of this change is influenced by the character of the inoculum. By the end of 6 weeks most warts have reached a height of 1.2 to 1.5 cm. Some grow larger and others regress. The warts are keratinized (horny) and are black or grayish in color. Pigmentation is determined by the presence or absence of melanoblasts in the epidermis affected. Although the melanoblasts appear not to be directly affected by the virus (*Molitor sylvilagi* H.), they participate in the growth (Beard, 1935). The warts frequently have an irregular or fissured upper surface. The lateral surfaces appear vertically striated because each growth is composed of closely packed and almost homogeneous vertical strands of tissue. The center of the diseased tissue is usually white or pinkish and fleshy. The warts may be knocked or pulled off fairly easily when full grown. When this happens a rather freely bleeding surface is left which usually heals without complications, though sometimes a second papilloma will develop at the site (Shope, 1933). There is no evidence of virus from primary warts spreading to other parts of the same animal and initiating secondary growths (Rous and Beard, 1934b). The papillomas are often vigorous at the start, and then although still comprised of proliferating cells, they remain stationary in size for many months. In more than half the cottontail rabbits infected by inoculation, the warts retrogress sooner or later. In the minority of cases, the papillomas may persist until death, that is, up to nearly 2 years (Rous, Kidd and Beard, 1936).

B. HISTOLOGY

The growths arise from the basal cells of the epidermis. Sections of the early stages show rapidly multiplying epithelial cells. These differ sharply from normal epithelial cells (Rous and Beard, 1934b) and cause definite localized thickenings. The growing masses of cells project down into the underlying tissue and extend laterally under the normal epithelium. In warts visible to the naked eye, mitoses are abundant even in cells some distance from the germinal layer. By the time the warts project as papillae, the cells show great variation in size. The tips of the papillae become necrotic as early as the 20th day, although mitoses continue to be numerous in the tissue below. The mature wart consists of closely arrayed, branching, filiform, epidermal processes with very narrow connective tissue cores. The germinal cells of the Malpighian layer are taller and narrower than normal and the polygonal and granular cell layers are greatly increased in depth. Monster cells with enormous vesicular nuclei occur, but no definite cellular inclusions are present. Some infiltration of the underlying tissue with mononuclear and polymorphonuclear leucocytes may occur (Hurst, in Shope, 1933). Frequently, however, there is no inflammatory reaction around young papillomas, and when there is, it may be due to wounds, necrosis, or bacteria and not to the papilloma as such (Rous and Beard, 1934b). In old warts the keratinized papilloma cells at the tip are not desquamated or scaled off as the growth increases in size but form a dry, elastic or horny covering for the mass of moist, amorphous, keratinized cells they enclose (Bryan and Beard, 1941).

3. *The Virus*

The agent responsible for papillomatosis is filterable through Berkefeld filters that retain bacteria. It is a resistant virus, withstanding a temperature of 67°C. for 30 minutes but not 70°C. (Shope, 1933). It can be preserved in the refrigerator for several years at least, in warts stored in a mixture of 50% glycerol and 50% physiological salt solution. The virus is stable between pH3.0 and 7.5 (Bryan and Beard, 1941).

The papilloma virus has a highly specific affinity for the epithelium of the skin. It does not infect the epithelium of other organs or even embryonic skin (Shope, 1933; Rous and Beard, 1934a).

The rabbit papilloma virus is apparently antigenically distinct from the virus causing papillomas of cattle and that causing papillomas in dogs (Beard and Kidd, 1936).

The virus can be concentrated and purified by differential centrifugation (Beard and Wyckoff, 1937). The warts are mostly a mass of cell debris comprised of particles of pigment, keratin (an insoluble protein that is the basic substance in skin and hair) and insoluble denatured protein. Extraction of the warts ground with sand in 10-20 times their weight of 0.9% NaCl for 12 hours removes about 90% of the virus. The amount of virus (measured as protein) that can be recovered from papillomas varies from 0.008 mg. to 1 mg. per g. of wart tissue. Fortunately, because of the nature of the warts the extracts contain little of the viscous proteins ordinarily so difficult to eliminate from extracts of animal tissues.

The virus has been obtained in a highly purified state as tested by the analytical ultracentrifuge, diffusion experiments (Neurath *et al.,* 1941), electrophoretic measurements (Sharp, Taylor, Beard and Beard, 1942a) and electron micrographs (Sharp, Taylor, Hook and Beard, 1946).

Some viruses appear to take up or release water depending on the osmotic properties of solutions in which they are suspended. In order to reduce possible osmotic effects in the study of papilloma virus density, bovine serum albumin solutions of various concentrations and densities were used as a medium for careful sedimentation studies of the virus in the ultracentrifuge. From such studies, the density of the virus in aqueous suspension was calculated to be 1.133. Water to the amount of 58% was determined to be associated with the virus particles and the hydrated units were calculated to have a diameter of 66 mμ (Sharp, Taylor and Beard, 1946). Under the electron microscope, the virus shadowed with gold appears as a sphere that has been flattened a little against the plastic film as a result of the dessication and heating necessary to the technique (Sharp, Taylor, Hook and Beard, 1946). Dessication probably also accounts, in part, for the fact that under the electron microscope the particles measure only about 44 mμ in diameter (Sharp, Taylor, Beard and Beard, 1942b).

Analysis of purified papilloma virus preparations indicates the following percentages of elements expressed as fractions of the dry weight: C 49.56, H 7.15, N 14.99, P 0.944, S 2.2 and ash 2.5 (Beard, Bryan and Wyckoff, 1939). The virus shows no evidence of ribonucleic acid, but between 6.8 and 8.7% of its dry weight consists of thymus nucleic acid. The evidence indicates that it also contains 1.46% fat (Taylor, Beard, Sharp and Beard, 1942). As a result of their investigations (Sharp, Taylor and Beard, 1946), the authors expressed the opinion that the virus particles had properties more like those of a living organism than those of a molecule.

4. *Papillomas on Domestic Rabbits*

The virus causes large vigorously growing papillomas on domestic rabbits (*Oryctolagus cuniculus* L.) but when such growths are employed as a source of virus for inoculations on either cottontail or domestic rabbits, they ordinarily prove noninfectious (Shope, 1933). Centrifugal techniques that have yielded highly infectious preparations from cottontail rabbit papillomas have failed to yield virus from domestic rabbit papillomas (Beard and Wyckoff, 1937; Bryan and Beard, 1941). However, it is possible to transmit some strains of the virus in series through domestic rabbits, though with difficulty. There are indications that in the process the virus becomes somewhat adapted to domestic rabbits (Shope, 1935). Moreover, when extracts from noninfectious domestic rabbit papillomas are injected into other rabbits, the animals become immune to subsequent inoculations with infectious virus extracts, and they develop neutralizing antibodies in their blood. Such results indicate that the virus is present in noninfectious domestic rabbit papillomas (Shope, 1937).

The technique of inoculating rabbits has been greatly improved during the experimental study of the disease. In early studies, fluid containing the virus was rubbed on skin that had been shaved and scarified with sandpaper until there occurred a barely perceptible oozing of blood-tinged fluid (Shope, 1933). However, if one paints the shaven skin 4 to 7 times at 2- to 7-day intervals with 0.3% methylcholanthrene in benzene or with a 50-50 mixture of turpentine and acetone, the skin forms a thick proliferating layer, and, after scarification, it is then susceptible to dilutions of virus preparations 10 to 100 times greater than is unpainted skin. If the inoculated skin is immediately covered with paraffined gauze and sealed in with adhesive tape, necrosis and scabbing are almost completely prevented and infections are obtained with dilutions an additional 10 or 100 times greater. The over-all increase in sensitivity over the original method amounts to 100 to 10,000 times. With such technique, virus can be demonstrated in domestic rabbit papillomas that would otherwise be classed as noninfectious. There is nevertheless much less virus in such warts than there is in cottontail papillomas (Friedewald and Kidd, 1944; Friedewald, 1944).

5. *Immunity*

It was observed early in the study of the disease that rabbits bearing warts are partially or completely immune to re-infection and that their blood contains antibodies that neutralize the virus (Shope, 1933). The neutralizing power of the blood develops soon after the papillomas appear, and in general the more papillomatous tissue the rabbit carries the faster the neutralizing ability increases. Development of neutralizing antibodies in the blood coincides with increasing resistance to re-infection but seems to have no effect on the growth of papillomas already established.

Serum from immune animals also fixes complement specifically in the presence of the virus (Kidd, 1938b). Filtration, heat treatment, and pH experiments show that the virus and the complement-binding antigen parallel each other, indicating that the complement-binding antigen is the virus (Kidd, 1938c). Moreover, the complement-fixing and neutralizing activities always parallel each other showing that a single antibody is responsible for both effects (Friedewald and Kidd, 1940). The antibody also causes flocculation of the virus when mixed with it in optimal proportions. In other words, the same antigen, namely, the virus, and the same antibody are involved in the neutralizing, complement-fixing and precipitin reactions. Antibody and virus are each capable of absorbing the other in great excess *in vitro*. The union between antibody and virus *in vitro* cannot be dissociated in any demonstrable degree by either dilution or centrifugation. A small proportion of virus particles remains infectious in mixtures of antibody and virus except where the antibody titer is very high. In neutralizing virus the antibody does not alter or attenuate it but reduces the number of infective particles (Kidd, Beard and Rous, 1936a). There appears to be no soluble antigen produced by this virus in contrast to some others. When extracts of papillomas are centrifuged at high speed the supernatant does not react with antibody; all of the reacting material is in the sediment containing the virus (Friedewald and Kidd, 1940).

The antibody as well as the virus occurs in the papillomas themselves, and there it may act as an inhibitor. In domestic rabbit papillomas antibody is usually present in excess over virus whereas in the papillomas of cottontails the reverse is usually true (Friedewald, 1940).

Rabbits may be immunized against the disease by injecting virus intraperitoneally in such a way that infection of the skin is avoided. The animals develop antibodies and become resistant or immune to infection (Shope, 1937).

Large, fissured papillomas of cottontails may contain pockets filled with blood and serum. When the blood of the rabbit has a high antibody content such papillomas may be noninfectious. Usually extracts of such papillomas injected into rabbits induce the formation of antibody indicating that virus is present in the extract. However, sometimes the antibody content of the papilloma extracts is so high that they are nonantigenic as well as noninfectious. Such extracts may transfer enough antibody to injected rabbits as to render them passively resistant to re-infection. The fact that noninfectious extracts may be nonantigenic therefore does not mean that virus is absent. In smaller, discrete, papillomas of cottontails, the virus can usually be recovered irrespective of the antibody content of the blood (Kidd, 1939; Kidd, 1941).

In addition to the phenomenon of acquired immunity, there also exist variations in the resistance or susceptibility of individual rabbits (Friedewald and Kidd, 1944) which probably depend on their genetic constitution.

6. Regression of the Papillomas

Retrogression of the papillomas occurs in a minority of domestic rabbits and a majority of cottontails. The greater the number of papillomas initially produced the sooner regression occurs and the more quickly it is consummated. When a number of animals are each inoculated with a number of virus sources differing in pathogenicity the growths on any one animal tend to enlarge or retrogress together. The retrogression appears to depend on a generalized resistance of host origin. During regression the virus may remain highly infectious. The virus antibody content of the blood does not seem to be a factor. In some rabbits the growths enlarge progressively, although the blood of the host has a high virus antibody content while in other rabbits with regressing papillomas the antibody content of the host may be low. Histologically the retrogression is accompanied by the same cellular changes that are directed against transplanted tissues that retrogress. All indications point to the resistance being directed against the cells and not against the virus. During regression the papilloma cells do not revert to normal cells but instead mature and die as papilloma cells (Beard and Rous, 1934; Kidd, Beard and Rous, 1936a; Kidd, 1938a).

Roentgen irradiation of the papillomas of domestic and cottontail rabbits causes eventual death of the cells and rapid regression of the papillomas without having any appreciable effect on the virus they contain (Friedewald and Anderson, 1943).

7. *Natural Progression to Cancer in Domestic Rabbits*

If bits of young papilloma tissue are implanted in the internal organs of the rabbit from which they came, growth will occur. In the new sites the papilloma tissue proliferates actively, often invading and destroying adjacent tissue. Excision of such growths may result in accidental dissemination of the tumor tissue or recurrence of the growth at the original focus. Penetration into the blood and lymph vessels surrounding such growths frequently occurs. A cellular reaction about the tumor may occur, or may be absent, particularly if proliferation is rapid (Rous and Beard, 1934a). Usually, rabbits other than the one from which the papilloma tissue came are resistant to implantation with the wart tissue although susceptible to the virus it contains. This resistance is probably directed against cells of a foreign genetic constitution and has nothing to do with resistance to the virus (Rous and Beard, 1934b).

The papillomas produced on domestic rabbits generally grow vigorously, frequently becoming large enough to prove fatal. Progressive changes in the direction of malignancy occur, and after 200 days or so, cancer is a common occurrence. However, this outcome is not inevitable; in a minority of domestic rabbits regression of the papillomas takes place (Rous and Beard, 1935). By gradual stages, the papillomas progress to cystic papilloma, malignant papilloma and squamous cell carcinoma. The malignant, metastasizing tumors that develop from the papillomas in the domestic rabbit are all cutaneous in origin. The transition to malignancy may occur over varying distances beneath the papilloma, but as a cellular process, it appears to be gradual. It always proceeds in the same direction, that of greater malignancy. Although the original papilloma is remarkably constant in its morphology, there is a great variety in the individual tumors that arise from it. Different ones appear to represent different stages of the transformation process or to be stabilized, for a time at least, at a particular stage. In the extreme, there is little cell differentiation and frequent metastasis. For a more detailed account of the evolution to cancer, the reader should consult the original description of these changes (Rous and Beard, 1935).

The shorter the incubation period and the more vigorous the growth of the papillomas, the more likely is cancer to ensue and the greater the tendency to have multiple cancer foci. The more concentrated the virus used in inoculating, the more likely are the papillomas to produce cancers. Even among confluent masses of papillomas, those starting from more concentrated virus suspensions give rise to cancer more frequently than those starting from less concentrated preparations. However, there also appear to be strains of virus differing in their carcinogenic abilities because even at high dilution some samples of virus consistently cause vigorous growths and others cause warts that regress.

Individual rabbits differ in their susceptibility to the transformation, and in the most favorable rabbits, numerous malignant changes occur. There is a tendency for all growths on an animal to enlarge or retrogress together. Even so, some virus infected cells and their progeny are more liable to the change to cancer than others on the same rabbit or even in the same papilloma. Correlated with this are differences in pigmentation and rate of growth in the cell families. The cancers arise most frequently on pigmented areas of the skin, although the cell families most likely to result in cancer are themselves non-pigmented or soon become so (Rous, Kidd and Beard, 1936). Extracts of the cancers are usually noninfectious. However, by special inoculation techniques virus can be demonstrated in small amounts in some cancers in early passages in new born rabbits (Smith, Kidd and Rous, 1947). The cancers contain an inhibitor of the virus (Syverton and Berry, 1935; Kidd and Rous, 1940a). This inhibitor appears to be identical with the virus antibody (Friedewald, 1940).

Most of the cancers that originate from virus-induced papillomas are not transplantable, or transplantable with great difficulty to rabbits other than the one in which they originate,—not a surprising result when the animals are not homozygous. However, one squamous cell carcinoma so derived, called Carcinoma V2, has been successfully transferred through many rabbits in series. It now grows rapidly in a considerable proportion of hosts, metastasizes frequently and kills hosts early. The tumor has none of the morphological features of the papilloma from which it came. Extracts of the V2 carcinoma are noninfectious. During the first 22 serial passages in rabbits the animals in which the tumor grew developed antibodies to the papilloma virus in high titer. Normal rabbits and rabbits bearing other types of tumors did not. It seems virtually certain therefore that the virus responsible for the tumor from which the cancer developed was still present in the growth during this period. The cancer was grown in series for a period of almost 8 months through 5 successive groups of rabbits hyperimmunized against the virus. In these hosts the cancer grew as well as in normal rabbits, and when it was returned to normal rabbits, the latter still developed antibodies to the papilloma virus. This procedure had been found effective in ridding other cancers of "passenger" viruses, that is, viruses they have acquired in passage through virus-infected hosts. As a result of these experiments, it was thought that the papilloma virus might have a special relationship to the V2 carcinoma (Kidd, Beard and Rous, 1936b; Kidd and Rous, 1940b; Kidd, 1942). However, experiments with the 46th and 50th passages of the cancer showed that the host rabbits were no longer immunized against the papilloma virus and it now seems probable that the virus is no longer present in the growth. Nevertheless, the carcinoma still has the same morphology (Smith, Kidd and Rous, 1947).

Papillomas produced by the virus on jack rabbits (*Lepus californicus* Gray) and snowshoe rabbits (*Lepus americanus* Erxleben) become cancerous in much the same way as those on domestic rabbits (Kidd and Rous, 1940a).

Although cancer may develop naturally from papillomas in cottontails, most cottontails acquire a resistance to the continued growth of the warts and when cancer does occur in this species the growths are frequently multiple indicating that the individual rabbit may be different in this respect from the rest of the species.

8. *Progression to Cancer Aided by Chemicals*

Virus injected intravenously into rabbits which previously have had patches of skin tarred becomes localized in these areas and will produce papillomas. If high concentrations of papilloma virus are injected intravenously into susceptible domestic rabbits with patches of skin that have been tarred repeatedly for a long time (for example, twice weekly for about 3 months) the virus induces promptly, in the tarred skin, a considerable variety of benign and malignant tumors. To obtain this result the tarring should be continued nearly to the extent that will produce tar tumors. Strangely enough, however, some rabbits that already have tar tumors produce only papillomas when virus is injected whereas others that show no outward effects of the tarring develop anomalous tumors or cancers. Frequently, these growths have a multicentric origin as indicated by their composite character and the speed with which they arise. The benign tumors so produced have papillomatous characteristics, and the malignant tumors resemble those that arise naturally from ordinary virus papillomas. This variety of effects must be attributed to changes already caused in individual cells by the tarring (Rous and Kidd, 1938; Kidd and Rous, 1938).

Benign tumors elicited on the skin of domestic rabbits by prolonged tarring are unable to establish themselves when implanted in the rabbit from which they came. However, if the papilloma virus is added to the finely cut tar tumor tissue before implantation, many of the tumors are then able to establish themselves. Some of the tumors are stimulated to active proliferation without change in their morphology; some are converted to virus papillomas, and still others have a blend of characteristics of both types of growth. Some tar tumors so treated may become cancerous at once without intervening papillomatosis. Some slow growing tar cancers are stimulated to more rapid growth. However, on some tar tumors it has no effect. Since the virus has been shown to have these effects on tar tumors, it has been suggested that it may have the same effect on the tumors it itself initiates (Rous and Kidd, 1940).

When a 0.3% solution of methylcholanthrene in ether containing 2% mineral oil is applied to virus papillomas, striking results are secured. If the applications are begun as soon as the skin inoculated with virus begins to heal and are continued thrice weekly for 2 to 4½ months, numerous cancers arise with unprecedented rapidity from a single papillomatous mass. The later applications are made after stripping away the keratinized layer overlying the growths. On domestic rabbits methylcholanthrene alone does not produce papillomas for nearly 2 months, usually not till much later, whereas cancer arises only after 9 months to 2 years and infrequently even then. As already described, the virus alone, on the other hand, immediately starts papillomas that may become cancerous in 6 months to a year. The cancers induced by the above treatment resemble histologically those elicited by the virus alone. Rabbits that show little or no effect on a patch of skin treated with the chemical alone may have many cancers develop on a patch of treated papillomas and vice versa. Many of the cancers produced have a histology that continues to show the effects of the virus. Variation of the virus has been suggested as a possible cause of the cell changes that occur when papilloma cells become cancerous. Tar applications have similar effects. Scharlach R in olive oil, on the other hand, will cause papillomas to proliferate wildly and appear cancerous, but when applications are stopped the growths revert to the papillomatous state (Rous and Friedewald, 1941 and 1944).

VIII. Mammary Carcinoma of the Mouse

1. *Introduction*

The extensive scientific literature dealing with mammary carcinoma of the mouse has been thoroughly reviewed in several excellent treatises (Members Nat. Cancer Inst., 1945; Bittner, 1947, a, b; Shimkin and Andervont, 1945). Except where otherwise indicated the following account has been drawn from these reviews. Readers interested in more detailed information about the disease and about the many scientists who have contributed to our knowledge of it, may consult these publications for references to the original literature.

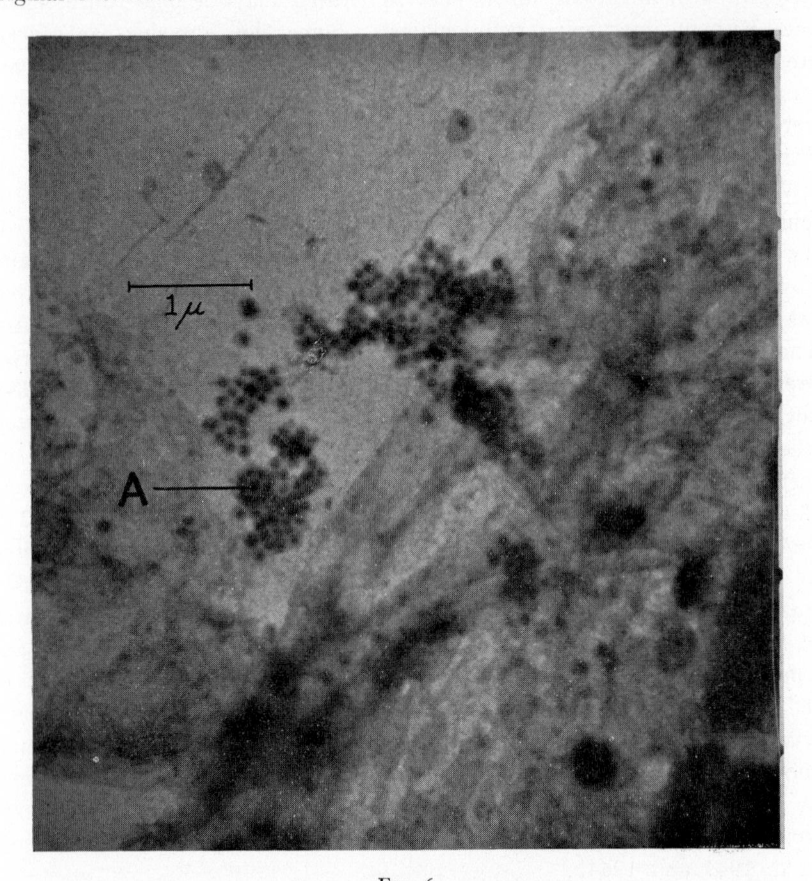

Fig. 6

Clumps of virus-like particles in a cell from a mammary carcinoma of the mouse. The individual particles have a dense center and a less dense periphery and there is a distinct variation in size. An interesting rosette arrangement of the particles may be seen at A. (Courtesy of the *Journal of Experimental Medicine*)

Mammary carcinoma is a common disease in the mouse. The mammary tumors are confined in nature to the female of the species; hormones, genes and a virus are involved in their causation.

2. *The Tumor*

The mammary tissue in the normal female mouse is comprised of five pairs of glands and is very extensive, running from behind the ears to the base of the tail. During lactation it includes a considerable portion of the subcutaneous tissues between these two regions. Invariably the tumors arise in the mammary tissue and are most frequent where the bulk of that tissue is greatest.

The growths are usually enclosed in an indistinct capsule and at autopsy can be readily shelled out of the surrounding tissue. Sometimes, however, they are adherent to neighboring structures because of an inflammatory reaction and infiltrative extensions. Metastases are infrequent but may occur in the lungs and rarely in other internal organs. The relative infrequency of metastases in this disease may be due to the looseness of the connective tissue, the ready expansibility of the region in which the tumor grows, the small size of the lymphatic channels and the short life span of the mouse. Spontaneous regression of the tumors is extremely rare. The tumors are transplantable and were considered malignant and comparable to carcinoma in man before any virus involvement was demonstrated. Usually, death of the host mouse is due to the tumors growing to such a size that they interfere with the movement and feeding of the animal; sometimes it is brought about by necrosis and secondary infection of the tumors.

The first microscopic evidence of tumor development is considered to be a nodular hypertrophy of the mammary epithelium varying from a slight increase in the number of normal acini to definite nodules. The changes do not appear to arise in a single cell or even in a few scattered single cells but whole areas of the mammary epithelium seem to begin to proliferate simultaneously. Only cells of epidermal origin become tumorous. Their nuclei cannot be distinguished from those of normal cells although the pattern of the Golgi material is different. Involvement of more than one gland is common. There exist a great many intergrading tumorous conditions between these first stages and definite cancer. Early investigators established the similarity between these mammary tumors in the mouse and certain breast cancers in man. All the histologic groups trace back to the normal structure of the mammary gland through a basic type of acinous structure which closely resembles the alveoli or ultimate lobules of the normal mammary gland. The histologic variations include solid cell forms, cystic and hemorrhagic types, keratinizing tumors and forms which on transplantation developed spindle-cell tumors. It seems obvious therefore that the mammary gland epithelium is capable of producing tumors of many morphologic forms. Two or more of these forms may be present in the same tumor and one form grades into another so that they are not sharply distinguishable one from another. Tumors may evolve at various stages in their growth from a glandular form to a less glandular, more solid type.

Biochemically, mammary carcinoma is like other tumor growth. The tissue accumulates more lactic acid than normal tissue when supplied glucose under aerobic conditions. It has a lower pH and a higher rate of anaerobic glycolysis than most normal tissues. The vitamin concentration is near the upper level for other growths and the enzyme pattern is similar to that of other mouse tumors. The carcinomas depress the catalase activity of the liver and kidney of mice bearing them and lower the hemoglobin level.

3. *The Virus*

The experimental study of mammary carcinoma of the mouse began early in the present century. Except for some early suggestions that it might be caused by a virus little attention was given to this hypothesis until genetic investigations culminated in crosses between inbred lines of mice having low tumor incidence (about 1%) and others having high tumor incidence (about 90%). When crosses were made between infected fathers from low tumor incidence strains and infected mothers from high incidence strains the progeny had a high rate of tumor development. Crosses in the reverse direction gave progeny with a low tumor rate. These results clearly indicated that some factor not transmitted in the chromosomes was important in determining the tumor rate in the progeny of such crosses. Experiments to determine whether this agent was transmitted to the next generation in the cytoplasm of the egg, from the uterus to the young embryo or from the mother's milk to the suckling mice have shown unmistakably that the agent reaches the young by way of the mother's milk. This may be shown by removing the young from highly susceptible mothers before or immediately after birth and nursing them only on noninfected females.

The agent is a virus with most intriguing properties. One of the most remarkable things about this virus is that it went undiscovered for about 30 years. During this time mammary carcinoma of the mouse was the object of intensive investigation in many laboratories in a number of different countries. The fact that the virus remained hidden so long is mentioned not in any way to reflect on the scientists who studied this disease but to emphasize the difficulties in the way of demonstrating virus in some tumors even when the host is such an excellent experimental animal as the mouse.

The virus, so important in the etiology of mouse mammary carcinoma, is not necessary for other kinds of mouse tumors. Transfer of the virus to other species such as deer mice (*Peromyscus*) has not caused tumors. However, the virus can be injected into developing chick embryos and recovered after 9 serial passages. The virus can be transmitted through many generations of susceptible mice without detectable dilution and is present in the milk of infected susceptible mice throughout the lactation period. It may be transmitted through the milk of infected animals that do not themselves develop mammary tumors. The young become thoroughly infected by nursing susceptible infected mothers for the first day after birth. Because of the high concentration of the virus in the milk it is probable that there is a chance of infection with even the shortest periods of nursing. Young mice that have acquired the virus from their mothers appear perfectly healthy until 6-24 months later when tumors will begin to develop in susceptible females. Animals are susceptible until about 4 or 5 weeks of age and become increasingly resistant to successful inoculation as they grow older. Heavily inoculated adult mice may not develop tumors but may pass on the virus so that their young do.

Although the only symptoms of disease occur in the cells of the mammary epithelium, the virus has been recovered by inoculating susceptible healthy animals, not only with extracts from the mammary tumors but also with extracts from every tissue of infected mice that has been thoroughly tested. These include the spleen, thymus, seminal vesicle, liver and lactating mammary gland. It has also been recovered from the serum and from red blood cells.

The virus of mammary carcinoma of the mouse passes through filters that retain bacteria and, of course, host cells, but it is not dializable. That it is present in high concentration in some tissues is indicated by the fact that some tissue extracts are infective when diluted 1 to 1,000,000. It is destroyed by a temperature of 61°C. for 30 minutes. In 50% glycerin in saline it remains active for 7-9 days. The virus has been shown by Dmochowski (Imp. Cancer Res. Fund Ann. Rept., 1946) to remain active for at least 2 years in tumor tissue dessicated in vacuo over phosphorus pentoxide and stored in the ice chest.

The virus is antigenic in rats and rabbits. Injection of rats and rabbits with extracts containing the virus results in the formation of antibodies that will neutralize the virus *in vitro*. If the antibodies are given to mice before they are inoculated with the virus they fail to develop mammary tumors. Administration of the antibodies after the animals receive the virus has no effect.

Early work (Visscher *et al.*, 1942; Bryan *et al.*, 1942) demonstrating that the virus is sedimentable in the ultracentrifuge has been confirmed and extended. Electron micrographs of some preparations have revealed bodies that may be virus but the identity of such particles with the virus has not yet been demonstrated (Graff *et al.*, 1947; Passey *et al.*, 1947). Recently electron micrographs have been obtained showing what may be the virus in the tumor cells (Porter and Thompson, 1948). The bodies photographed by Porter and Thompson are spherical, vary considerably in size and show an inner dense sphere about 75 mμ in diameter and an outer less dense zone which makes the over-all diameter about 130 mμ (Fig. 6). It should be pointed out that there is a very great difference in the sizes of the bodies suspected of being the virus by different workers.

4. *The Genes*

More than 20 years before the presence of the virus was demonstrated, it was well established that heredity had an important influence on the incidence of mammary tumors in mice. It is now known that many genetic factors in the mouse affect the tumor incidence by determining the susceptibility of the mammary tissue to the virus or to the hormones and by affecting the hormone system itself. Inbred strains with high, low and intermediate tumor rates can be selected. In some inbred strains of mice virgin females have a low incidence and breeding females a high incidence, whereas in other inbred strains the virgins have as high a rate as their breeding sisters. Some factors affecting the development of mammary tumors are linked with known single factor traits; in one case lower incidence is linked with a coat-color gene known as lethal yellow and in another case higher incidence is linked with a gene for brown coat color.

Inbred resistant strains of mice exist with various degrees of immunity to the virus. If nursed when young by highly susceptible infected mothers a certain percentage of them usually develop mammary tumors (in one such case about 10%). Different incidences in different low incidence lines so tested suggest different susceptibilities and many genetic factors exerting an influence. That these resistant lines of mice have a lower concentration of virus in their milk seems clear. This may be one reason why the tumor incidence in certain resistant lines drops within a few generations after an initial increase due to heavy inoculation with the virus. Resistant individuals may pass on the virus in their milk even though they do not develop tumors themselves.

It should be mentioned in passing that an inbred strain of mice may be very susceptible to the mammary carcinoma virus and yet have a low incidence of other types of tumors and vice versa. In other words there is no known linkage between the hereditary factors influencing susceptibility to the virus, and genes affecting the incidence of other types of tumors.

5. *The Hormones*

The fact that mammary carcinoma of the mouse appears in the female but not in the male suggests in itself that the sex hormones have an important effect on the disease. The mammary gland is rudimentary in the male. Removal of the ovaries from very young females may completely inhibit or greatly delay the development of mammary tumors. On the other hand, castrated males of an infected susceptible stock into which ovaries are successfully grafted will develop mammary tumors. Also when castrated susceptible infected males are supplied with female sex hormones, either natural or synthetic, they may be induced to develop mammary tumors. Estrone, estradiol, equilin, equilenin, diethylstilbestrol and triphenylethylene have been successfully employed in such experiments. In general, the incidence of the tumors in estrogen-treated males belonging to different infected stocks parallels the incidence of the disease in females of the same lines. The incidence tends to increase with increasing dose of estrogenic chemical until the toxic concentration is reached. However, there is no evidence that the hormone complex need be abnormal for tumors to develop.

6. *The Environment*

Mammary carcinoma of the mouse is a disease unusually sensitive to environmental conditions. Underfeeding of susceptible mice infected with the virus reduces the incidence of the tumors. On the other hand a high fat diet has increased the tumor rate. Diets deficient in specific nutrients essential for the growth of young mice, such as the essential amino acids, cystine, lysine, tryptophan, and methionine, also reduce the incidence. Such deficiencies may operate either through inhibiting all growth, preventing development of the mammary gland, or interfering with the hormone system.

Some vitamin deficiencies have an effect on tumor growth. Pantothenic acid deficiency may cause severe interference in the utilization of food by mice and retard mammary tumor growth. Pyridoxine deficiency on the other hand does not appear to have this effect.

There is some evidence that mice which are kept at high temperatures (90°-91°F.) and which eat about half as much as animals kept at 65°F., are suppressed in growth and develop fewer tumors. There is even evidence that mice kept several to a cage eat less and develop mammary tumors later than isolated mice.

All these observations indicate the importance of nutrition in the expression of this disease. However, it has not been possible to suppress the tumors effectively by diet without also rendering the animals almost completely sterile.

The incidence of mammary carcinoma in the mouse tends to be higher in breeding females than in non-breeding females and in some strains the incidence increases with the number of litters the females bear.

7. *Other Features of the Disease*

It should be pointed out that mammary tumors of the mouse are unusual in that a low incidence of tumors, apparently of the same type, may occur in stocks in which the virus cannot be demonstrated to be present by current techniques (Andervont, 1945; Andervont and Dunn, 1948a; Andervont and Dunn, 1948b). It is to be hoped that future work will clarify this anomalous feature of the disease.

In this connection it may be of interest to mention that among many hundreds of sweet clover plants free of the wound-tumor virus, only two have been observed with tumors. Each plant had but a single tumor on the stem. Both plants belonged to an inbred line of sweet clover that proved to give the most tumorous reaction of any tested with the virus.

Although the virus may be spread by injecting it into susceptible mice, the only demonstrated natural mode of dissemination is from mother to young through the milk. Since infected populations operate at a biological disadvantage compared with uninfected ones it seems necessary to assume that the virus is disseminated by some additional and at present unknown method. Spread by arthropod vectors has been suggested and the possibility that virus-free stocks may become re-infected must be borne in mind. The possible transmission of the virus during mating is suggested by its demonstration in the contents of the seminal vesicle (Andervont and Dunn, 1948a).

It is thought-provoking to try to visualize the difficulty of recognizing or even suspecting virus involvement in this disease if mouse populations had the characteristics of human populations. With a mixture of virus-bearing and virus-free individuals, heterozygous in their response to infection, living under a variety of conditions, cross-breeding relatively freely, and with inbreeding taboo, there would be little outward evidence of its infectious nature.

IX. General Considerations

1. *Comparison of Plant and Animal Tumors*

The different characteristics of tumor growth in plants and animals appear to emphasize the degree to which such growths, in spite of their abnormalities, retain features of the normal growth characteristics of corresponding healthy cells. Differences between animal and plant tumors appear to be related more to differences in the normal histogenesis of animals and plants than to differences in their inciting agents. The cells that form tumors in animals and plants are "sick" cells of types normally existing in the organism. There is no evidence that a virus infection is capable of inducing the formation of a distinctly new cell type foreign to the host.

The multiplication of animal cells induced by viruses is regularly followed by cellular differentiation; such differentiation is the basis for the pathologist's descriptive classifications of tumors. The possibilities of such differentiation are naturally limited to the potentialities of the cells from which the growths start. In animals, the potentialities of the normal generative cells, have become limited in various degrees, sometimes to the production of a single cell type. In plants such limitation of the potentialities of generative or meristematic cells does not take place, at least not in such degree. The limitation of the potentialities of generative cells in animals is illustrated by the growth of various isolated cell types as such in tissue cultures. The totipotency of plant generative cells is illustrated by the common if not complete failure to grow single cell types in tissue culture (White, 1948) and by regeneration of whole plants from various plant fragments such as root segments, pieces of stems or leaves. In the light of the foregoing, it is therefore not surprising that plant tumors are composed of several cell types whereas animal tumors may be composed of a single cell type.

Some animal tumor cells penetrate into surrounding tissues and this characteristic makes them more dangerous to the life of the host. However, in normal growth and development many animal cells penetrate through other tissues and some exhibit amoeboid movements (Speidel, 1948). They may assume special relationships with cells from a different germ layer and together with them form organs. Stimuli and responses that control such inter-related growth still find expression in animal tumor development. For example, in the normal development of the breast in the mouse (Turner and Gomez, 1933; Dalton, 1945), the epithelial cells grow inward into the mesenchyme, and penetrate through it in branching columns, the mesenchyme forming a supporting stroma in the process. The cooperative, almost "symbiotic," development of these two different tissues results in the formation of the breast. When the breast epithelium renews its growth under the influence of the mammary carcinoma virus, any penetration it makes into mesenchyme and any mesenchymal response forming stroma would seem to be traceable to normal growth processes of these tissues. Corresponding processes are not characteristic of normal plant growth. It is not surprising, therefore, that stroma formation is absent in plant tumor growth.

The most common example of plant cells growing through other cells of the same plant is that of an embryonic branch root. Here the mass of cells of the embryonic root grows outward as a unit through the overlying tissues. There is no intimate cooperative growth with overlying tissues; there is no penetration between these overlying cells; they are crushed, digested or pushed aside as a mass. Invasive or penetrating normal tissue development in plants is at best extremely rare.

In general, plant organs develop from masses of embryonic cells which differentiate into the different types in the structure depending apparently on their position within the mass. Plant tumor growth retains in abnormal fashion something of this manner of growth. Tumors penetrate other plant tissues but only in mass, that is, there are no finger-like invasive tissue extensions such as characterize certain animal tumors. If haustorial cells of dodder could be rendered tumorous, perhaps a penetrating invasive type of plant tumor would result. However, even in such an instance there is no basis in normal plant growth for expecting the development of a stroma.

Some animal tumors metastasize. No plant tumors are known to do so. It is not difficult to understand metastasis in certain types of tumors (for example, lymphomatosis of chickens) where the normal cell prototype meanders through the body. The basis for it is not apparent in the case of tumors, the normal cell prototype of which has a fixed position in some tissue. Why cells of certain tumors should metastasize more frequently to certain locations than to others is also mystifying when the routes of the blood or lymph channels do not afford a ready explanation. The failure thus far to find real metastasis in plants, may be due, in part, to the presence of a firm wall around each cell that is cemented to the walls of neighboring cells. Moreover, in plants the channels of transport are inside individual cells, and although sometimes large enough to allow the passage of smaller cells of the same plant, they certainly do not provide the free path that blood and lymph channels do for animal cells. For here the channels are much larger and are intercellular in origin. Certain cells not only pass through these channels normally but some even penetrate through their walls normally (Speidel, 1948). The writer wishes to suggest for consideration rather than imply, that differences between plant and animal tumors are related to differences between the normal life processes of plants and animals rather than to differences in the tumor-inciting agents.

In comparing the malignancy of plant tumor diseases with that of animals, it should be pointed out that plants are not so vulnerable to tumor growth as are animals. An animal has several vital organs, the loss of any one of which will kill it. This is not true of plants. The loss of a leaf, a stem or a root usually does not cause death but calls into play regenerative powers of growth which the higher animals lack in any comparable degree.

It is instructive to consider the important similarities that exist between the wound-tumor disease in plants and an animal disease such as mammary carcinoma of the mouse. In both, a virus plays an important rôle in tumor production and apparently in both many genetic factors influence the outcome. Other factors such as wounds or hormones that affect cell multiplication are also involved in the formation of the tumors. In both, too, there is at the present time a suggestion that some tumors may occur in the absence of the virus.

2. *Berry-Dedrick Transformation*

This phenomenon was described in the section on infectious myxoma and infectious fibroma of rabbits. In their classical paper Berry and Dedrick (1936a) suggested that transformation was accomplished by some heat stable ingredient of the myxoma virus increasing the virulence of the fibroma virus. Nevertheless, Berry (1937) recognized that the possible reactivation of myxoma virus by something from the fibroma virus had not been disproved. The character of the myxoma virus produced by transformation is determined by the strain of the inactivated myxoma virus employed and is not influenced by the strain of the fibroma virus used. These facts would require that if the transformation is accomplished by passage of some ingredient from myxoma virus to fibroma virus, this ingredient (in addition to its ability to increase the virulence of fibroma virus and confer upon it all characters distinguishing the myxoma from the fibroma agent) must also have the ability to determine whether ordinary myxoma, neuromyxoma or 80A myxoma will be produced. It would be a remarkable coincidence if this hypothetical particle should determine all of these properties. On the other hand, the alternative hypothesis requires only that an essential element in myxoma virus inactivated by heat, occurs in fibroma virus too and may be passed from fibroma virus into inactivated myxoma virus. In this connection it is worth noting that the fibroma virus is inactivated at the same low temperature as the myxoma virus.

The Berry-Dedrick transformation may be the first instance of a phenomenon found in other viruses. It is possible that the transfer of characters from one bacterial virus to another (Hershey, 1946; Delbrück and Bailey, 1946; Luria, 1947) is a related phenomenon. Here, some sort of linkage of genetic viral factors has been demonstrated (Hershey and Rotman, 1948).

3. *Tumors and Host Resistance*

Duran-Reynals and Shrigley (1944) have emphasized the role of a balance between host resistance and virus virulence in producing new growths from host cells. Where the host is very susceptible in relation to the virulence of the virus, host cell growth tends to be minimal and destructive effects maximal. At the other extreme, resistance may be so great that no disease results from inoculation. In certain intermediate relationships between virus virulence and host susceptibility, cell growth tends to be maximal and cell destruction minimal. Many examples of this general principle in animal tumor diseases may be recalled from the above surveys. Perhaps the fact that sweet clover, one of the most tumorous hosts of the wound-tumor virus, shows no vein enlargement as do other less tumorous hosts is an expression of the same phenomenon in plants.

There is very little in the literature to suggest that infection by tumor viruses of hosts ordinarily considered immune results in enhanced tumor growth. Sanarelli (1898) reported that he infected a female dog with the myxomatosis virus, a virus highly specific for the rabbit. The dog developed cancers of the breast that were myxomatous in their histology. However, Hyde and Gardner (1933) failed to confirm Sanarelli when they inoculated twelve dogs of various breeds with massive doses of the virus.

4. *Virus Tumors and Cancer*

Many excellent treatises have been published on the general subject of viruses in relation to cancer, among them the papers by Andrewes (1934, 1939b), Duran-Reynals and Shrigley (1944), Kidd (1946), Rous (1936, 1943a,b, 1946) and Shimkin (1945a,b).

Cancer cells, when examined under the light microscope show no evidence of the presence of microorganisms that might be responsible for their malignant behavior. No organisms have been isolated from them, which after growth in culture media reproduced the disease upon inoculation into a suitable host. That these generally accepted facts do not necessarily eliminate such organisms as the agents converting normal cells into cancer cells is indicated by the recent work of Braun and White on the crown gall disease of plants (1943). More recently Braun (1947) has shown very clearly that the bacterium [*Agrobacterium tumefaciens* (Smith and Townsend) Conn.] responsible for this tumor disease of many plant species need only be in contact with plant tissues for 4 days immediately after the tissues are wounded in order to convert normal cells into tumor cells. After the conversion, the cells continue to grow as tumor cells indefinitely even in the absence of the bacteria.

But, in particular, the failure to see a microorganism in cancer cells or to isolate one from such cells leaves the possibility open that viruses could be the cause of their transformation. This is true because none but the very largest of the viruses is visible under the light microscope even with the most specialized staining techniques and they are characterized as a group by their failure to grow on cell-free media.

Theoretical deductions excluding viruses as a cause of cancer must give way to the experimental facts which clearly indicate that viruses cause cancers of the Rous sarcoma type in chickens and cause tumors that progress to cancer in the case of mammary carcinoma of the mouse, kidney carcinoma of frogs and papillomas of rabbits. In the case of the Rous sarcoma, the virus converts the normal cells to cancer cells at once. In the other cases, the virus converts normal cells to benign tumors that progress by stages to cancer. In addition, viruses cause other tumors in animals and plants, the more important of which have been dealt with in this paper. These cannot be considered as unrelated growth processes as distinguished from cancers except by arbitrary standards erected in our present state of ignorance. One may well doubt if such arbitrary distinctions have any real significance to a natural system of knowledge.

It is worth mentioning here that Andrewes' arguments for considering the Rous sarcoma a true cancer and its causal agent a virus are more cogent today in the light of the strides made in virus research than they were in 1934. Many exceptional properties of viruses have been discovered since that time. For example, the production of myxoma virus from fibroma virus and heat inactivated myxoma virus, the transfer of characters from one bacteriophage particle to another, the remarkable cycle which the swine influenza virus may undergo, the crystallization of some plant viruses, the multiplication of some plant viruses in their insect vectors, etc., all emphasize the diverse and remarkable properties that may occur among the viruses and have broadened the virologist's concept of their attributes. The path of a virus from one host to another may be obvious or it may be very obscure. There is a sound basis of experimental fact behind the knowledge that transmission may be very devious, complicated and extremely difficult to unravel. There is no experimental basis for resort to hypotheses of spontaneous origin where the means of transmission is not known.

It should be pointed out that the interpretations of experimental findings set forth in this survey are not without challenge. For example, Kidd (1946) holds that "it seems premature to attempt to decide at the present time whether the agents responsible for fowl sarcomas and that implicated in the etiology of the mouse mammary adenocarcinoma should be classified as viruses—as much because of the prevailing uncertainties about the nature of the latter—as because the tumor agents are atypical of the generality of viruses in one or more respects (e.g., in lacking antigenicity within the susceptible species, in lacking infectivity under natural conditions or in lacking definitive pathogenicity)." The reader should be warned that this survey has not been written from such a viewpoint but rather from the position that a great deal is known about viruses, even though much more undoubtedly remains to be discovered, and that one is warranted in regarding the above entities as viruses. They possess the important common features of viruses in regard to size, inability to grow on cell-free media, and ability to reproduce and cause disease when introduced into susceptible hosts. Many recognized viruses have unusual properties in one respect or another.

Kidd (1946) also holds that "the tumors which provide causative agents separable from their cells are actually limited to the small group of naturally occurring fowl sarcomas and allied growths." He points out that there is no proof that the rabbit papilloma virus causes the conversion of the benign papillomas to cancers or that the virus of mammary carcinoma of the mouse causes the conversion of the benign adenomas it first induces in the breasts of mice into malignant growths. It must be admitted that except in the case of the fowl sarcoma viruses, the others causing tumors have not been shown to be responsible for the change of benign tumor cells to malignant tumor cells nor for the continued growth of the cells in this state. Such cells have not yielded a virus causing an immediate malignant transformation of susceptible cells. This is a serious experimental deficiency and bears out Kidd's contention that in all cases but the fowl sarcomas, the cause for the conversion of the cells to the malignant state is not known.

In very interesting work with a typical transplantable cancer of rabbits of unknown cause (the Brown-Pearce carcinoma) Kidd (1946) has discovered that they contain an entity serologically unrelated to other serological entities detectable in rabbit tissues, either normal or tumorous. The transplantable V2 carcinoma of rabbits, which originated from a rabbit papilloma, also contains a similar entity. It is unrelated serologically to normal rabbit antigens and to the papilloma virus. It is not detectable in rabbit papillomas. The properties of these entities have been extensively studied. They are sedimentable along with the microsomes of the host cells. Kidd has considered the possibility that they are the cause of malignancy. However, because they have invariably proven incapable of initiating disease of any sort, proof in this case also, is lacking for their causal relation to malignancy.

One of the puzzling features of the Rous sarcoma virus and the other viruses producing similar tumors is their source. They do not appear to pass from one bird to another in nature. However, it is much more likely that their appearance follows some scheme already known in virology than that they arise spontaneously (*de novo*).

It is possible that each of these tumors arises because of a mutation of a virus present in the animal but not recognized. Such a virus might be very common in chickens. The development of antibodies to the Rous virus in many normal chickens as they grow older supports such a hypothesis. One would expect that the mutations would usually differ from each other in various ways and so cause tumors varying in a number of respects. In other words, variation in the mutants would be the rule rather than the exception. Such is the case with these fowl tumors related to the Rous sarcoma. Yet all the mutants would be related as is the case with the viruses known to cause these growths. That the mutants might arise from the virus or viruses causing the fowl leucosis complex is not excluded by any experimental facts known today. Moreover, the isolation (Furth and Stubbs, 1934; Furth, 1936a, b; Oberling and Guérin, 1937) of strains of the leucosis virus with leucotic and sarcomatous effects lends credence to the idea.

A disease of plants is interesting in this connection. There occurs in petunias (Kunkel, 1948) a masked strain of tobacco mosaic virus. Plants with the virus appear healthy. Occasionally a yellow spot appears on a leaf of a plant carrying the virus. From this spot, a mutant of the tobacco mosaic virus is readily isolated. It causes yellow mottling on petunias. The mutants usually vary one from another and the mutant strains are not known to spread in petunias in nature.

The possibility that malignant growths may in general be caused by viruses has been considered by a number of writers (Andrewes, 1939b; Duran-Reynals and Shrigley, 1944; Rous, 1946). Latency in virus infections, mutations of viruses, the effect of carcinogens on virus tumor infections make it impossible to dismiss the idea lightly. Genetic variability in response to virus infection, devious routes of virus transmission, long incubation periods, resistant individuals serving as sources of infection, may easily mask the infectious nature of a virus malady. It has been suggested that when a cancer arises in an animal a latent virus already present suddenly induces cell proliferation and tumor formation and that this activity happens at that particular time because other influences such as carcinogenic chemicals or irradiation establishes a cellular environment favorable for the action of the virus. It has also been suggested that a mutation of the latent virus, sometimes induced by external factors such as carcinogens, suddenly causes cancerous cell growth. These speculations enrich the field of experimental endeavor. The extent to which they are accepted as generally applicable will, of course, depend on the number of specific instances in which they are shown to be true.

The possibility that a multiplicity of agents causes cancers seems more probable to the writer. A weakness of the virus etiology of cancers as a concept of wide applicability resides in the small number of cancers that have been shown to be virus induced. However, this weakness must be considered in the light of the many difficulties that may attend the demonstration of a causal virus. Some of these have been considered earlier and need only be recalled here: the difficulty of demonstrating papilloma virus in papillomas on domestic rabbits, the non-filterable phases of the Rous sarcoma, the decades of research on mammary carcinoma of the mouse before tangible evidence of a virus etiology was discovered. Whenever man is the subject of investigation, the difficulties are enormously increased. Because of the demonstration of virus etiology in some cancers, it seems important that the virus approach to the problem be vigorously prosecuted. Only by strenuous attempts to verify the hypothesis of virus etiology whereever it is indicated (and perhaps also where it is not indicated) can the virus concept make its full contribution to an understanding of tumors and cancer.

References

Ahlström, C. G. 1938. The histology of the infectious fibroma in rabbits. *Jour. Path. and Bact.* **46**: 461-472.

Ahlström, C. G. 1940a. On the anatomical character of the infectious myxoma of rabbits. *Acta Path. et Microbiol. Scand.* **17**: 377-393.

Ahlström, C. G. 1940b. The reaction of tarred rabbits to the myxoma virus. *Acta Path. et Microbiol. Scand.* **17**: 394-416.

Ahlström, C. G., and Andrewes, C. H. 1938. Fibroma virus infection in tarred rabbits. *Jour. Path. and Bact.* **47**: 65-86.

Anderson, T. F. 1946. Morphological and chemical relations in viruses and bacteriophages. *Cold Spring Harbor Symposia on Quantitative Biology* **11**: 1-13.

Andervont, H. B. 1945. Relation of milk influence to mammary tumors of hybrid mice. *Jour. Nation. Cancer Inst.* **5**: 391-395.

Andervont, H. B., and Dunn, T. B. 1948a. Mammary tumors in mice presumably free of the mammary tumor agent. *Jour. Nation. Cancer Inst.* **8**: 227-233.

Andervont, H. B., and Dunn, T. B. 1948b. Efforts to detect a mammary tumor agent in strain C mice. *Jour. Nation. Cancer Inst.* **8**: 235-240.

Andrewes, C. H. 1932. The transmission of fowl-tumors to pheasants. *Jour. Path. and Bact.* **35**: 407-413.

Andrewes, C. H. 1933a. The active immunization of pheasants against fowl tumors. *Jour. Path. and Bact.* **37**: 17-25.

Andrewes, C. H. 1933b. Further serological studies on fowl tumor viruses. *Jour. of Path. and Bact.* **37**: 27-44.

Andrewes, C. H. 1934. Viruses in relation to the aetiology of tumors. *Lancet* **2**: 63-69; 117-124.

Andrewes, C. H. 1936. A change in rabbit fibroma virus suggesting mutation. I. Experiments on domestic rabbits. *Jour. Exptl. Med.* **63**: 157-172.

Andrewes, C. H. 1939a. The occurrence of neutralizing antibodies for Rous sarcoma virus in the sera of young "normal" chicks. *Jour. Path. and Bact.* **48**: 225-227.

Andrewes, C. H. 1939b. Latent virus infections and their possible relevance to the cancer problem. *Proc. Roy. Soc. Med.* **33**: 75-86.

Andrewes, C. H., and Ahlström, C. G. 1938. A transplantable sarcoma occurring in a rabbit inoculated with tar and infectious fibroma virus. *Jour. Path. and Bact.* **47**: 87-99.

Andrewes, C. H., Ahlström, C. G., Fouldes, L., and Gye, W. E. 1937. Reaction of tarred rabbits to the infectious fibroma virus (Shope). *Lancet* **2**: 893-895.

Andrewes, C. H., and Shope, R. E. 1936. A change in rabbit fibroma virus suggesting mutation. III. Interpretation of findings. *Jour. Exptl. Med.* **63**: 179-184.

Asmundson, V. S., and Biely, J. 1932. Inheritance of resistance to fowl paralysis (neurolymphomatosis gallinarum). I. Differences in susceptibility. *Can. Jour. Res.* **6**: 171-176.

Bawden, F. C. 1943. Plant Viruses and Virus Diseases. Chronica Botanica Co., Waltham, Mass., 294 pp.

Beard, J. W. 1935. Conditions determining melanosis of a virus-induced rabbit papilloma (Shope). *Proc. Soc. Exptl. Biol. and Med.* **32**: 1334-1336.

Beard, J. W., and Kidd, J. G. 1936. Antigenic individuality of certain papilloma viruses. *Proc. Soc. Exptl. Biol. and Med.* **34**: 451-453.

Beard, J. W., and Rous, P. 1934. A virus induced mammalian growth with the characters of a tumor (the Shope rabbit papilloma). II. Experimental alterations of the growth on the skin: Morphological considerations: the phenomena of retrogression. *Jour. Exptl. Med.* **60**: 723-740.

Beard, J. W., and Wyckoff, R. W. G. 1937. The isolation of a homogeneous heavy protein from virus-induced rabbit papillomas. *Science* **85**: 201-202.

Beard, J. W., Bryan, W. R., and Wyckoff, R. W. G. 1939. The isolation of the rabbit papilloma virus protein. *Jour. Inf. Dis.* **65**: 43-52.

Berry, G. P. 1937. The transformation of the virus of rabbit fibroma (Shope) into that of infectious myxomatosis (Sanarelli). *Proc. Amer. Phil. Soc.* **77**: 473-476.

Berry, G. P. 1940. The fibroma-myxoma "spectrum" of viruses. 1939 3rd International Congress for Microbiology. N. Y. Report of Proceedings, pp. 343-344.

Berry, G. P., and Dedrick, H. M. 1936a. A method for changing the virus of rabbit fibroma (Shope) into that of infectious myxomatosis (Sanarelli). *Jour. Bact.* **31**: 50-51.

Berry, G. P., and Dedrick, H. M. 1936b. Further observations on the transformation of the virus of rabbit fibroma (Shope) into that of infectious myxomatosis (Sanarelli). *Jour. Bact.* **32**: 356.

Berry, G. P., and Lichty, J. A., Jr. 1936. Immunological and serological evidences of a close relationship between the viruses of rabbit fibroma (Shope) and infectious myxomatosis (Sanarelli). *Jour. Bact.* **31**: 49-50.

Bittner, J. J. 1947a. The causes and control of mammary cancer in mice. Harvey Lectures. 1946-47: 221-246.

Bittner, J. J. 1947b. The mammary tumor milk agent. *Annals New York Acad. Sci.* **49**: 69-73.

Black, L. M. 1944. Some viruses transmitted by agallian leaf-hoppers. *Proc. Amer. Phil. Soc.* **88**: 132-144.

Black, L. M. 1945. A virus tumor disease of plants. *Amer. Jour. Bot.* **32**: 408-415.

Black, L. M. 1946a. Plant tumors induced by the combined action of wounds and virus. *Nature* **158**: 56.

Black, L. M. 1946b. Variation in host susceptibility to wound-tumor virus. *Amer. Jour. Bot.* **33** supplement: 13a.

Black, L. M. 1947. Virus tumors in plants. Growth Supplement. Sixth Growth Symposium pp. 79-84.

Brandly, C. A., Waters, N. F., and Hall, W. J. 1942. Fowl paralysis and other forms of the avian leukosis complex. In "Keeping Livestock Healthy." U. S. Dept. Agric. Yearbook 1942. pp. 944-962.

Braun, A. C. 1947. Thermal studies on the factors responsible for tumor initiation in crown gall. *Amer. Jour. Bot.* **34**: 234-240.

Braun, A. C., and White, P. R. 1943. Bacteriological sterility of tissues derived from secondary crown-gall tumors. *Phytopath.* **33**: 85-100.

Briggs, R. 1942. Transplantation of kidney carcinoma from adult frogs to tadpoles. *Cancer Res.* **2**: 309-323.

Briggs, R., and Grant, R. 1943. Growth and regression of frog kidney carcinoma transplanted into the tails of permanent and normal tadpoles. *Cancer Res.* **3**: 613-620.

Brown, J. C., and Cross, J. C. 1941. A probable agent for the transmission of fowl paralysis. *Science* **93**: 528.

Bryan, W. R., and Beard, J. W. 1941. Studies on the purification and properties of the rabbit-papilloma-virus protein. *Jour. Nation. Cancer Inst.* **1**: 607-673.

Bryan, W. R., Kahler, H., Shimkin, M. B., and Andervont, H. B. 1942. Extraction and ultracentrifugation of mammary tumor inciter of mice. *Jour. Nation. Cancer Inst.* **2**: 451-455.

Burmester, B. R. 1945. The incidence of lymphomatosis among male and female chickens. *Poultry Sci.* **24**: 469-472.

Burmester, B. R. 1947. Studies on the transmission of avian visceral lymphomatosis. II. Propagation of lymphomatosis with cellular and cell-free preparations. *Poultry Sci.* **26**: 534.

Burmester, B. R., and Nelson, N. M. 1945. The effect of castration and sex hormones upon the incidence of lymphomatosis in chickens. *Poultry Sci.* **24**: 509-515.

Carr, J. G. 1942. The absence of a seasonal influence upon the Rous No. 1 sarcoma in young chicks. *Brit. Jour. Exptl. Path.* **23**: 339-342.

Carr, J. G. 1943a. Some investigations upon the nature of the resistance of an inbred line of fowls to the development of the Rous No. 1 sarcoma. *Brit. Jour. Exptl. Path.* **24**: 127-132.

Carr, J. G. 1943b. The relation between age, structure, and agent content of Rous No. 1 sarcomas. *Brit. Jour. Exptl. Path.* **24**: 133-137.

Carr, J. G. 1943c. Prolonged antibody production following recovery of fowls from Rous No. 1 sarcoma. *Brit. Jour. Exptl. Path.* **24**: 138-140.

Claude, A. 1937. Preparation of an active agent from inactive tumor extracts. *Science* **85**: 294-295.

Claude, A. 1939a. Properties of the inhibitor associated with the active agent of chicken tumor I. *Amer. Jour. Cancer* **37**: 59-63.

Claude, A. 1939b. Chemical composition of the tumor-producing fraction of chicken tumor I. *Science* **90**: 213-214.

Claude, A. 1940. Particulate components of normal and tumor cells. *Science* **91**: 77-78.

Claude, A., Porter, K. R., and Pickels, E. G. 1947. Electron microscope study of chicken tumor cells. *Cancer Res.* **7**: 421-430.

Clemmesen, J. 1939. The influence of Roentgen radiation on immunity to Shope fibroma virus. *Amer. Jour. Cancer* **35**: 378-385.

Dalton, A. J. 1945. Histogenesis of the mammary gland of the mouse. In A Symposium on Mammary Tumors in Mice. *A.A.A.S. Publ.* **22**: pp. 39-46.

Davis, O. S., Doyle, L. P., Walkey, F. L., and Cenker, L. K. 1947. Studies in avian leukosis. III. The incidence of avian leukosis in various breeds of chickens. *Poultry Sci.* **26**: 499-507.

Delbrück, M., and Bailey, W. T. 1946. Induced mutations in bacterial viruses. *Cold Spring Harbor Symposia on Quantitative Biology* **11**: 33-37.

De Ome, K. B. 1943. Intraperitoneal injection of lymphomatous nerve tissue into resistant or susceptible chickens. *Poultry Sci.* **22**: 381-394.

Dienes, L. 1948. Pleuropneumonia and pleuropneumonia-like organisms (Borrelomycetaceae). Supplement No. 3 in Bergey's Manual of Determinative Bacteriology. 6th Edition. Williams and Wilkins Co., Baltimore, pp. 1287-1296.

Doerr, R., and Hallauer, C. (Editors). 1938 and 1939. Handbuch der Virusforschung. Julius Springer, Vienna, 1384 pp.

Duran-Reynals, F. 1940a. Neutralization of tumor viruses by the blood of normal fowls of different ages. *Yale Jour. Biol. and Med.* **13**: 61-76.

Duran-Reynals, F. 1940b. A hemorrhagic disease occurring in chicks inoculated with the Rous and Fuginami viruses. *Yale Jour. Biol. and Med.* **13**: 77-98.

Duran-Reynals, F. 1942. The reciprocal infection of ducks and chickens with tumor-inducing viruses. *Cancer Res.* **2**: 343-369.

Duran-Reynals, F. 1943. The infection of turkeys and guinea fowls by the Rous sarcoma virus and the accompanying variations of the virus. *Cancer Res.* **3**: 569-577.

Duran-Reynals, F. 1947. A study of three new duck variants of the Rous chicken sarcoma. *Cancer Res.* **7**: 99-102.

Duran-Reynals, F., and King, J. W. 1947. Reciprocal effects of natural immune bodies from chickens and ducks on variants of a sarcoma virus. *Cancer Res.* **7**: 21-25.

Duran-Reynals, F., and Shrigley, E. W. 1944. Virus infection as an etiologic agent of cancer. *A.A.A.S. Research Conference on Cancer,* pp. 1-23.

Duran-Reynals, F., and Shrigley, E. W. 1946. A study of five transplantable chicken sarcomas induced by viruses. *Cancer Res.* **6**: 535-544.

Durant, A. J., and McDougle, H. C. 1939. Studies on the origin and transmission of fowl paralysis (neurolymphamatosis) by blood inoculation. *Missouri Agr. Exptl. Sta. Res. Bull.* **304**: 1-23.

Elford, W. J., and Andrewes, C. H. 1935. Estimation of the size of a fowl tumor virus by filtration through graded membranes. *Brit. Jour. Exptl. Path.* **16**: 61-66.

Elford, W. J., and Andrewes, C. H. 1936. Centrifugation studies: II. The viruses of vaccinia, influenza and Rous sarcoma. *Brit. Jour. Exptl. Path.* **17**: 422-430.

Ellermann, V. (Preface date 1921). The Leucosis of Fowls and Leucemia Problems. Gyldendal, 11 Hanover Square, London W1, pp. 105.

Feldman, W. H., and Olson. C., Jr. 1943. Fowl Leukosis. Pp. 558-564. In Diseases of Poultry. Edited by H. E. Biester and L. Devries. 1945 edition. The Collegiate Press, Inc., Ames, Iowa, 1005 pp.

Foulds, L. 1934. The Filterable Tumors of Fowls: A Critical Review. Supplement to the 11th Scientific Report on the Investigations of the Imperial Cancer Research Fund. Taylor and Francis, London, 41 pp.

Friedewald, W. F. 1940. Identity of "inhibitor" and antibody in extracts of virus-induced rabbit papillomas. *Jour. Exptl. Med.* **72**: 175-200.

Friedewald, W. F. 1944. Certain conditions determining enhanced infection with the rabbit papilloma virus. *Jour. Exptl. Med.* **80**: 65-76.

Friedewald, W. F., and Anderson, R. S. 1943. The effects of Roentgen rays on cell-virus associations. Findings with virus induced rabbit papillomas and fibromas. *Jour. Exptl. Med.* **78**: 285-304.

Friedewald, W. F., and Kidd, J. G. 1940. Union in vitro of the papilloma virus and its antibody. *Jour. Exptl. Med.* **72**: 531-558.

Friedewald, W. F., and Kidd, J. G. 1944. The recoverability of virus from papillomas produced therewith in domestic rabbits. *Jour. Exptl. Med.* **79**: 591-605.

Furth, J. 1932. Studies on the nature of the agent transmitting leucosis of fowls. I. Its concentration in blood cells and plasma and relation to the incubation period. *Jour. Exptl. Med.* **55**: 465-478.

Furth, J. 1936a. The relation of leukosis to sarcoma of chickens. II. Mixed osteochondrosarcoma and lymphomatosis (Strain 12). *Jour. Exptl. Med.* **63**: 127-144.

Furth, J. 1936b. The relation of leukosis to sarcoma of chickens. III. Sarcomata of strains 11 and 15 and their relation to leukosis. *Jour. Exptl. Med.* **63**: 145-156.

Furth, J., and Miller, H. K. 1932. Studies on the nature of the agent transmitting leucosis of fowls. II. Filtration of leucemic plasma. *Jour. Exptl. Med.* **55**: 479-493.

Furth, J., and Stubbs, E. L. 1934. Tissue culture studies on relation of sarcoma to leukosis of chickens. *Proc. Soc. Exptl. Biol. and Med.* **32**: 381-383.

Gardner, R. E., and Hyde, R. R. 1942. Transformation of rabbit fibroma virus (Shope) into infectious myxomatosis (Sanarelli). *Jour. Inf. Dis.* **71**: 47-49.

Graff, S., Moore, D. H., Stanley, W. M., Randall, H. T., and Haagensen, C. D. 1947. The Milk Agent. Program 4th Int. Cancer Research Congress. p. 144. St. Louis 1947.

Green, R. G. 1935. On the nature of filterable viruses. *Science* **82**: 443-445.

Green, R. G., Anderson, T. F., and Smadel, J. E. 1942. Morphological structure of the virus of vaccinia. *Jour. Exptl. Med.* **75**: 651-656.

Heisdorf, A. J., Brewer, N. R., and Lamoreux, W. F. 1947. The genetic relationship between mortality from induced and spontaneous lymphomatosis. *Poultry Sci.* **26**: 67-73.

Hershey, A. D. 1946. Spontaneous mutations in bacterial viruses. *Cold Spring Harbor Symposia on Quantitative Biology* **11**: 67-77.

Hershey, A. D., and Rotman, R. 1948. Linkage among genes controlling inhibition of lysis in a bacterial virus. *Proc. Nation. Acad. Sci. U. S.* **34**: 89-96.

Hobbs, J. R. 1928. Studies on the nature of the infectious myxoma virus of rabbits. *Amer. Jour. Hyg.* **8**: 800-839.

Hobbs, J. R. 1931. The occurrence of natural and acquired immunity to infectious myxomatosis of rabbits. *Science* **73**: 94-95.

Hoffstadt, R. E., and Pilcher, K. S. 1938. The use of the chorioallantoic membrane of the developing chick embryo as a medium in the study of virus myxomatosum. *Jour. Bact.* **35**: 353-368.

Hoffstadt, R. E., and Pilcher, K. S. 1939. Immunological reactions of elementary bodies and of virus free filtrates from myxoma infected chick membranes with hyper-immune rabbit serum. *Jour. Inf. Dis.* **65**: 103-112.

Hoffstadt, R. E., and Pilcher, K. S. 1941. A study of the IA and OA strains of the Shope fibroma virus with special reference to the Berry transformation. *Jour. Inf. Dis.* **68**: 67-72.

Hoffstadt, R. E., Omundson, D. V., and Donaldson, P. 1941. Cultivation of the virus of infectious myxoma on the chorioallantoic membrane of the developing duck embryo. *Jour. Inf. Dis.* **68**: 213-219.

Holmes, F. O. 1929. Local lesions in tobacco mosaic. *Bot. Gaz.* **87**: 39-55.

Holmes, F. O. 1937. Inheritance of resistance to tobacco-mosaic disease in the pepper. *Phytopath.* **27**: 637-642.

Holmes, F. O. 1948. Order virales. The filterable viruses. Supplement No. 2 in Bergey's Manual of Determinative Bacteriology. 6th Edition. Williams and Wilkins, Baltimore, pp. 1125-1286.

Hurst, E. W. 1937a. Myxoma and the Shope fibroma. I: The histology of myxoma. *Brit. Jour. Exp. Path.* **18**: 1-15.

Hurst, E. W. 1937b. Myxoma and the Shope fibroma. II: The effect of intracerebral passage on the myxoma virus. *Brit. Jour. Exptl. Path.* **18**: 15-22.

Hurst, E. W. 1937c. Myxoma and the Shope fibroma. III. Miscellaneous observations bearing on the relationship between myxoma, neuromyxoma and fibroma viruses. *Brit. Jour. Exptl. Path.* **18**: 23-30.

Hurst, E. W. 1938. Myxoma and the Shope fibroma. 4. The histology of Shope fibroma. *Aust. Jour. Exptl. Biol. and Med. Sci.* **16**: 53-64.

Hutt, F. B., and Cole, R. K. 1947. Genetic control of lymphomatosis in the fowl. *Science* **106**: 379-384.

Hyde, R. R. 1939. Infectious myxomatosis of rabbits (Sanarelli) versus the fibroma virus (Shope) with especial reference to the time interval in the establishment of concomitant immunity. *Amer. Jour. Hyg.* **30**: Sect. B, 47-56.

Hyde, R. R., and Gardner, R. E. 1933. Infectious myxoma of rabbits. *Amer. Jour. Hyg.* **17**: 446-465.

Hyde, R. R., and Gardner, R. E. 1939. Transmission experiments with the fibroma (Shope) and myxoma (Sanarelli) viruses. *Amer. Jour. Hyg.* **30**: Sect. B, 57-63.

Imperial Cancer Research Fund. 1946. *43rd Ann. Rept.* **1945-46**: 9-10.

Jensen, J. H. 1933. Isolation of yellow-mosaic viruses from plants infected with tobacco mosaic. *Phytopath.* **23**: 964-974.

Johnson, E. P. 1937. Transmission of fowl leukosis. *Poultry Sci.* **16**: 255-260.

Jungherr, E. 1943. The avian leukosis complex. In Diseases of Poultry. Edited by H. E. Biester and L. Devries. 1945 edition, 1005 pp. The Collegiate Press, Ames, Iowa, Chap. 18, pp. 367-413.

Kelly, S. M., and Black, L. M. 1949. The origin, development and cell structure of a virus tumor in plants. *Amer. Jour. Bot.* **36**: 65-73.

Keogh, E. V. 1938. Ectodermal lesions produced by the virus of Rous sarcoma. *Brit. Jour. Exptl. Path.* **19**: 1-9.

Kessel, J. F., Prouty, C. C., and Meyer, J. W. 1931. Occurrence of infectious myxomatosis in southern California. *Proc. Soc. Exptl. Biol. and Med.* **28**: 413-414.

Kidd, J. G. 1938a. The course of virus-induced rabbit papillomas as determined by virus, cells, and host. *Jour. Exptl. Med.* **67**: 551-574.

Kidd, J. G. 1938b. Immunological reactions with a virus causing papillomas in rabbits. I. Demonstration of a complement fixation reaction: Relation of virus-neutralizing and complement-binding antibodies. *Jour. Exptl. Med.* **68**: 703-724.

Kidd, J. G. 1938c. Immunological reactions with a virus causing papillomas in rabbits. II. Properties of the complement-binding antigen present in extracts of the growths: Its relation to the virus. *Jour. Exptl. Med.* **68**: 725-736.

Kidd, J. G. 1939. The masking effect of extravasated antibody on the rabbit papilloma virus (Shope). *Jour. Exptl. Med.* **70**: 583-604.

Kidd, J. G. 1941. The detection of a "masked" virus (the Shope papilloma virus) by means of immunization. Results of immunization with mixtures containing virus and antibody. *Jour. Exptl. Med.* **74**: 321-344.

Kidd, J. G. 1942. The enduring partnership of a neoplastic virus and carcinoma cells. Continued increase of virus in the V2 carcinoma during propagation in virus-immune hosts. *Jour. Exptl. Med.* **75**: 7-20.

Kidd, J. G. 1946. Distinctive constituents of tumor cells and their possible relations to the phenomena of autonomy, anaplasia, and cancer causation. *Cold Spring Harbor Symposium on Quantitative Biology* **11**: 94-112.

Kidd, J. G., Beard, J. W., and Rous, P. 1936a. Serological reactions with a virus causing rabbit papillomas which become cancerous. I. Tests of the blood of animals carrying the papilloma. *Jour. Exptl. Med.* **64**: 63-77.

Kidd, J. G., Beard, J. W., and Rous, P. 1936b. Serological reactions with a virus causing rabbit papillomas which become cancerous. II. Tests of the blood of animals carrying various epithelial tumors. *Jour. Exptl. Med.* **64**: 79-96.

Kidd, J. G., and Rous, P. 1938. The carcinogenic effect of a papilloma virus on the tarred skin of rabbits. II. Major factors determining the phenomenon: the manifold effects of tarring. *Jour. Exptl. Med.* **68**: 529-562.

Kidd, J. G., and Rous. P. 1940a. Cancers deriving from the virus papillomas of wild rabbits under natural conditions. *Jour. Exptl. Med.* **71**: 469-494.

Kidd, J. G., and Rous, P. 1940b. A transplantable rabbit carcinoma originating in a virus-induced papilloma and containing the virus in masked or altered form. *Jour. Exptl. Med.* **71**: 813-838.

Kunkel, L. O. 1948. Correspondence with the writer.

Ledingham, J. C. G. 1937. Studies on the serological inter-relationships of the rabbit viruses, myxomatosis (Sanarelli, 1898) and fibroma (Shope, 1932). *Brit. Jour. Exptl. Path.* **18**: 436-449.

Littau, V. C., and Black, L. M. 1949. Cytoplasmic inclusions associated with wound-tumor in Rumex acetosa. *Phytopath.* **39**: 13.

Lucké, B. 1934. A neoplastic disease of the kidney of the frog. *Rana pipiens. Amer. Jour. Cancer* **20**: 352-379.

Lucké, B. 1938a. Carcinoma of the kidney in the leopard frog: the occurrence and significance of metastasis. *Amer. Jour. Cancer,* **34**: 15-30.

Lucké, B. 1938b. Carcinoma in the leopard frog: its probable causation by a virus. *Jour. Exptl. Med.* **68**: 457-468.

Lucké, B. 1939. Characteristics of frog carcinoma in tissue culture. *Jour. Exptl. Med.* **70**: 269-276.

Lucké, B. 1940. Physical factors influencing the growth of cancer (experimental studies based on renal adenocarcinoma in animals). *Jour. Urology* **44**: 545-558.

Lucké, B., and Schlumberger, H. 1939. The manner of growth of frog carcinoma, studied by direct microscopic examination of living intraocular transplants. *Jour. Exptl. Med.* **70**: 257-268.

Lucké, B., and Schlumberger, H. 1940a. Heterotransplantation of frog carcinoma; character of growth in the eyes of alien species. *Jour. Exptl. Med.* **72**: 311-320.

Lucké, B., and Schlumberger, H. 1940b. The effect of temperature on the growth of frog carcinoma. I. Direct microscopic observations on living intraocular transplants. *Jour. Exptl. Med.* **72**: 321-330.

Lucké, B., and Schlumberger, H. 1949. Induction of metastasis of frog carcinoma by increase of environmental temperature. *Jour. Exptl. Med.* **89**: 269-278.

Luria, S. E. 1945. Mutations of bacterial viruses affecting their host range. *Genetics* **30**: 84-99.

Luria, S. E. 1947. Reactivation of irradiated bacteriophage by transfer of self-reproducing units. *Proc. Nation. Acad. Sci. U. S.* **33**: 253-264.

Lush, D. 1937. The virus of infectious myxomatosis of rabbits on the chorioallantoic membrane of the developing egg. *Aust. Jour. Exptl. Biol. and Med. Sci.* **15**: 131-139.

Lush, D. 1939. The serological relationship of myxoma and Shope's fibroma viruses. *Aust. Jour. Exptl. Biol. and Med. Sci.* **17**: 85-88.

Maramorosch, K. 1949. The influence of temperature on the incubation of the wound-tumor virus in the insect *Agallia constricta*. *Phytopath.* **39**: 14.

Mellanby, E. 1938. The transmission of the Rous filterable agent to the normal tissues of fowls. *Jour. Path. and Bact.* **47**: 47-64.

Members of the Staff of the National Cancer Institute. 1945. A Symposium on Mammary Tumors in Mice. A.A.A.S. Publ. **22**, p. 223.

Milford, J. J., and Duran-Reynals, F. 1943. Growth of a chicken sarcoma virus in the chick embryo in the absence of neoplasia. *Cancer Res.* **3**: 578-584.

Moses, A. 1940. Infectious rabbit myxomatosis. *Ann. Acad. Brasil. Sci.* **12**: 231-239.

Murphy, J. B., and Rous, P. 1912. The behavior of chicken sarcoma implanted in the developing embryo. *Jour. Exptl. Med.* **15**: 119-132.

Neurath, H., Cooper, G. R., Sharp, D. G., Taylor, A. R., Beard, D., and Beard, J. W. 1941. Molecular size, shape, and homogeneity of the rabbit papilloma virus protein. *Jour. Biol. Chem.* **140**: 293-306.

Oberling, C., and Guérin, M. 1937. La production de tumeurs avec l'agent de la leucémie transmissible des poules. 2nd Internat. Cong. for Micro. Report of proceedings, pp. 94-95.

Oster, G., and Stanley, W. M. 1946. An electron microscope study of the contents of hair cells from leaves diseased with tobacco mosaic virus. *Brit. Jour. Exptl. Path.* **27**: 261-265.

Parker, R. F. 1940. Studies of the infectious unit of myxoma. *Jour. Exptl. Med.* **71**: 439-444.

Parker, R. F., and Thompson, R. L. 1942. The effect of external temperature on the course of infectious myxomatosis of rabbits. *Jour. Exptl. Med.* **75**: 567-573.

Passey, R. D., Dmochowski, L., Astbury, W. T., and Reed, R. 1947. Electron microscope studies of normal and malignant tissues of high- and low-breast cancer strains of mice. *Nature* **160**: 565.

Philip, C. B. 1942. Mechanical transmission of rabbit fibroma (Shope) by certain haematophagous bugs. *Jour. Parasitol.* **28**: 395-398.

Porter, K. R., Claude, A., and Fullam, E. F. 1945. A study of tissue culture cells by electron microscopy. *Jour. Exptl. Med.* **81**: 233-246.

Porter, K. R., and Thompson, H. P. 1948. A particulate body associated with epithelial cells cultured from mammary carcinomas of mice of a milk-factor strain. *Jour. Exptl. Med.* **88**: 15-24.

Price, W. C. 1940. Generalized defense reactions in plants. *Amer. Naturalist* **74**: 117-128.

Ratcliffe, H. L., and Stubbs, E. L. 1935. Attempts to transmit chicken leukosis by mosquitoes and by mites. *Jour. Inf. Dis.* **56**: 301-304.

Rhodes, A. J. 1938. The effect of intracerebral passage of the virus of infectious myxomatosis of rabbits. *Jour. Path. and Bact.* **46**: 217-218.

Rivers, T. M. 1930. Infectious myxomatosis of rabbits. Observations on the pathological changes induced by virus myxomatosum (Sanarelli). *Jour. Exptl. Med.* **51**: 965-976.

Rivers, T. M., and Ward, S. M. 1937. Infectious myxomatosis of rabbits. Preparation of elementary bodies and studies of serologically active materials associated with the disease. *Jour. Exptl. Med.* **66**: 1-14.

Rivers, T. M. *et al.* 1928. Filterable Viruses. Williams and Wilkins Co., Baltimore, 428 pp.

Rivers, T. M., Ward, S. M., and Smadel, J. E. 1939. Infectious myxomatosis of rabbits. Studies of a soluble antigen associated with the disease. *Jour. Exptl. Med.* **69**: 31-48.

Rose, S. M., and Wallingford, H. M. 1948. Transformation of renal tumors of frogs to normal tissues in regenerating limbs of salamanders. *Science* **107**: 457.

Rous, P. 1910a. A transmissible avian neoplasm. (Sarcoma of the common fowl.) *Jour. Exptl. Med.* **12**: 696-705.

Rous, P. 1910b. Metastasis and tumor immunity. Observations with a transmissible avian neoplasm. *Jour. Amer. Med. Assoc.* **55**: 1805.

Rous, P. 1911. A sarcoma of the fowl transmissible by an agent separable from the tumor cells. *Jour. Exptl. Med.* **13**: 397-411.

Rous, P. 1912. An avian tumor in its relation to the tumor problem. *Proc. Amer. Phil. Soc.* **51**: 201-205.

Rous, P. 1913. Resistance to a tumor-producing agent as distinct from resistance to the implanted tumor cells. Observations with a sarcoma of the fowl. *Jour. Exptl. Med.* **18**: 416-427.

Rous, P. 1936. The virus tumors and the tumor problem. *Amer. Jour. Cancer* **28**: 233-272.

Rous, P. 1943a. Viruses and Tumors. In Virus Diseases. The Messenger Lectures, Cornell University Press, Ithaca, N. Y., pp. 147-170.

Rous, P. 1943b. The nearer causes of cancer. *Jour. Amer. Med. Assoc.* **122**: 573-581.

Rous, P. 1946. Concerning the cancer problem. *Amer. Sci.* **34**: 329-358.

Rous, P., and Beard, J. W. 1934a. A virus-induced mammalian growth with the characters of a tumor (the Shope rabbit papilloma). I. The growth on implantation within favorable hosts. *Jour. Exptl. Med.* **60**: 701-722.

Rous, P., and Beard, J. W. 1934b. A virus-induced mammalian growth with the characters of a tumor (the Shope rabbit papilloma). III. Further characters of the growth. General Discussion. *Jour. Exptl. Med.* **60**: 741-766.

Rous, P., and Beard, J. W. 1935. The progression to carcinoma of virus-induced rabbit papillomas (Shope). *Jour. Exptl. Med.* **62**: 523-548.

Rous, P., and Friedewald, W. F. 1941. The carcinogenic effect of methylcholanthrene and of tar on rabbit papillomas due to a virus. *Science* **94**: 495-496.

Rous, P., and Friedewald, W. F. 1944. The effect of chemical carcinogens on virus-induced rabbit papillomas. *Jour. Exptl. Med.* **79**: 511-538.

Rous, P., and Kidd, J. G. 1938. The carcinogenic effect of a papilloma virus on the tarred skin of rabbits. I. Description of the phenomenon. *Jour. Exptl. Med.* **67**: 399-428.

Rous, P., and Kidd, J. G. 1940. The activating, transforming, and carcinogenic effects of the rabbit papilloma virus (Shope) upon implanted tar tumors. *Jour. Exptl. Med.* **71**: 787-812.

Rous, P., Kidd, J. G., and Beard, J. W. 1936. Observations on the relation of the virus causing rabbit papillomas to the cancers deriving therefrom. I. The influence of the host species and of the pathogenic activity and concentration of the virus. *Jour. Exptl. Med.* **64**: 385-400.

Rous, P., and Murphy, J. B. 1911. Tumor implantations in the developing embryo. Experiments with a transmissible sarcoma of the fowl. *Jour. Amer. Med. Assoc.* **56**: 741-742.

Rous, P., and Murphy, J. B. 1912. The nature of the filterable agent causing a sarcoma of the fowl. *Jour. Amer. Med. Assoc.* **58**: 1938.

Rous, P., and Murphy, J. B. 1914a. On the causation by filterable agents of three distinct chicken tumors. *Jour. Exptl. Med.* **19**: 52-69.

Rous, P., Murphy, J. B., and Tytler, W. H. 1912a. The role of injury in the production of a chicken sarcoma by a filterable agent. *Jour. Amer. Med. Assoc.* **58**: 1751.

Rous, P., Murphy, J. B., and Tytler, W. H. 1912b. The relation between a chicken sarcoma's behavior and the growth's filterable cause. *Jour. Amer. Med. Assoc.* **58**: 1840-1841.

Rous, P., Murphy, J. B., and Tytler, W. H. 1912c. A filterable agent the cause of a second chicken tumor, an osteochondrosarcoma. *Jour. Amer. Med. Assoc.* **59**: 1793-1794.

Sanarelli, G. 1898. Das myxomatogene Virus. Beitrag zum Studium der Krankheitserreger ausserhalb des Sichtbaren. *Zentr. Bakt. 1 Abt.* **23**: 865-873.

Schlesinger, M., and Andrewes, C. H. 1937. The filtration and centrifugation of the viruses of rabbit fibroma and rabbit papilloma. *Jour. Hyg.* **37**: 521-526.

Schlumberger, H., and Lucké, B. 1949. Serial intraocular transplantation of frog carcinoma for fourteen generations. *Cancer Res.* **9**: 52-60.

Shaffer, J. G. 1941. Antigenic relationship of infectious myxoma and fibroma viruses of the rabbit. *Amer. Jour. Hyg.* Sect. B **34**: 102-120.

Sharp, D. G., Taylor, A. R., Beard, D., and Beard, J. W. 1942a. Electrophoresis of the rabbit papilloma virus protein. *Jour. Biol. Chem.* **142**: 193-202.

Sharp, D. G., Taylor, A. R., Beard D., and Beard, J. W. 1942b. Study of the papilloma virus protein with the electron microscope. *Proc. Soc. Exptl. Biol. and Med.* **50**: 205-207.

Sharp, D. G., Taylor, A. R., and Beard, J. W. 1946. The density and size of the rabbit papilloma virus. *Jour. Biol. Chem.* **163**: 289-299.

Sharp, D. G., Taylor, A. R., Hook, A. E., and Beard, J. W. 1946. Rabbit papilloma and vaccinia viruses and T_2 bacteriophage of *E. coli* in "shadow" electron micrographs. *Proc. Soc. Exptl. Biol. and Med.* **61**: 259-265.

Shimkin, M. B. 1945a. General and historical introduction. In "A Symposium on Mammary Tumors in Mice." *A.A.A.S. Publ.* **22**, 1-6.

Shimkin, M. B. 1945b. Conclusions—Including discussion of the possible implications for man. In A Symposium on Mammary Tumors in Mice. *A.A.A.S. Publ.* **22**, 209-223.

Shimkin, M. B., and Andervont, H. B. 1945. Properties and nature of the milk agent in the genesis of mammary tumors in mice. In A.A.A.S. Research Conference on Cancer. Gibson Island, 1944: 97-105.

Shope, R. E. 1932a. A transmissible tumor-like condition in rabbits. *Jour. Exptl. Med.* **56**: 793-802.

Shope, R. E. 1932b. A filterable virus causing a tumor-like condition in rabbits and its relationship to virus myxomatosum. *Jour. Exptl. Med.* **56**: 803-822.

Shope, R. E. 1933. Infectious papillomatosis of rabbits. *Jour. Exptl. Med.* **58**: 607-624.

Shope, R. E. 1935. Serial transmission of virus of infectious papillomatosis in domestic rabbits. *Proc. Soc. Exptl. Biol. and Med.* **32**: 830-832.

Shope, R. E. 1936a. Infectious fibroma of rabbits. III. The serial transmission of virus myxomatosum in cottontail rabbits, and cross-immunity tests with the fibroma virus. *Jour. Exptl. Med.* **63**: 33-41.

Shope, R. E. 1936b. Infectious fibroma of rabbits. IV. The infection with virus myxomatosum of rabbits recovered from fibroma. *Jour. Exptl. Med.* **63**: 43-57.

Shope, R. E. 1936c. A change in rabbit fibroma virus suggesting mutation. II. Behavior of the variant virus in cottontail rabbits. *Jour. Exptl. Med.* **63**: 173-178.

Shope, R. E. 1937. Immunization of rabbits to infectious papillomatosis. *Jour. Exptl. Med.* **65**: 219-231.

Shope, R. E. 1938. Protection of rabbits against naturally acquired infectious myxomatosis by previous infection with fibroma virus. *Proc. Soc. Exptl. Biol. and Med.* **38**: 86-89.

Shope, R. E. 1941. The swine lungworm as a reservoir and intermediate host for swine influenza virus. II. The transmission of swine influenza virus by the swine lungworm. *Jour. Exptl. Med.* **74**: 49-68.

Shrigley, E. W., Greene, H. S. N., and Duran-Reynals, F. 1945. Studies on the variation of the Rous sarcoma virus following growth of the tumor in the anterior chamber of the guinea pig eye. *Cancer Res.* **5**: 356-364.

Smadel, J. E., Ward, S. M., and Rivers, T. M. 1940. Infectious myxomatosis of rabbits. II. Demonstration of a second soluble antigen associated with the disease. *Jour. Exptl. Med.* **72**: 129-138.

Smith, K. M. 1934. Recent Advances in the Study of Plant Viruses. P. Blakiston's Son & Co., Inc., Philadelphia, Pa., 423 pp.

Smith, K. M. 1937. A Textbook of Plant Virus Diseases. P. Blakiston's Son & Co. Inc., Philadelphia, Pa., 615 pp.

Smith, W. E., Kidd, J. G., and Rous, P. 1947. Recovery and disappearance of the rabbit papilloma virus (Shope) from the carcinomas that originate from papilloma cells. Program 4th International Cancer Research Congress. St. Louis, p. 84.

Speidel, C. C. 1948. Living cells in action. *Amer. Sci.* **36**: 237-257.

Stanley, W. M. 1935. Isolation of a crystalline protein possessing the properties of tobacco-mosaic virus. *Science* **81**: 644-645.

Stein, C. D. 1942. Equine infectious anemia or swamp fever. In Keeping Livestock Healthy. U. S. Dept. Agric. Yearbook, p. 392-401.

Stern, K. G., and Kirschbaum, A. 1939. On the nature of the agent causing leucosis in fowls. *Science* **89**: 610-611.

Stubbs, E. L., and Furth, J. 1935. The relation of leukosis to sarcoma of chickens. I. Sarcoma and erythroleukosis (Strain 13). *Jour. Exptl. Med.* **61**: 593-616.

Swan, C. 1941. The route of transmission of the virus of infectious myxomatosis of rabbits to the central nervous system. *Aust. Jour. Exptl. Biol. and Med. Sci.* **19**: 113-115.

Syverton, J. T., and Berry, G. B. 1935. Carcinoma in the cottontail rabbit following spontaneous virus papilloma (Shope). *Proc. Soc. Exptl. Biol. and Med.* **33**: 399-400.

Taylor, A. R., Beard, D., Sharp, D. G., and Beard, J. W. 1942. Nucleic acid of the rabbit papilloma virus protein. *Jour. Inf. Dis.* **71**: 110-114.

Taylor, L. W., Lerner, I. M., De Ome, K. B., and Beach, J. R. 1943. Eight years of progeny-test selection for resistance and susceptibility to lymphomatosis. *Poultry Sci.* **22**: 339-347.

Teixeira, J. de C., and Smadel, J. E. 1941. Further studies on the serological reactions of the soluble antigens of infectious myxomatosis. *Jour. Bact.* **42**: 591-603.

Traub, E. 1936. Persistence of lymphocytic choriomeningitis virus in immune animals and its relation to immunity. *Jour. Exptl. Med.* **63**: 847-862.

Traub, E. 1939. Epidemiology of lymphocytic choriomeningitis in a mouse stock observed for four years. *Jour. Exptl. Med.* **69**: 801-817.

Turner, C. W., and Gomez, E. T. 1933. The normal development of the mammary gland of the male and female albino mouse. *Missouri Agr. Exptl. Sta. Res. Bull.* **182**: 3-43.

Valleau, W. D. 1947. Clubroot of tobacco: a wound-tumorlike graft-transmitted disease. *Phytopath.* **37**: 580-582.

van Rooyen, C. E. 1937. Elementary (Paschen) bodies in infectious myxomatosis of the rabbit (Virus Myxomatosum Sanarelli). *Zentr. Bakt. Orig.* **139**: 130-137.

van Rooyen, C. E., and Rhodes, A. J. 1937. Centrifugation of the elementary bodies of infectious myxomatosis of the rabbit. *Zentr. Bakt. Orig.* **140**: 117-120.

van Rooyen, C. E., and Rhodes, A. J. 1948. Virus diseases of man. Thomas Nelson and Sons, New York, 1202 pp.

Visscher, M. B., Green, R. G., Bittner, J. J., Ball, Z. B., and Siedentopf, H. A. 1942. Characterization of milk influence in spontaneous mammary carcinoma. *Proc. Soc. Exptl. Biol. and Med.* **49**: 94-96.

Waters, N. F. 1945. Natural transmission of avian-lymphomatosis. *Poultry Sci.* **24**: 226-233.

Waters, N. F. 1947a. Factors involved in mortality from avian lymphomatosis. *Poultry Sci.* **26**: 639-647.

Waters, N. F. 1947b. The contagious nature of a lymphoid tumor in chickens. *Science* **106**: 246-247.

Waters, N. F., and Prickett, C. O. 1946. Types of lymphomatosis among different inbred lines of chickens. *Poultry Sci.* **25**: 501-508.

Watson, M. A., and Roberts, F. M. 1940. Evidence against the hypothesis that certain plant viruses are transmitted mechanically by aphids. *Ann. Appl. Biol.* **27**: 227-233.

White, P. R. 1948. Correspondence with the writer.

Hormones and the Differentiation of Sex

BY ROBERT K. BURNS

Carnegie Institution of Washington, Department of Embryology, Baltimore, Maryland

I. Introduction

The knowledge that the various organs of the genital system in vertebrate animals depend in some manner upon the gonads for their normal function and for maintenance of normal structure is very old. Among ancient and primitive peoples castration of domestic animals and caponization of fowl were widely practiced, and the effects of eunuchism in the human species were also familiar. However, the nature of the essential relationship between the gonads and the accessory organs of sex, that is to say, the intermediate mechanism by which the gonads are able to exert an influence over distantly located structures (such as the head furnishings of the cock), was mysterious and long remained so. It was not quite 100 years ago that the oft cited experiment of Berthold resulted in the first clear conception of control through the medium of a substance carried by the blood. The name *hormone* was not applied to such an agent until much later. Berthold showed quite simply that a capon exhibiting the typical symptoms of castration could be restored to a normal condition by grafting living testis tissue beneath the skin or in other atypical positions. Since such grafts are well vascularized, but usually are not secondarily supplied with nerves, the conclusion was reached that a specific substance, having a restorative effect on the accessory sex structures and secondary sex characters, is produced in the engrafted testis tissue and transmitted through the blood.

With the gradual appreciation of the principle of hormonal regulation in the reproductive physiology of adult animals, it was inevitable that this mode of control would suggest itself as an appropriate mechanism for determining the development of sex structures in the embryo. It is not practicable to trace the origin and the progress of this idea; as a general concept it was plausible from the first since nothing was known to contradict it directly, but before pure hypothesis could be transformed into a concrete theory, capable of experimental test, it was necessary to obtain a more exact knowledge of the processes of normal sex differentiation, and to find methods of experimental attack adaptable to the special conditions of embryonic development. The necessary information and understanding accumulated slowly.

It is often said that Nature herself first provided a crucial experiment;

however it can also be said without accusing Nature of favoritism that she is often obliging in this respect in the presence of an acute and appreciative observer. Such a man in 1916 was F. R. Lillie, and Nature's particular problem, now ripe for solving, was the ancient and hitherto baffling riddle of the "freemartin." In that year Lillie first proposed in round outline all the essential features of the modern physiological theory of sex differentiation; postulating that hormone substances produced in the differentiating gonads of an embryo are transmitted through the circulating blood, exercising a special selective action upon the primordial sex structures in the course of their differentiation. His theory was supported factually in the following year by his classical analysis of the freemartin case (Lillie, 1917).

A freemartin is a sexually abnormal female calf, born as twin to a normal male, with reproductive organs strongly modified in the male direction. Evidence that the creature is genetically a female need not concern us here. The gonads of the freemartin are rudimentary in size and show well developed testis tubules locally which, however, are always sterile. A complete male duct system is typically found, but the female genital tract also is represented by a variable development of the internal structures—oviducts, uterus, vagina—or may be altogether lacking. The mammary glands and external genitalia, however, are predominantly of female type.

Freemartins occur only when twins are of different sex, and only the female member of the pair is abnormal. The fetal membranes and placentas of such twins are always found to be fused so as to allow free transfusion of blood; in the absence of vascular union the freemartin effect is lacking—the female calf is normal. Other evidence suggested that internal secretion begins in the testis much earlier than in the ovary, thus providing for the fact that the female calf alone is modified. From these main considerations Lillie was led inevitably to the conclusion that a hormone, originating in the gonads of the male twin, passed into the circulation of the female at an early stage of development, altering thereafter the course of differentiation.

Lillie's theory of the freemartin may be said to have initiated the modern era in the physiology of sex differentiation. It immediately stimulated experimental investigation from several directions, not only by indicating the nature and the source of the physiological agents involved in the differentiation of sex, but also by defining more clearly than before the part played by the rudimentary sex structures of the embryo, and some of the conditions which govern their reactions to hormones. From time to time various aspects of Lillie's theory have been questioned in the light of seemingly incompatible evidence from other quarters, adjudged incompatible on an unjustifiable assumption that the conditions postulated in the freemartin will be encountered in virtually the same form among all classes of vertebrates. The theory has even been questioned in its entirety, partly on the basis of such discrepancies, but chiefly as a result of one type of experiment—castration—performed under conditions later shown to have been less crucial than first appeared. However, the net result of recent work has been to reinstate the theory, in its general form, more firmly than before; and regardless of its ultimate verification in detail, it has served one of the most important functions of every good theory by clearly visualizing the ways and means by which its final validity may be determined.

A great impetus was given to the experimental study of sex differentiation with the advent of chemically pure hormones, physiologically more potent and far less toxic than the crude preparations first available. Originally identified as active principles obtained from tissue extracts or certain body fluids, they were eventually isolated as crystalline materials, and are now commonly made by synthesis. In keeping with their varied biological origins they occur in many different forms which are alike, however, in having the basic molecular structure of sterols. From this fact they are called steroid hormones. From the effects which they typically exert on the structure and function of the reproductive organs they are broadly classified as *androgenic* or *estrogenic,* but their biological activities vary greatly with the particular compound used, the animal group or species employed in testing, and the particular structure or function chosen as an indicator. Behavior varies also, as would be expected, with dosage, the stage or degree of differentiation of the reacting structure and other experimental variables. Consequently in designating a substance as an *androgen* or an *estrogen,* or in describing its activity as androgenic or estrogenic, caution must be used, having in mind not only the general quality of the effect, but the particular experimental conditions under which it is manifested.

The variety of sources from which the steroid hormones were originally obtained would in itself challenge the propriety of regarding all of them as "sex hormones" in any strict sense. Indeed, it may be fairly questioned whether any of the substances, in the exact molecular structure which we know, represents a hormone as it functions in a living organism. Prototypes for the male and the female hormones are recognized tentatively in substances originally extracted from gonad tissues—*testosterone* obtained from mammalian testis tissue, and *estradiol* from the follicular fluid of the ovary. Hereafter the terms *male hormone* or *female hormone* will generally refer to these substances or their compounds. Related steroid compounds which have similar activity (*androsterone* and *estrone*) have been recovered under many conditions from urine, but are usually less potent. They are considered as metabolic byproducts probably derived from the gonad hormones. Estrogenic substances are found also in the fluids of the fetal membranes, and have been extracted in quantity from the placenta of many animals. Finally, the adrenal cortex is known to produce a number of androgenic steroids, as well as estrogen, and there are other sources which need not be considered.

II. The Structural Basis for Sex Differentiation in the Embryo

Thus far we have dealt only with the history of hormones and their role as physiological agents in sex differentiation; but this is to neglect the other aspect of the problem which is of equal importance and much greater complexity. This complementary aspect is the part taken by the embryonic genital system; it involves the over-all plan, or organization, of the system as a whole, and it depends upon a specific character or "determination" within each part, which prescribes its individual response to a hormone. Indeed, the essential problem in sex differentiation is found in this highly specific relationship between the hormone and the reacting structures or tissues.

Up to a point in early development each embryo is equipped with all the basic parts necessary for the differentiation of either sex, in other words it is potentially bisexual. The duration of this condition varies widely in different animal groups. We may now review briefly the actual structures present in the bisexual phase, as providing a common base for normal development and for all types of experimental transformation.

The gonads are represented by paired *genital ridges,* in which there is at first no visible structure identifying sex; however two distinct histological zones gradually appear, with the potentialities of testis and ovary. As long as both elements are present the gonad is potentially bisexual, but in the course of differentiation one histological component is destined to become dominant while the other will remain rudimentary or eventually disappear. Experimental methods are quite effective in controlling this process in the gonads of many animals. There are present, also, primitive sex ducts, male and female—the *mesonephric* or *Wolffian ducts* and the primitive oviducts (*Müllerian ducts*). In the embryos of most vertebrates there is a stage of development in which both ducts are simultaneously present and fully formed (Fig. 3), but in some cases the oviduct in the male embryo may begin to degenerate locally before it is completely laid down. Such local defects in the formation of embryonic primordia lead to predictable variations in experimental results.

The two pairs of embryonic sex ducts extend posteriorly to join the cloacal chamber. In the lower vertebrates this primitive arrangement is but little modified, but in mammals the sex ducts connect with a subdivision of the cloaca—the *urinogenital sinus*—which is partitioned off as a common genitourinary passage (Fig. 3). Copulatory organs are developed in many groups, represented in the bisexual stage of the embryo by a small prominence on the ventral body wall at the external opening of the urinogenital sinus. This structure—the *genital tubercle*—like the genital ridge, remains morphologically undifferentiated for some time, retaining meanwhile the capacity to form genitalia of male or female type. From these simple structures of the early embryo are differentiated all the basic parts of the genital tracts of both sexes (Burns, 1942).

Both from the developmental and the phylogenetic standpoint, many of the accessory organs of sex are primarily somatic or asexual structures. They first arise as parts of other organ systems, and temporarily or permanently, function as such; only secondarily are they incorporated into the reproductive tract. Since in embryological origin many of them long antedate the gonads, their early development can hardly depend in any way on the differentiation of the latter. Evidently it is determined according to the general principles which govern the formation of a limb, or an eye, or any other organ. On the other hand, many sex structures arising later in development appear to be dependent from an early stage on the gonad; and in some cases, indeed, the presence or absence of a part can be wholly controlled by hormone treatments. Each embryonic structure, therefore, presents an individual problem as to the stage in development at which it becomes responsive to hormones.

III. The Present Status of the Problem

In view of the very large amount of work in this field in recent years, and the evident complexities, it is not surprising that considerable disagreement has existed among investigators, both as regards actual findings, and their interpretation within the general framework of the theory. However, it is not difficult to find broad common ground on which most would agree; difficulty arises only in setting limits to this area which will be generally accepted. The recent trend has undoubtedly been in favor of more general agreement on major questions. Before attempting further discussions it may be helpful at this point to summarize as briefly as possible the essential points of the hormone theory as it now appears, and the nature of the supporting evidence. Such a summary will of necessity introduce in advance the main conclusions to be developed later; however this may be an advantage if only by way of defining the target and clarifying the general aim. Incidentally it will also serve to indicate the chief lines of experimental attack and the methods used in pressing them.

(1). At the beginning of the period of sex differentiation the vertebrate embryo possesses dual sets of primordia, representing in prospect all the structures necessary for the development of the genital system of either sex. Differentiation of an ovary, or a testis, is normally followed by development of the corresponding set of accessory structures. This bisexual plan of organization in the young embryo provides a basic morphological pattern, or "substrate" on which hormone action is exerted.

(2). In experimental studies of the differentiation of the gonads, marked differences have been found among various groups in their responses to hormones. In fishes, amphibians and birds there is extensive evidence, both from grafting experiments and from the administration of pure hormones, that the differentiation of the gonad as testis or as ovary is itself reversible, the histological structure being transformed in accordance with the type of hormone. As yet such evidence is lacking in mammalian embryos, and in this respect the freemartin with its highly modified gonad (sterile testis) stands in marked contrast with other forms.

(3). The role of hormones in the differentiation of the accessory sex structures laid down as primordia during the bisexual stage of development, has been studied by several methods. Various grafting techniques have been utilized, designed to introduce a hormone of one type into an embryo of the other sex; also the direct administration of hormones has been widely employed, first in the form of crude extracts, later as pure preparations. Conversely, castration of mammalian embryos has been successfully carried out in recent years, providing a clear test of the capacity of the sex primordia to differentiate in the absence of hormonal guidance from the gonad. From the results of these widely different experimental approaches the following general conclusions may be ventured subject to modifications, or reservations, which will appear in the proper place:

(4). The results of castration show that the embryonic testis is essential for normal development of the male genital tract and other accessory structures; in the absence of the testis some parts fail entirely to appear, some already present retrogress, still others are arrested in their development and assume a female character. The female duct system—which normally degenerates—persists in male castrates and develops. In the female, however, the consequences of castration are less severe, and a special problem enters here in the possible effects of maternal hormones. The severity of castration effects depends in general upon the stage of development at which the operation is performed.

(5). The effects of hormone treatment on the other hand, are positive, and the modifications induced are of the same character, whether the hormone is "natural" (i.e., elaborated by living tissues) or in the form of a chemically pure preparation. Male hormones induce accelerated differentiation and hypertrophy of all parts of the male genital system in male embryos, and differentiation of the corresponding male rudiments in females; on the other hand, female hormones stimulate the development of female structures in embryos of either sex, and in some cases powerfully inhibit the differentiation of male parts. Thus, in the highly selective actions which they exert upon the individual sex primordia, and upon the developing genital system as a whole, hormones appear to behave as specific differentiating agents. The extent to which these general statements must be qualified in dealing with different animal groups and many different experimental conditions, is best considered as the evidence is presented.

(6). The weight of evidence at present favors the view that the hormones, or sex differentiating principles, of the embryonic gonads are identical in nature with those of adult animals.

IV. Differentiation of the Gonad

Bisexual structure of the gonad is a widespread and highly variable phenomenon in vertebrates. In some cyclostomes, for example, early bisexual structure is retained and the adults are hermaphroditic; but in most vertebrates the condition is transient, although hermaphroditic or "intersexual" individuals occur not infrequently as anomalies.

1. Amphibians

Bisexuality is found in typical form in the immature gonads of amphibians, which themselves show wide variation from group to group, and even within species or different geographical races. In some forms the condition persists throughout larval life. Histologically, the undifferentiated gonad shows two distinct zones: an inner *medulla,* representing the male or testicular component, and an outer *cortex*—the ovarial constituent (Fig. 1). One of these components, prescribed by genetic constitution, is destined to develop into the definitive gonad—testis or ovary; the other undergoes involution, or persists, subject to much variation, in a rudimentary condition.

In normal differentiation it is maintained that the genetically dominant constituent of the gonad exerts a direct, inhibitory effect on its opponent, at the same time activating its own differentiation. This dual role is mediated in theory by means of hypothetical *inductor substances*—"medullarin" or "corticin"—which exert their effects locally, and are transmitted by diffusion through the tissues rather than through the circulation. By definition, therefore, the inductors are humoral in nature, but not hormones. Under some circumstances, however, their influences may be extended beyond the confines of the gonad, affecting adjacent organs, but presumably involving the same mode of transmission. There has been much incon-

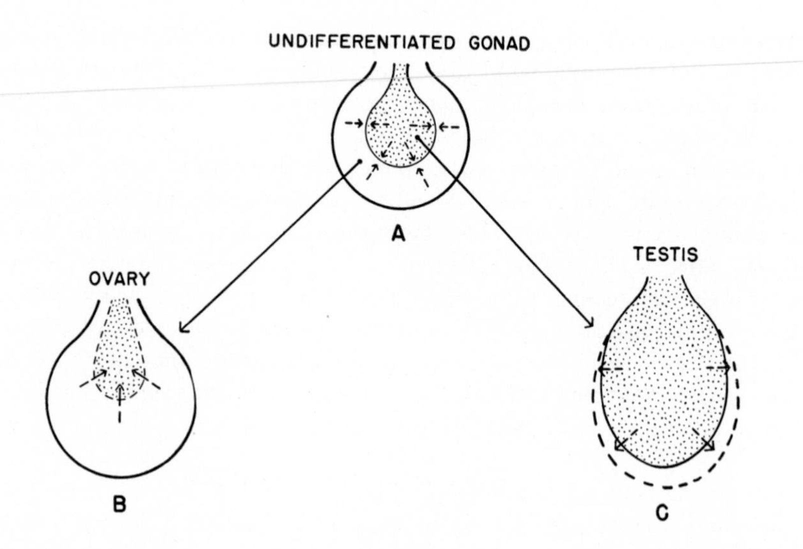

FIGURE 1

Diagrams illustrating the histological components in the bisexual stage of the amphibian gonad and their role in the differentiation of ovary and testis. The centrally placed *medulla* (stippled) represents the testicular component, and the peripheral *cortex* the ovarial element. The arrows indicate the antagonistic or inhibitory action exerted by each component against the other until final dominance of one is established.

clusive debate regarding the identity of inductor substances with the sex hormones—a question which must be left for later consideration.

The type of gonad organization just described exhibits in most amphibians a remarkable lability, and it should be pointed out at once that genetic constitution is itself an important factor in determining the capacity for experimental reversal. This is indicated by marked differences in behavior between major groups, species, or even between geographic races (Witschi, 1939). Genotypic variations are commonly manifested in the bisexual stage of the gonad by visible differences in the cortex-medulla ratio, or by the persistence of the bisexual or undifferentiated condition for a longer period of time.

It has been possible by a number of experimental means, such as various grafting procedures, or by *parabiosis,* in which whole organisms are united, to induce every degree of intersexuality in the structure of the gonad, as reflected by progressive changes in the cortex-medulla ratio (Fig. 2). The extent of reversal is influenced, as would be expected, by various factors such as the species used, time of initiation and the duration of the experiment, etc. In some cases reversal may end in complete sexual transforma-

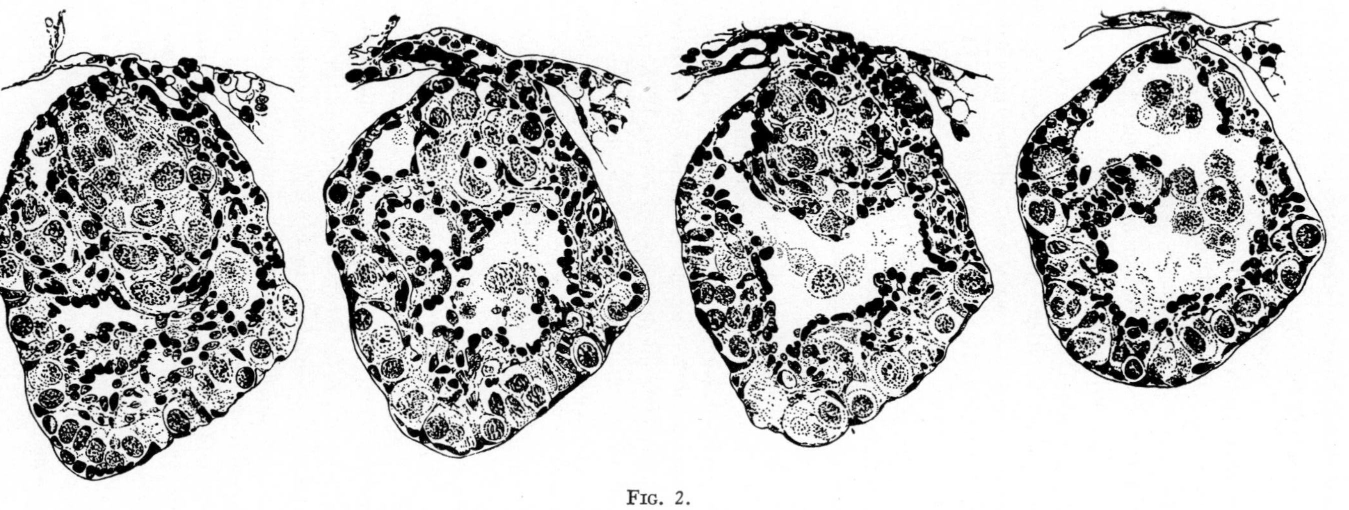

FIG. 2.

Four transverse sections at equal intervals through the testis of a male salamander, grafted as a parabiotic twin to a large female of another species. This gonad is in course of transformation into an ovary by progressive degeneration of its medullary component. In the section at the left the medulla is still well represented but is separated by incipient spaces from the outlying cortical zone. By enlargement and confluence of these spaces (primary cavities of the rete cords) the medulla is gradually broken down and replaced by a large central ovarian cavity in which scattered medullary germ cells still survive. The cortical zone, surrounding the ovarial cavity, has a structure approaching that of a normal ovary, although transformtion is not yet complete.

tion, with production of functional gametes of the opposite sex. It is clear in such instances that differentiation of the germ cells is conditioned by the transformation of their histological environment. When reversal is slow, or remains incomplete, there may be reversion to the primary sex, if the reversing stimulus is withdrawn or weakened (Humphrey, 1942).

However, reversal of sex in the gonad is also readily induced in many species by the use of pure hormones; and in such case the histological changes are virtually identical with those which follow parabiosis or grafting. The general statement may be made that the undifferentiated gonads of anuran larvae are readily reversible in either direction by treatment with androgens or estrogens; in later stages the ovary can still be transformed, but the testis—through deterioration of its cortical component—has largely lost its reversibility (Mintz *et al.* 1945). In urodele amphibians the picture is less clear, and the capacity for reversal appears to depend within wide limits on species, dosage, timing and such experimental factors. Under some conditions the effects of certain androgenic hormones are inconsistent. They have produced—in addition to the expected effects on male characters—a stimulation of the cortex of the gonad. It has been definitely shown in some instances that this *paradoxical effect* occurs only when the dose is very large and is not found at lower dosages (Vannini, 1946). This is an important matter, which will be considered again in connection with other problems. The fact that all the experimental agencies known to induce reversal in the gonad seem to operate at the same level of development, by altering the cortex-medulla balance, also raises questions for future consideration.

2. *Birds*

The gonads of birds exhibit a similar bisexual structure in early development, with complications in the better known species introduced by marked lateral asymmetry—especially in the female. In the chick—the form most thoroughly studied—asymmetry is extreme. The left ovary (destined to be the functional organ) develops both *cortex* and *medulla,* with cortex strongly preponderant; the right ovary suffers an early arrest of development, before the formation of cortex, and remains thereafter a mere rudiment composed virtually of medullary tissue. In male embryos asymmetry is less marked; a cortical component is present on both testes, although much better developed on the left. The consequences, in terms of experimental reversibility, are interesting and entirely consistent with the embryonic structure (Willier, 1939).

Treatment of female embryos with certain *male hormones* (*testosterone* compounds) induces development of the *medullary component* in both ovaries and there is regression of the cortex of the left, more or less complete according to dosage. Testicular differentiation is initiated in both ovaries through hypertrophy and development of the medullary tissue. If the cortex is not entirely suppressed, the left ovary may remain an ovo-testis. The gonads of male embryos remain essentially normal. When male "urinary hormones" (*androsterone* and related forms) are used, the effects upon ovaries are like those induced by testosterone; but in male embryos there may be differentiation of the cortical component of the left testis—a paradoxical result like that just described in some experiments with amphibians.

If chick embryos are exposed to *female hormones* the effects are more consistent. In the male chick (in which medullary and cortical components are present in both gonads) female hormone induces development of cortex. This response is more marked in the left gonad which becomes an ovo-testis, or (with large doses) an almost normal ovary. The right gonad is less reactive, because of weaker representation of cortex, but becomes intersexual with larger dosages. Female embryos are always normal.

These results show that, as in amphibian gonads, reversal of differentiation by hormones is effected by an appropriate response of medullary or cortical elements, laid down in the bisexual stage of the gonad, and specifically organized as to sex. In such experiments there is again a tendency to revert to the normal pattern when the reversing influence is withdrawn, as in some experiments with amphibians. Similar effects have been produced by hormones in the embryos of ducks and a few other birds (Witschi, 1939).

Until recently, attempts to induce modifications in the chick embryo by grafts had been wholly negative, a cause for much speculation in view of the success of grafting techniques in amphibian embryos, and the demonstrated ability of chick gonads to undergo transformation as a result of hormone treatment. Transplantation of gonad tissue to the embryonic membranes of differentiating embryos produced no significant changes; and the converse experiment—transplanting undifferentiated gonads to the membranes of older embryos—was also without effect. The reasons for these failures are not yet fully apparent. However, quite recently changes similar in all respects to those induced by hormones, have been obtained by implanting differentiated gonad grafts directly into the body cavity of the embryo (Wolff, 1946-1947). When graft and host are of different sex, the host becomes intersexual. Ovarian grafts in male hosts induce differentiation of cortex on the left testis, to such an extent that it may show locally the structure of a normal ovary. This effect is most marked in the vicinity of the graft, indicating that the concentration of the agent is important. The right testis is less affected, histologically (as was the case also after hormone treatment) but its growth is greatly inhibited. Testicular grafts in female embryos have but little effect on the gonads, but other structures are greatly modified.

Studies of reptilian embryos have shown the same type of gonad organization as in birds, but with less asymmetry; and the response to hormones is, on the whole, quite similar.

3. *Mammals*

In the embryos of mammals the gonads again show bisexual organization after still another pattern. It appears to be essentially limited to the ovary. Although traces of cortex have been described on the testes of a few mammals (Willier, 1939), it is apparently not of constant occurrence in any species, and in comparison with the condition in amphibians or birds is almost negligible. On the other hand the embryonic ovary develops a medullary region, typical in structure and relationships, remains of which persist even in the adult. The simple plan exemplified in amphibians has been variously modified in other groups. For example, the cortical constituent is virtually lacking in mammalian testes, is unequally developed in the testes of birds (strongly on the left testis, rather weakly on the right—linked with the peculiar lateral asymmetry) and is strangely absent again in the right "ovary" of birds!

On the basis of structure alone, the ovaries of mammals should be amenable to reversal by virtue of possessing a medullary component, whereas the testes should lack capacity for transformation. In actual experience, all attempts to induce transformation experimentally in mammalian gonads of either sex have thus far failed. This statement is based on results of administration of hormones during the period of differentiation in a number of species; it is quite possible, however, that the gonad has not been exposed sufficiently early. On the other hand, the gonad of the freemartin (often called "Nature's experiment") is greatly modified, and it is conceivable that an appropriate method of grafting might prove effective, as was eventually demonstrated after many failures in the chick.

V. Differentiation of the Sex Ducts

1. *Amphibians*

In amphibians the sex ducts are simple in structure and show little regional specialization. The male ducts (mesonephric or *Wolffian ducts*) serve at first as kidney ducts in both sexes, and the genital function in the male is secondarily acquired. The oviducts (*Müllerian ducts*) develop later, during larval life. In the male of some species they are temporary, but in others they persist throughout life as complete, if somewhat rudimentary canals. Thus, with respect to the ducts, the bisexual phase may be confined to the larval period or may exist indefinitely. Normally the ducts show little functional differentiation until after metamorphosis, when growth of the gonads is markedly accelerated. It is then usually observed that the segments of the ducts immediately alongside the gonads are the first to show increased growth and coiling. This circumstance suggests a direct influence emanating from the gonad.

Transformation of sex in the gonad results, after some delay, in corresponding changes in the ducts, which react slowly under the influence of the dominant component of the gonad. When an hermaphroditic condition prevails for some time, both ducts may differentiate together, a behavior which indicates direct stimulation of the proper duct by each gonad constituent. Injected hormones induce precocious development even in larval life, apparently by direct action. *Testosterone* stimulates differentiation of the Wolffian duct in either sex, but the effect on the Müllerian duct varies with the stage at which the hormone acts. In early development differentiation is completely suppressed; later the same hormone may suppress the hinder region of the duct (still in course of differentiating) whereas the anterior portion (already formed) undergoes hypertrophy (Humphrey, 1942; Mintz, 1947). This is a type of paradox that is frequently encountered in the responses of the sex ducts. The manner in which the double action is mediated is still obscure; but evidence to be discussed later shows that in addition to timing, dosage is an essential factor.

Female hormones readily induce hypertrophy of the oviduct in either sex, but have no inhibitory action on the male duct.

2. *Birds*

In birds information on development of the ducts comes mainly from the use of hormones in the chick embryo. Disregarding variations based on lateral asymmetry, the results conform rather closely with those described in amphibians. *Male hormones* induce development of the *male ducts in both sexes;* but the effects on the oviducts again differ in detail with the type of hormone, the genetic sex of the embryo, and the laterality factor. There is general agreement that compounds of *testosterone* have only a masculinizing effect, inhibiting the oviduct; but when urinary androgen (*androsterone*) is used, the paradoxical effect which was noted in the gonad, is again encountered (Willier, 1939; Wolff, 1938). In male embryos the anterior ends of the *oviducts* instead of disappearing, survive and grow, presenting a parallel with the situation in amphibians, in which the anterior portion undergoes hypertrophy, whereas the region as yet undifferentiated is suppressed. In the female the main part of the functional oviduct is suppressed, but the anterior end behaves as in the male. The final effect is thus to reduce the female to the same status as the male, which is perhaps less of a paradox than first appeared.

The effects of *female hormones* are, as in amphibians, entirely consistent. The *oviducts undergo hypertrophy* in both sexes, with development in the male of a complete left oviduct, closely approximating the normal female pattern. There is again no inhibiting influence of female hormones on the mesonephric duct which, as the kidney duct, is, of course, an essential organ.

Once established, these effects of hormones on the embryonic oviduct are apparently *permanent*. Continuation of development, in the modified form, is insured even in the post-hatching period. In the male embryo (in which normally the Müllerian duct has disappeared by the fourteenth day of incubation) injection of estrogens at any time prior to the tenth day, induces permanence or "stabilization" of the anterior part of the duct; and certain androgens—by virtue of the paradoxical effect—have the same stabilizing power (Wolff, 1938). The permanent nature of these changes in the ducts is in contrast with the transient effects in the gonads, where continued treatment after hatching is necessary to maintain reversal.

It has been shown recently that identical modifications in the ducts are induced when gonads of older embryos, well advanced in differentiation, are implanted into the body cavity of younger embryos (Wolff, 1946-1947). The effects are in some respects more marked than those induced by hormone treatment, and likewise permanent; that is to say, the "stabilization effect" is also exerted by embryonic grafts.

3. Development of the Sex Ducts in Mammals

The embryonic sex ducts of mammals develop in the usual way, but in later differentiation show marked regional specialization. The main features are illustrated in Figs. 3 and 5. Efforts at various times to induce modifications of the duct systems in mammals by different types of grafting have yielded negative results (Moore, 1947; Price, 1947), but the method has its difficulties and has perhaps not been adequately tested. The recent success of gonad grafts in the chick embryo, after a long period of negative findings, should be borne in mind. Hormone administration, however, has produced striking effects upon the ducts in a number of species. These effects generally resemble those already reviewed, consequently emphasis will be laid mainly on certain differences and points of special significance. Since treatment with hormones has not thus far caused essential changes in the structure of the gonads in mammals, the effects upon the ducts may be ascribed to direct action.

Because of the early stage at which the embryos of marsupials are born, these primitive mammals offer an unusual opportunity for experiment (Burns, 1942; Moore, 1941). The embryos are sexually undifferentiated when born, and direct access to the young in the brood pouch permits treatment without surgical intervention. At birth only the male sex duct is present, in its capacity as mesonephric duct (Fig 3A). The Müllerian duct develops between the third and tenth day of pouch life, and at 10 days a bisexual stage is attained (Fig. 3B). The gonads, however, are by this time well differentiated. In females both sex ducts are complete and connect with the urinogenital sinus, but in males the Müllerian duct is usually defective posteriorly. Regression sets in, apparently, before connection is made with the sinus.

Injection of *male hormone* (*testosterone*) from birth onward has striking effects. In male embryos differentiation of all derivatives of the Wolffian duct is accelerated, and with larger doses hypertrophy becomes extreme; in female embryos an anatomically complete male duct system is developed, only slightly smaller than in treated males. But with large doses of the hormone, there is in both sexes stimulation of the Müllerian ducts as well. Females typically exhibit hypertrophy of all regions of the female genital tract, although in some cases the vaginal canal is suppressed. Male embryos (in which the Müllerian ducts normally atrophy) have well-developed oviducts and uteri (Fig. 4B) but vaginal canals (rudiments for which are lacking, as we have seen) are never found. In this marked reaction of the female duct to androgen we again have the now familiar *paradoxical effect* manifested in typical form.

However, further experiments with the opossum throw light on this puzzling phenomenon, showing that the paradox is in this case at least, entirely a matter of dosage. If the dose is diminished by steps the paradoxical reaction of the female duct declines, and at very low dosages disappears altogether. But a dose which has no detectable effect on the Müllerian duct, is still adequate to stimulate all male duct derivatives markedly (Burns, 1942). This fact seems of some importance since it shows that at a concentration properly adjusted to the responding structures the hormone acts in an orthodox and sex-specific manner. The empirical demonstration of this relationship, however, is not in itself conclusive.

Female hormone, even in small doses, causes great hypertrophy of the female genital tract in young opossums of both sexes, except that vaginal canals are absent in males. But in some circumstances there is stimulation of the *male duct* as well (Moore, 1947), (an effect which will be seen again in the rat). Here then is a paradoxical effect exerted by an estrogenic hormone.

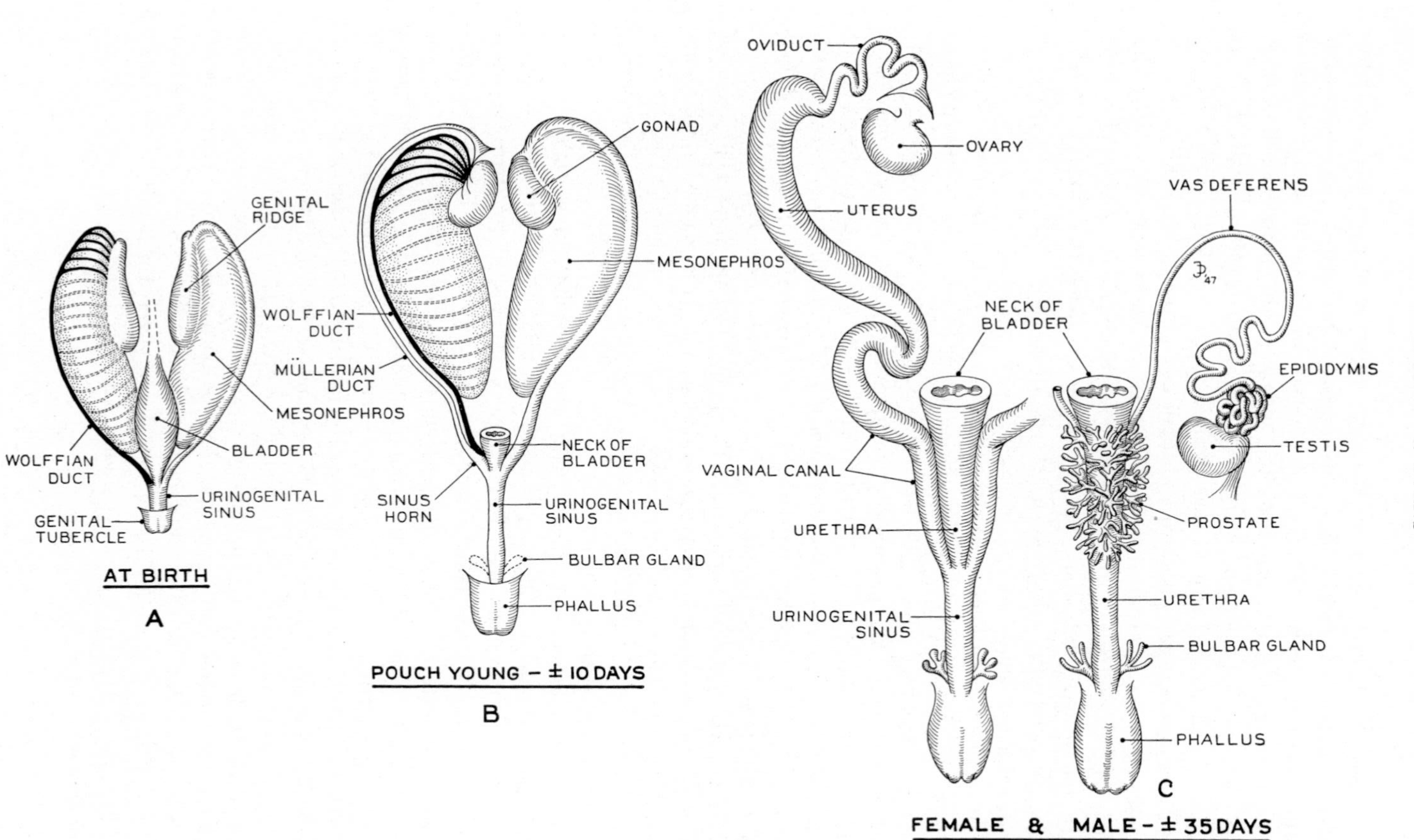
GENITAL RIDGE
WOLFFIAN DUCT
MÜLLERIAN DUCT
MESONEPHROS
BLADDER
WOLFFIAN DUCT
URINOGENITAL SINUS
GENITAL TUBERCLE
AT BIRTH
A
GONAD
MESONEPHROS
NECK OF BLADDER
SINUS HORN
URINOGENITAL SINUS
BULBAR GLAND
PHALLUS
POUCH YOUNG – ± 10 DAYS
B
OVIDUCT
OVARY
UTERUS
VAS DEFERENS
NECK OF BLADDER
EPIDIDYMIS
TESTIS
VAGINAL CANAL
PROSTATE
URETHRA
URETHRA
URINOGENITAL SINUS
BULBAR GLAND
PHALLUS
C
FEMALE & MALE – ± 35 DAYS

FIGURE 3.

FIG. 3.

Semidiagrammatic drawings of the sex structures at three stages of development in the opossum. *A*. At birth: the genital ridge is histologically undifferentiated, Wolffian ducts are present as ducts of the mesonephros, a short urinogenital sinus has formed by separation from the cloaca, and a small genital tubercle represents the copulatory organ. *B*. About 10 days after birth: the gonad is now well differentiated histologically. The female sex duct, or Müllerian duct, has just completed its development, connecting with the urinogenital sinus alongside the Wolffian duct (the condition pictured represents the *female*—in males the Müllerian duct is incomplete at its posterior end). The urinogenital sinus has elongated greatly, and the genital tubercle has become the phallus, in which the rudiments of the erectile bodies are well differentiated but as yet in an indifferent condition. *C*. Female and male genital tracts at the end of morphogenesis. The Müllerian duct has differentiated regionally into oviduct, uterus and vaginal canal; the Wolffian duct (with certain mesonephric tubules previously indicated in black) has given rise to the epididymis and vas deferens. In each case the heterologous sex duct has been reduced to insignificant vestiges, not illustrated. The urinogenital sinus shows marked dimorphism, characterized by profuse growth of prostatic glands in the male, and changed relationships due to vaginal differentiation in the female.

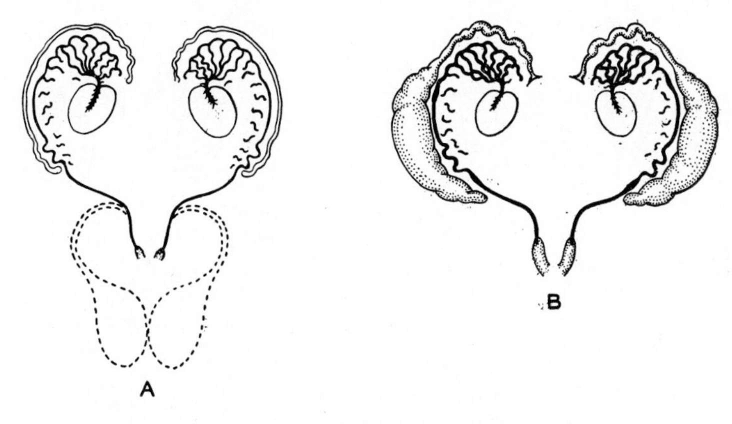

FIG. 4.

Semidiagrammatic drawings illustrating the paradoxical action of large doses of *testosterone propionate* in male opossums treated for 50 days after birth. *A*. Normal male: the male duct system—epididymis and vas deferens—is displayed (in black) in the primitive position, after dissection and removal of the testes from the scrotal sacs, which are indicated in dotted lines. A slender undifferentiated segment of the Müllerian duct (uncolored), representing the oviducal and part of the uterine region, survives. *B*. The ducts in a treated male, showing pronounced hypertrophy and differentiation of the persistent regions of the female duct into oviduct and uterus, induced by large doses of androgen. (In females the vaginal region is also present and all parts are enormously hypertrophied.) After Burns, 1939. *Jour. Morphol.* **65**, 105. By permission of the Wistar Institute.

In placental mammals[1] there are important differences as compared with opossums. The results reported for the rat may be considered typical (Greene, 1942). *Male hormones* do not affect the differentiation of male embryos (in opossums there is a strong accelerating effect) but all females develop a complete male duct system (Fig. 5, left). Because the derivatives

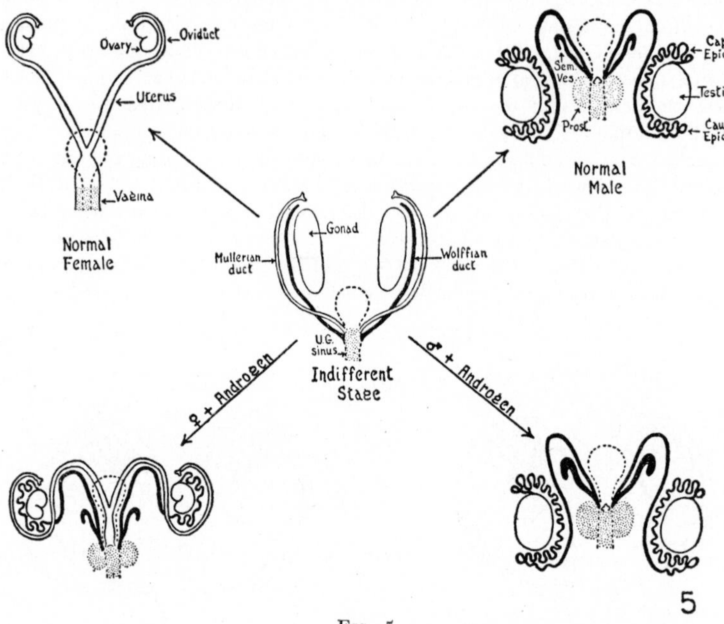

FIG. 5.

Modifications induced in the genital systems of rat embryos exposed *in utero* to the action of androgen. The bisexual stage of differentiation is shown in the center. Differentiation of the male embryo is not modified except for slight enlargement of prostate and seminal vesicles (lower right). A complete male duct system is differentiated in female embryos (lower left) which also retain the female duct in a slightly inhibited condition. Compare with the normal female above. From Greene, 1942. *Biological Symposia*, **9**, 107. By permission of the Ronald Press Company.

of the Müllerian duct are also developed, such females are completely intersexual. Retention of the Müllerian duct in this case may be due to lack of adequate inhibition by the androgen, or to intervention of the paradoxical influence.

---

[1]A number of the common laboratory animals have been used with results which are generally very similar, among them the *rat, mouse, guinea pig, hamster* and *monkey*. The method used is injection of the pregnant female with large doses of hormone during the period of sex differentiation in the embryo. The procedure is simple but, because of severe physiological disturbances, the mortality is high during the earlier stages of pregnancy. The dose which reaches the embryo cannot be determined.

Estrogens seriously impair the differentiation of male embryos. The Wolffian duct may be almost completely suppressed, or local remnants may survive. The Müllerian duct (which in normal males has disappeared at birth) is stimulated to such an extent that large portions of the definitive oviduct and uterine region persist (Fig. 6, right). In the female embryo estrogens cause marked hypertrophy of the female tract (Fig. 6, left) and

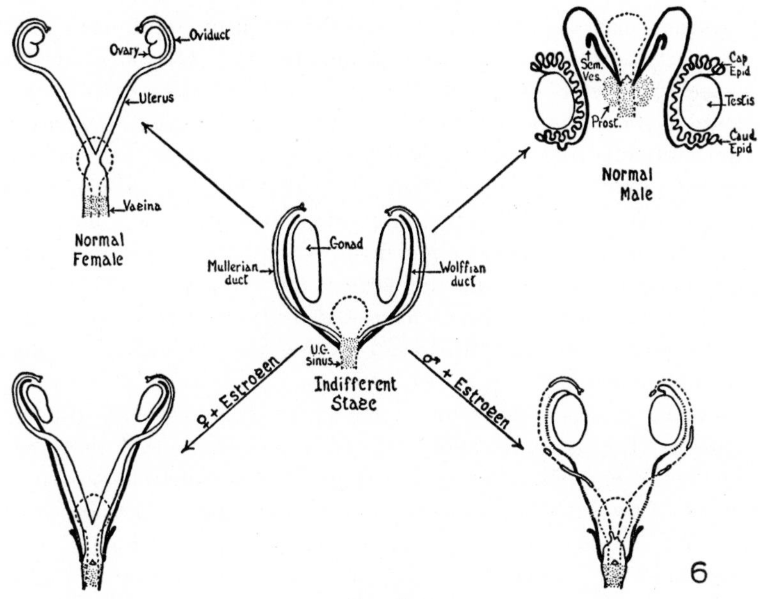

FIG. 6.

Modifications induced in the genital systems of rat embryos exposed *in utero* to the action of estrogen. The bisexual stage of differentiation is shown in the center. Differentiation of the Wolffian duct in male embryos (lower right) is strongly repressed, only fragments of the male duct persisting. At the same time considerable portions of the Müllerian ducts (lacking in normal males—see above) are retained. In female embryos (lower left) the female genital tract shows marked hypertrophy, and paradoxically the male duct is also present in a nearly normal condition (compare with normal female above). From Greene, 1942. *Biological Symposia,* **9**, 109. By permission of The Ronald Press Company.

at the same time the male duct (instead of disappearing, as in normal development, or being partially inhibited, as in the treated male), also develops—again a paradoxical effect of a *female hormone* on the male duct.

It will be noted, that in addition to the commonly reported paradoxical effect of androgen upon the female duct, we have now two instances in mammals of a converse effect of estrogen upon the male duct. For androgen it was shown that in all probability the paradox is an effect of high dosage.

Whether the paradoxical effect of estrogen is also a function of dosage cannot be determined, since the method of administration does not permit estimation of the dose. However, in the rat, circumstances which will be discussed further on suggest this explanation.

4. *Effects upon the Duct Systems Summarized*

At this point a brief summary of the effects of sex hormones upon the duct systems may be attempted, since the frequent appearance of paradoxical effects cannot fail to confuse the picture. *Male hormones* have always the expected *positive action* on the male, and in many cases a decided *inhibitory action* on the female ducts; but, paradoxically, the latter are sometimes stimulated. There appear to be two significant factors in this unexpected response. In amphibians and birds the state of differentiation of the duct when the stimulus is applied is evidently important; for (in the former) the paradoxical action involves only the portions of the duct already differentiated, or (in the latter) those parts which are last to regress in male subjects. In each case it is the anterior region—a fact seemingly related to the chronological order of development. Because experimental conditions are so varied, it is not possible to say in these cases whether dosage is a factor in the paradoxical response, although in the opossum, this is undoubtedly so. It is possible indeed that the two factors are closely related, with the stage of differentiation of the tissue influencing a threshold of response, above which the paradoxical response occurs. We must consider, therefore, whether paradoxical effects are not essentially the product of special experimental conditions. *Female hormones* are, on the whole, more consistent in their actions, and although paradoxical effects are found, they present less of a problem.

It should be pointed out that the derivatives of the duct systems are particularly prone to paradoxical responses because their development proceeds from separate primordia—the primitive sex ducts of the embryo. Thus it is possible for structures which normally represent alternative pathways of development to differentiate together, without direct interference. Consequently, when two tendencies—the normal and the paradoxical—coexist, both may be realized; they do not compete for control of the same primordium. In the development of many sex structures the latter situation is found, and paradoxical effects are not encountered.

VI. Differentiation of the Urinogenital Sinus

The *urinogenital sinus* of the mammalian embryo is formed from the cloaca early in development by separation of the ventral portion, into which the sex ducts open (Figs. 3A, 5). It is a primordium which gives rise to definitive structures in each sex. Unlike sex ducts, the sinus in its final differentiation must follow one of two distinct courses, and cannot simultaneously give rise to both male and female types. In theory, then, the differentiation of the sinus provides a simpler test of hormone action, because paradoxical effects are virtually excluded. Experimental findings support this assumption; the effects of androgens, or of estrogens, on the sinus and its derivatives are specific to a high degree.

In its later development the urinogenital sinus acquires in each sex a characteristic anatomical form (Fig. 3C). In the female this form is in part the result of changes imposed by vaginal development; and in both sexes it is influenced by the character of the external genitalia. The details of these changes must be passed over. A prominent feature of sinus development is found in the differentiation of prostatic glands, more or less elaborately developed in the males of all mammals. In placental mammals prostatic rudiments are present at first in both sexes, and so a bisexual stage exists; but in the female they survive only as vestiges, or disappear. In marsupials the female embryo lacks prostatic buds at all stages, and a morphologically bisexual stage is never realized; nevertheless, the potentiality exists in the sinus epithelium and prostatic development is readily evoked by androgens. In estimating the influence of hormones on the differentiation of the sinus, three main criteria are used: (1) the gross form of the sinus; (2) prostatic development, as a masculine trait, and (3) the differentiation of the sinus epithelium, which is equally characteristic in the female. The effects obtained in young opossums are typical (Burns, 1942a, b; Moore, 1941; Moore, 1947).

Treatment with *male hormone* greatly accelerates differentiation in male embryos. The prostatic buds appear somewhat earlier than normal, and proliferate enormously. In female embryos the sinus rapidly assumes the male form, and prostatic growth is only a little less profuse than in treated males, far exceeding that of normal males of the same age (Fig. 7). The amount of growth varies directly with the dosage. *Female hormone* has an exactly opposite effect. In the male, prostatic differentiation is completely suppressed and the sinus assumes the female form, with an epithelium characteristic of the mature female (Fig. 8). Exposure to a small dose of estrogen for a period of a few days at the time the prostatic buds should emerge is sufficient for complete inhibition (Burns, 1942a). Thus, the presence of androgen during the critical stage of sinus differentiation induces a purely male condition in female embryos; conversely, estrogen produces a sinus of female type. The effects upon prostatic differentiation are permanent. Glands induced in females persist indefinitely in the absence of further treatment (Moore, 1947); and development in the male is not resumed once the early rudiments have been inhibited (Burns, 1942a).

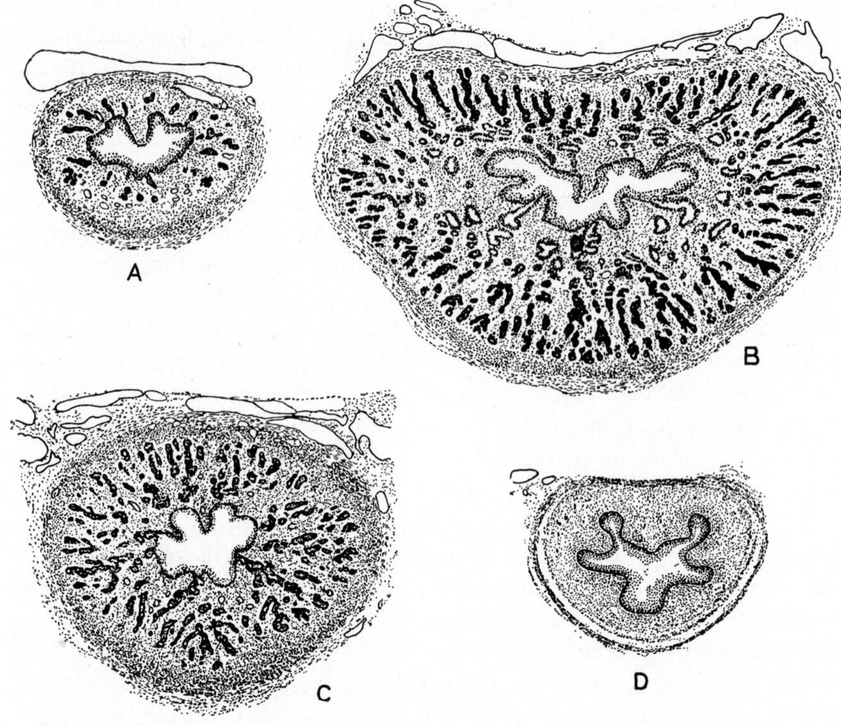

FIG. 7.

The effects of large doses of androgen (*testosterone propionate*) on the differentiation of the urinogenital sinus and prostate glands in young opossums treated from birth to an age of 50 days. *A*. Normal male, aged 50 days. The branching prostatic glands are shown in black. *B*. Hypertrophic development of the prostate, induced by androgen, in a male littermate of the specimen shown in *A*.

The female opossum (*D*) does not normally develop prostatic rudiments at any stage. Five prominent longitudinal folds are seen in cross-section, of which the upper pair represent the terminations of the vaginal canals (cf. Fig. 3C). In *C* appears the prostatic differentiation induced by male hormone in a female littermate of the others. Note that the differentiation is far greater than in the normal male (above) but less than in the treated male, although the dosage was the same.

VII. Differentiation of the External Genitalia

The development of the external genitalia closely parallels that of the sinus in that from identical primordia two distinct anatomical types are finally differentiated. The first rudiment of the copulatory structures—the *genital tubercle*—is present in a young opossum at birth as a protuberance of the body wall at the external opening of the sinus (Fig. 3A). In the early postnatal period the tubercle enlarges, forming a sexually indifferent

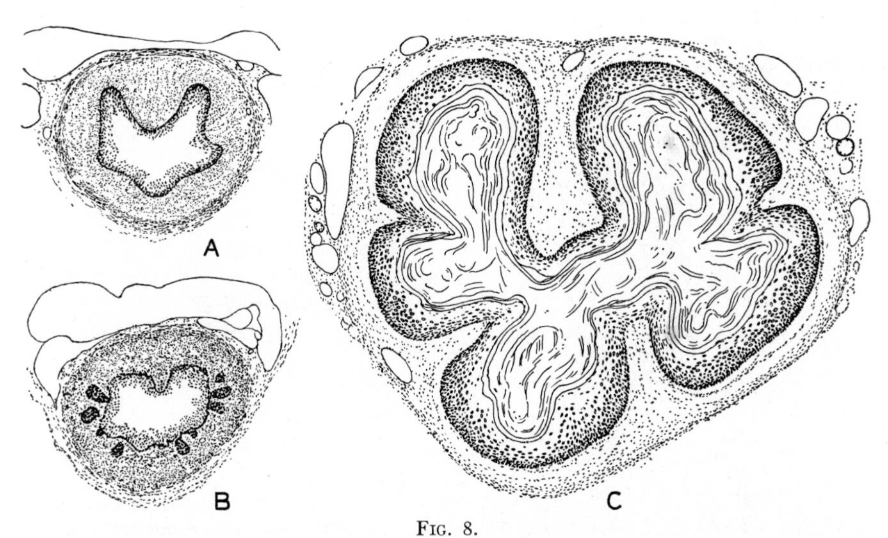

FIG. 8.

The effects of estrogen (*estradiol dipropionate*) on the differentiation of the urinogenital sinus and prostatic glands in young opossums treated from birth to an age of 30 days. *A*. Normal female, aged 30 days. The longitudinal folds seen in cross-section are less prominent than at 50 days; and there are no rudiments of prostatic glands. *B*. Normal male, aged 30 days, showing solid, unbranched prostatic buds, and bi-lobed cross-section characteristic of the male sinus. *C*. The sinus of a male treated from birth with estrogen. There is enormous hypertrophy of the sinus, and a greatly thickened, cornified epithelium like that of the adult female. Prostatic glands are lacking, and will not subsequently develop after such treatment. Note that the 5-lobed form of the cross-section is characteristic of the female (cf. *A* and Fig. 7D).

phallus (Fig. 3B) in which the rudiments of the erectile bodies are clearly defined as localized condensations in the mesenchyme. Distinct morphological differentiation is not apparent until about the age of 30 days, and the final form is largely determined by the fate of the erectile bodies, which are highly developed in the penis, vestigial in the clitoris.

The two alternative types are developed precociously and conditioned in a striking way by sex hormones. The effects of treatment with *testosterone propionate,* or with *estradiol dipropionate,* over the first 20 days of postnatal life, are contrasted in two male embryos in Fig. 9. *Male hormone* has a remarkable effect upon the development of the erectile bodies in embryos of either sex, inducing rapid differentiation and gross hypertrophy. The transformed female organ is structurally identical with that of the male but always remains slightly smaller (Figs. 10A and B). *Estrogens* suppress the differentiation of the erectile bodies (Burns, 1942b) and characteristically female genitalia develop in treated males (Figs. 10C and D). Comparable effects on the external genitalia have been shown in the rat,

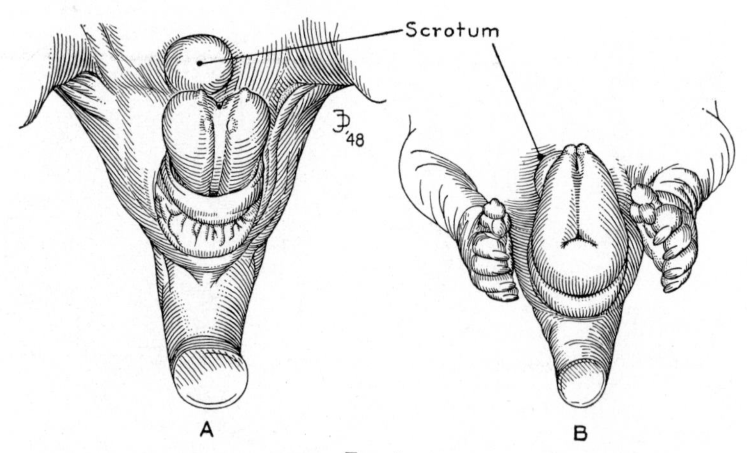

FIG. 9.

The typical effects of large doses of androgen (*testosterone propionate*) and estrogen (*estradiol dipropionate*) on the differentiation of the phallus in young opossums treated from birth to an age of 20 days. *A*. The effect of the male hormone on the form of the phallus in a young male, identified by the scrotum just anterior to the phallus. The size and form of the structure is determined mainly by hypertrophy and precocious differentiation of the erectile bodies. *B*. Female type of genitalia produced in another *male* (note the partially hidden scrotum at the left) by estrogen. In two male embryos either of two distinct types of genitalia is produced by the proper hormone. Had both embryos been female the result would have been the same.

mouse and other forms. Androgens cause hypertrophy of the phallus, which assumes a penis-like form in both sexes. Estrogens induce retention of the urethral cleft (hypospadias) and genitalia of female type.[2]

VIII. EMBRYONIC CASTRATION AND THE HORMONE THEORY

Striking as are the demonstrated effects of hormones in the differentiation of many sex structures, the conclusion that they are therefore the determiners of normal differentiation does not inevitably follow. The question may be directly tested, however, by castration of the embryo. The difficulties of this operation are obvious, and only recently have convincing results been obtained, which confirm in a striking manner the theory that differentiation is dependent on a hormone from the gonad.

[2]The males of some birds possess a well-developed copulatory organ within the cloacal vent which develops from a small conical structure regarded as homologous with the *genital tubercle* of mammalian embryos. This structure is unusually well developed in the male duck. In duck embryos the differentiation of the penis can be controlled by hormones in exactly the same way as in mammals; *androgen* conditioning development of the organ in either sex, and *estrogen* causing its suppression (Wolff and Wolff, 1947).

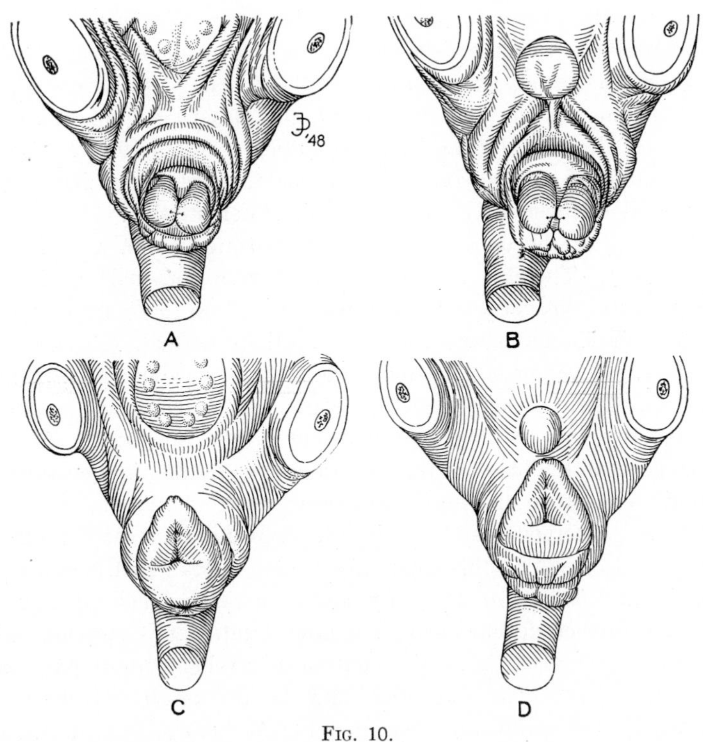

FIG. 10.

The effects of the same androgen and estrogen as in Fig. 9, in older opossums. Genetic sex is identified by the presence of the pouch in females (left) and the scrotum in males. *A.* and *B.* Littermate specimens treated with androgen from birth to an age of *50 days.* The form of the phallus in the two cases is identical and independent of genetic sex. *C.* and *D.* Corresponding effects of estrogen in female and male littermates, treated from birth to an age of *30 days.* The result is again independent of the genetic sex of the subject. The same effects may be obtained if hormone treatment is begun at any age up to ±25 days, and perhaps even later in the case of male hormone in large dosages. Suppression of the development of erectile tissue by estrogen is even more extreme than in younger stages.

In defining the differentiation period it is arbitrary to distinguish sharply between pre- and post-natal stages. In animals born in a relatively immature condition, structures that appear late in development may continue to differentiate actively after birth; for example, the prostate gland. Some years ago it was reported that castration of the newborn rat is followed by atrophic changes in the male, affecting particularly the *seminal vesicles* and *external genitalia.* The changes were prevented when male hormone was administered. Castration in females caused no appreciable atrophy until the approach of puberty. These observations (with others) were used to support a so-called "mon-hormonic theory" of sex differentiation in mammals, according to which male development is dependent upon a hormone produced in the testis; development of the female system, on the other hand, does not depend upon the ovary, but occurs automatically, so to speak, in the absence of male hormone (Wiesner, 1934-1935). The backward projection of this reasoning into prenatal development has suggested that maternal estrogen may control female differentiation.

Pouch young of the opossum have been castrated at an age of 20 days (Moore, 1947). There is no definite atrophy of the male genital tract, and the prostate continues to develop more or less, up to an age of 100 days. In female castrates development is also essentially normal. Young opossums at 20 days are developmentally about the stage of newborn rats, permitting comparisons. There is agreement as to the lack of effect of castration in the female, but the continued development of the prostate is in contrast with the general findings in the rat; and the results in opossums were considered to disprove the hormone theory of differentiation. But it may be questioned whether castration in the opossum was carried out early enough to be decisive. In this connection we must recall that prostate glands *induced in the female opossum by androgen* retain their structure and capacity for further development long after treatment is stopped (Moore, 1947). In both species, also, the continued development of parts of the female genital tract after castration may be the result of earlier conditioning, as in the "stabilizing effect" on the Müllerian ducts of the chick, where the permanent character of changes induced in the sex ducts by hormones has been clearly demonstrated (Wolff, 1938; Wolff, 1946-1947).

Castration in *prenatal development* has been accomplished in two mammalian species—the rat and the rabbit. In the former (Wells, 1946) the results are of a preliminary nature, and hardly conclusive because of the short period of observation. Male fetuses castrated in the uterus and recovered 2 to 3 days later (just prior to birth) show small but consistent reductions in the seminal vesicles and bulbo-urethral glands. Differentiation of these glands had already begun before castration, and regression of the heterologous sex ducts was also under way.

Castration has been performed in rabbit embryos at 1-day intervals between the 19th and the 24th days of gestation, and the fetuses removed for study on the 28th day, when sexual differentiation is virtually complete (Jost, 1947). Castration at 24 days is followed by normal development; on the other hand, in males castrated on the 21st day (when both sex ducts are present) the Wolffian ducts and their derivatives (ampullae, seminal vesicle) are absent, but the derivatives of the Müllerian ducts, which have disappeared in normal males, are well developed. The prostate is reduced in size and the genitalia are of female type. These male castrates closely resemble normal females. If castration is carried out between the 21st and 20th days only prostatic buds are formed, and if earlier still—before the 20th day—the prostate is absent altogether. It thus appears that a very brief period, just prior to the 20th day, is critical for development of the prostate; and that in this period the presence of the testis is essential. This result of castration in the fetal rabbit is entirely compatible with the effects of injected hormones in opossum embryos, in which, at a comparable stage, when the prostatic buds make their appearance in the male embryo, they are permanently suppressed by a small dose of estrogen. In the same period, androgen induces their differentiation in the female.

All of the effects of castration reported above are counteracted by male hormone administered at operation, and males castrated unilaterally remain *normal.*[3] In female rabbit fetuses, castrated at any age, the female genital tract is not significantly affected, as was noted also in the rat and the opossum. It must be emphasized that *castrates of both sexes, and normal females, are remarkably similar in their anatomy,* all possessing female but lacking male ducts.

We must conclude from this evidence that in the rabbit *the embryonic testis is necessary for differentiation of the male genital tract and accessory glands*—in its absence the Wolffian ducts fail to develop, and the Müllerian ducts, through lack of an inhibitory action, persist and differentiate as in the female. Development of the Müllerian ducts in the female however, is *not dependent on the ovary;* they develop also in castrates of both sexes. These results support the older "mon-hormonic theory," that in mammals only the male hormone is necessary to bring about differentiation; but we cannot dismiss the possibility that estrogen from the mother, known to be present in the fetal fluids of many mammals, including the rabbit (Price, 1947), is sufficient for differentiation of the female. This theory is adapted in particular to the conditions of mammalian development, and the rôle of the ovary in the development of lower forms is not called into question.[4]

---

[3]The last statement must be qualified slightly in a few instances of unilateral castration on or before the 20th day, i.e., near the early limits of the operation. In these early cases, there is a definitely *localized effect* of the remaining testis. The Wolffian duct on the side of the testis is preserved, but on the opposite side it is defective or lacking, and the Müllerian duct has survived. This interesting and significant result should be compared with local effects upon adjacent parts of the sex ducts, cited in amphibians, and a very similar effect of gonad grafts within the body cavity in chick embryos (Wolff, 1946-1947).

[4]A rare anomaly of development in the human female is of particular significance in this connection (Wilkins and Fleischmann, 1944). In the condition known clinically as *agenesis of the ovary,* that organ is so rudimentary or degenerate in character as

If the impressive evidence obtained from embryonic castration of the rabbit stood alone, its general validity might be doubted. However, in spite of certain puzzling features, Lillie's interpretation of the freemartin remains firmly established, and many characteristics of the freemartin are consistent in theory with the results of castration. In birds also it appears that the previously established belief that gonad grafts have no effect on sex differentiation must now be abandoned. Finally, in amphibians, the evidence from certain types of grafting, and from most parabiosis experiments, has always required the assumption of blood-borne differentiating agents, originating in the gonads. It has been suggested that in the freemartin the active agent may come from the whole organism rather than from the gonads. This hypothesis might conceivably apply to parabiotic twins, but could not apply to graft experiments, and it is contradicted by the results of castration. Until direct evidence compels a different conclusion it seems preferable to interpret all these cases on one basis.

IX. The Nature and Identity of Sex Differentiating Agents

New evidence supporting the rôle of embryonic hormones in sex differentiation, reopens old questions as to their identity, or essential similarity, with other sex differentiating agents which have been postulated. This problem may be approached at the three main levels of development at which such agents have been presumed to operate: (1) gonad differentiation, thought by some to be the special province of inductor substances; (2) development of the accessory parts, commonly considered to be dependent on a hormone from the embryonic gonad—a view now substantiated by the results of castration; and (3) the development and regulation of secondary sex characters, functions, and other phenomena of late development or maturity. The last category is of incidental interest only, since the rôle of hormones in this period has been long accepted.

Fundamental distinctions have been claimed between hormones and inductor substances, on the basis of chemical nature, mode of action and medium of transport. But these differences have not in the past been universally conceded, and can no longer be accepted as well established. Of chemical evidence there is none—inductor substances are as yet hypo-

to be in many cases no more than a slender cord of dense connective tissue, or stroma. Typical cases are recognized at the approach of puberty by the failure of the female secondary sex characters to appear and the absence of the menstrual cycle. A child-like physique is retained and growth is arrested. In these individuals, in which there is reason to believe that ovarian differentiation never occurred, there is a fully formed female genital tract although of infantile proportions. Early morphological development of all derivatives of the Müllerian duct was not impaired.

thetical. As for their other characteristics, inductors are assumed to exert local effects (primarily within the confines of the gonad) of a highly specific nature, inhibiting differentiation of the antagonistic gonad component while promoting the development of their own. They are typically transmitted by direct diffusion through tissue, but under suitable conditions may spread to adjacent organs. In some types of parabiosis, gonads of opposite sex are influenced directly in this way (Witschi, 1939). It has been noted, however, that the first indications of active differentiation in the sex ducts of amphibians often appear in the immediate vicinity of the gonads, before effects are evident in more distant regions. This situation suggests direct transmission of a stimulus. At the same period, however, the sex ducts react strongly to sex hormones. To which form of agent is this local effect on the ducts to be attributed? Instances are common also in which the influence of a gonad graft appears more strongly in its immediate vicinity (Wolff, 1946-1947); and certain effects of very early unilateral castration in the rabbit embryo should be recalled (see footnote 3). There is nothing in these facts, however, to show that the agent is other than hormonal in the ordinary sense.

It is also well known that minute amounts of sex hormones, applied directly, or injected into the dermal layer of the skin, have extremely localized effects on such tissues as the comb of fowls, or developing feather follicles. In the latter instance the maximal influence is seen only at the point of injection, the effect fading out rapidly within a short distance (Willier, 1939). It is unlikely that vascular transport is involved here. It seems reasonable to suppose that any humoral agent, originating locally, would first build up an effective concentration near the site of production—even though passing at the same time into the blood—and so be able to exert local influences before an adequate level could be maintained in the circulation. It may be questioned whether inductors and hormones are to be distinguished on the basis of how they are transmitted.

Differences in the thresholds at which various structures react may also be a factor in the evocation of "local" responses as, for example, when only a near-by gonad responds—a matter that does not seem to have received sufficient consideration.

Considering the problem from still another aspect, it has frequently been pointed out that there are no effects ascribed to gonad inductors which cannot be closely simulated by use of hormones (Wolff, 1947). In both amphibians and birds—in which the structure of the gonads is readily transformed by hormones—the progress of reversal is indicated by changes in the cortex-medulla ratio. Male hormones induce growth and differentiation of the medullary region of ovaries, and medullary development is accompanied by inhibition of the cortex. This is the role and the mode of action postulated for inductors. But the same histological picture appears also in gonads in which reversal is induced by the presence of a graft or, by a blood-borne substance infusing from a parabiotic partner. In each case the hormone introduced may be exercising one of the reciprocal functions (inhibition-stimulation) attributed to the inductor, or both.[5] In any event the hormone imposes its control by usurping the normal machinery. In view of a great deal of evidence of this kind it seems unnecessary, in the absence of more direct proof, to assume the existence of inductors as unique agents.

X. Specificity of Hormone Action and Paradoxical Effects

It has seemed plausible also, at various times and on various grounds, to discriminate between the hormones of the embryonic gonads, that control the development of the genital tract (classically illustrated in the freemartin case) and the sex hormones of adult organisms, with which the steroid substances of gonad origin have been tentatively identified. This distinction was first proposed in consequence of early failure to obtain evidence of sex reversal by the grafting of adult or well-differentiated gonads. Many experiments in mammals failed to do more than induce superficial changes in secondary sex characters and physiology. We have seen that such experiments in the chick were also negative. The first result was, of course, inevitable, as the host organisms were generally already fully differentiated. The causes for failure in the chick are not yet fully explained, but are to be sought in a number of experimental conditions. In any event, the negative results of early experimentation stood in sharp contrast with the clear-cut conditions exhibited by the freemartin, and the evident necessity of interpreting many parabiosis experiments in terms of a hormonal agent. The position therefore seemed justified that adult gonads

[5]On the basis of experiments in amphibians it has been shown that steroid hormones are capable of exercising independently each of the separate effects postulated for the gonad inductors (Vannini, 1946). The testis hormone (testosterone) induces testicular development by stimulating the medulla without evident effect on the cortex; the follicular hormone (estradiol) promotes cortical development without affecting the medulla. Thus the two gonad hormones each appear to have a positive, direct action upon the proper gonad component. Two other steroids are demonstrated to have actions complementary to those of the first pair. The corpus luteum hormone (progesterone) likewise promotes testis differentiation, but exerts its effect by inhibition of the cortex. An adrenal steroid (desoxycorticosterone) has a corresponding relationship to female differentiation, inducing ovarial development, but by inhibition of the medullary element.

no longer produce substances capable of modifying sex differentiation in the embryo.

With the advent of steroid hormones and the proof that they profoundly modify the *development* of sex structures in many animals, this position became less tenable; but scepticism still prevailed because of the obvious inconsistencies that resulted from the experimental use of steroids. Outstanding examples have already been described at some length as "paradoxical effects"—exerted more frequently by androgenic substances, but in some cases also by estrogens. On the basis of such paradoxical effects it has been maintained that the steroid substances cannot be actual hormones—that they are not sex-specific in their actions (because they sometimes induce differentiation of the structures of the opposite sex), that they have not in any case produced a completely authentic example of transformation. These criticisms are natural, but they largely ignore the fact that in such experiments many factors enter; the particular chemical form of the hormone is but one. It may be suggested, by way of analogy, that in experimental morphogenesis the "specificity" of a given embryonic inductor cannot be tested with accuracy except when a number of experimental conditions are known and controlled, particularly those that concern the previous history, organization, and present condition of the reacting systems. Let us consider some of the better known paradoxes to which objections have been raised.

The type most commonly encountered is the action of male hormones in inducing growth of different parts of the female genital tract. In some experiments this effect is entirely a matter of dosage. Only when the dose is at a level which is more than adequate to cause accelerated development of male parts, does the paradoxical effect emerge. This is true of the reaction of Müllerian duct derivatives in the opossum, treated with testosterone propionate; and a paradoxical growth of the cortex, induced by the same substance in the testes of certain frogs, is eliminated by reducing the dosage (Vannini, 1946). Other examples could be cited. Suggestive also is the situation in male rat embryos exposed to androgen, in which the paradox *does not occur* (Fig. 5). In these embryos development is normal; there is no marked acceleration of male differentiation (as occurs in opossums) and Müllerian duct derivatives are absent, as in control males. There is no way of determining the actual dose of androgen in this experiment, but since it was inadequate to overstimulate the male genital tract, it evidently was not excessive. A similar correlation is found in female rat embryos receiving estrogen, in which a paradoxical effect on the male duct does appear (Fig. 6). In such embryos the female genital tract is larger and better differentiated than in normal females, indicating an overdosage.

It is hardly convincing to urge that paradoxical effects of adult sex hormones disqualify them as agents in the differentiation of sex, in view of the fact that similar effects have often been obtained experimentally in adult physiology, in which their role is not questioned. Such observations are too numerous to be cited directly (Burrows, 1945), and in many instances the dosages used were unquestionably very large. In addition, paradoxes of the same order are not unknown in the antagonistic reactions of *differentiating gonads of the same sex,* under conditions which suggest that relative size of the interacting gonads is a significant factor. When embryos of two species of frog are united in parabiosis, a curious phenomenon is seen in ♀♀ pairs. The ovaries of one species become greatly hypertrophied; those of the other are at first strongly inhibited, and may secondarily undergo partial *reversal to testes* (Witschi, 1942). A nearly identical situation, involving the interaction of testes in two different species of salamander, is reported, in which a testis primordium of the larger species had been implanted in the place of one gonad of the host embryo. The larger testis exerted a strong adverse effect on that of the host, which attained an average size no more than half of normal (Humphrey, 1942). The anomalous reaction in each case is apparently correlated with a marked disparity in size, suggesting in turn that the effect is perhaps only another aspect of overdosage. Cases of this kind also raise the possibility that we are dealing not alone with quantitative differences in stimulus, but with differences in sensitivity, or capacity to react, represented by varying thresholds in the responding tissues of different species. Essentially the basis of a paradoxical response may lie in an unbalanced relation between stimulus and ability to respond, although the relationship may appear so simple only where direct action of the hormone upon the end-organ can be assumed. The situation is undoubtedly sometimes complicated by other factors. It would be interesting, but probably fruitless at present, to speculate on other ways by which paradoxical responses may be mediated.

In conclusion it may be pointed out that there is extensive evidence demonstrating consistent differences in reactivity to hormones on the part of many different embryonic sex structures, and also for the *same structure* in embryos of different age or sex (Burns, 1942b). Such differences in response are of great interest, and are demonstrated experimentally in the relative size which a particular organ will attain at a given stage, under uniform conditions of treatment. The paradoxical effect of large doses of androgen on the female genital tract provides an illustration that is now familiar, manifesting itself in the growth and differentiation of the Müllerian duct derivatives in *both sexes.* However, female structures responding in this way are without exception larger and better developed *in female subjects* than in males, as long as the dosage remains the same. Differences in reactivity of this kind are not confined to paradoxical responses, but have been demonstrated for practically all sex structures which have been observed over an extended period (cf. prostate differentiation, Fig. 7). Their basis evidently lies in genetically determined threshold differences associated with sex constitution. A parallel situation was demonstrated earlier, involving a difference in the response of the male and the female duct systems in the same individual to low dosages of androgens. The existence of a distinct difference in threshold seems necessary in this case, to explain the fact that a dosage level can be determined empirically which is high enough to cause accelerated differentiation of the male system, yet below the level required for the paradoxical stimulation of the female duct. Finally, it must be remembered that many individual sex structures in the embryo differ widely, both as to the stage when reactivity first appears, and thereafter with advancing stages of development. On such grounds, normal differentiation may be envisaged in terms of minutely integrated responses of a complex system of parts, in which hormone level and capacity to respond are progressively adjusted from stage to stage. On the whole there is little reason for surprise or disappointment that attempts at experimental control have in many details failed of the mark. As a matter of fact, so also very frequently does the natural mechanism, as witnessed by the anomalies and aberrations of development.

References

Because of the very large literature in this field it has been necessary to restrict references as far as possible to papers containing general discussion and review, in which extensive bibliographies will be found.

Burns, R. K. 1942a. Hormones and experimental modification of sex in the opossum. *Biological Symposia* **9**: 125-146.

Burns, R. K. 1942b. Hormones and the growth of the parts of the urinogenital apparatus in mammalian embryos. *Cold Spring Harbor Symposia on Quantitative Biology* **10**: 27-33.

Burrows, H. 1945. Biological actions of sex hormones. (Part III Androgens, Part IV Estrogens). Cambridge Univ. Press, Cambridge, England.

Greene, R. R. 1942. Hormonal factors in sex inversion: the effects of sex hormones on embryonic sexual structures of the rat. *Biological Symposia* **9**: 105-123.

Humphrey, R. R. 1942. Sex inversion in the amphibia. *Biological Symposia* **9**: 81-104.

Jost, A. 1947. The age factor in the castration of male rabbit fetuses. *Proc. Soc. Exptl. Biol. and Med.* **66**: 302-303.

Lillie, F. R. 1917. The free-martin: a study of the action of sex hormones in the foetal life of cattle. *Jour. Exptl. Zool.* **23**: 371-452.

Mintz, B. 1947. Effects of testosterone propionate on sex development in female amblystoma larvae. *Physiol. Zool.* **20**: 355-373.

Mintz, B., Foote, C. L., and Witschi, Emil. 1945. Quantitative studies on response of sex characters of differentiated Rana clamitans larvae to injected androgens and estrogens. *Endocrinology* **37**: 286-296.

Moore, C. R. 1941. On the role of sex hormones in sex differentiation in the opossum (Didelphys virginiana). *Physiol. Zool.* **14**: 1-45.

Moore, C. R. 1947. Embryonic sex hormones and sexual differentiation. Charles C Thomas, Springfield, Illinois.

Price, D. 1947. An analysis of the factors influencing growth and development of the mammalian reproductive tract. *Physiol. Zool.* **20**: 213-247.

Vannini, E. 1946. Sex differentiation in amphibia. *Nature* **157**: 812-815.

Wells, L. J. 1946. Effects of androgen upon reproductive organs of normal and castrated fetuses with note on adrenalectomy. *Proc. Soc. Exptl. Biol. and Med.* **63**: 417-19.

Wiesner, B. P. 1934-1935. The post-natal development of the genital organs in the albino rat. *Jour. Obst. and Gyn. British Empire* **41**: 867-922 and **42**: 8-78.

Wilkins, L., and Fleischmann, W. 1944. Ovarian agenesis. *Jour. Clin. Endocrinol.* **4**: 357-375.

Willier, B. H. 1939. The embryonic development of sex. Sex and internal secretions. Williams & Wilkins, Baltimore.

Witschi, E. 1939. Modification of the development of sex in lower vertebrates and in mammals. Sex and internal secretions. Williams & Wilkins, Baltimore.

Witschi, E. 1942. Hormonal regulation of development in lower vertebrates. *Cold Spring Harbor Symposia on Quantitative Biology* **10**: 145-151.

Wolff, Et. 1938. L'action des hormones sexuelles sur les voies génitales femelles des embryons de poulet. *Trav. Station Zool. Wimereux* **13**: 825-840.

Wolff, Et. 1946-1947. Recherches sur l'intersexualité expérimentale produite par la méthode des greffes de gonades à l'embryon de poulet. *Arch. d'Anat. microsc. et de Morphol. exp.* **36**: 69-90.

Wolff, Et. 1947. Essai d'interprétation des résultats obtenus récemment chez les vertébrés sur l'intersexualité hormonale. *Experientia* **3**: 1-25.

Wolff, Et., and Wolff, Em. 1947. Le rôle des hormones sexuelles dans la morphogénèse du pénis chez l'embryon de Canard. *Comp. Rend. Acad. Sci* (Paris) **224**: 1452-1453.

Growth Hormones and Tissue Growth in Plants

BY PHILIP R. WHITE

The Lankenau Hospital Research Institute and the Institute for Cancer Research, Philadelphia, Pennsylvania

SYNOPSIS

Growth hormones (auxins) are known to control a wide variety of phenomena in plants. The spread of these phenomena is so great that the "least common denominator" appears to be the physiology of the cell itself rather than at any higher level of organization. One of the most versatile and precise methods of studying the physiology of cells of complex organisms is the technique known as *tissue culture*. This technique as regards plants has been applied in the United States almost exclusively to the study of tumor tissues, which grow satisfactorily without external sources of hormones and hence tell us nothing about hormone physiology. In France, however, tissue cultures of nontumor tissues, which require external sources of growth hormones, have been extensively studied. Although these studies clearly demonstrate the important role which such substances play in all growth, they have also resulted in the accumulation of evidence that under certain circumstances the capacity of a tissue to produce these substances may become greatly enhanced over the level normal to that tissue. This altered capacity for hormone production appears to be responsible for the development of certain malignant types of tumors in plants. The mechanisms involved in this enhancement are not yet fully understood. They present several possibilities, each of which has its counterpart in the theories of the mechanisms of cancer production in animals and in man. Further elucidation of this problem should prove to be of considerable importance.

INTRODUCTION

Theophrastus divided plants first into root, stem and leaf, these into bark, wood and pith, and these in turn into sap, fiber, veins and flesh. The first are "organs," the second "tissues," and the third "materials." Without the microscope Theophrastus could not know that the flesh, veins and fibers were themselves made up of units, the cells. Hooke recognized cells as anatomical units. Schleiden and Schwann realized that they were more than that, that they were physiological units and that, as Schwann puts it, they are just as true individuals and quite as autonomous as are the bees in a swarm. The bee is an individual but cannot survive except when associated with other bees in the swarm-organism. The cell is an individual but cannot survive without other cells in the body-organism.

Primary Effects of Hormones

When a plant bends toward light we speak of its "phototropism" and trace its bending to a complex series of changes in the quantities and distribution of a growth "hormone." This hormone is called an auxin and has been tentatively identified as "indole acetic acid or something very similar thereto." When a plant responds to gravity by sending its roots downward and its stems upward we speak of its "geotropism," and trace the response to a different distribution of the same growth hormone. When a leaf drops in the fall or an apple fails to "set" properly in the spring we trace that drop to the formation of a layer of cork across the base of the leaf-petiole or the fruit-peduncle (abcission layer) which actually pushes the leaf or fruit off. This again we trace to a particular distribution of the same growth hormone.

The Common Denominator of These Effects

"Phototropism" and "geotropism" are rather similar processes, but leaf and fruit abcission are very different from the tropisms. The fact that a single substance is involved in such dissimilar responses tells us that we shall learn the true nature of the response only when we study it at some level in which all these responding organs are alike. They are not alike at the level of "root, stem, leaf" nor at the level of "bark, wood, pith." Only at the level of "sap, fiber, vein, flesh" or at the level of the constituent "cells" are all these responding members alike. It is therefore the *cell* which is the responding unit, and it is at the *cell* level that we must study the question in order to get a final set of answers.

Here we come up against the fact that although the literature abounds in papers on phototropism, geotropism, leaf fall, fruit fall, parthenocarpy (the production of fruit without fertilization by application of hormones), weed control (2-4-D etc.) and a variety of *organ-level* studies, there is very little at the cell level. There is some published material, but not much.

Tissue Culture. A Technique for Studying This Common Denominator

If one is to study the response of a cell to any substance one must isolate the cell from other cells as one would isolate a bee in studying its responses. This is not easy in higher organisms where the "social" function of each sort of cell has become rigidly standardized. It is made possible by use of the techniques grouped under the name of "tissue cultures." Tissue culture is the isolation of a cell (more commonly a group of similar cells) from the organism and the substitution of a set of carefully controlled conditions—of nutrition, temperature, acidity, etc.—for those which, in the intact organism, are supplied by the neighboring cells and tissues. Methods for doing this are available. For animal cells we owe our methods to Harrison, Carrel and a host of their followers. For plant cells we owe them chiefly to Gautheret and White.

Types of Cellular Response

Any substance, and the auxins are no exception, may affect a cell grossly in one of four ways. There may be no evident response. The cell may enlarge, as it does when large amounts of water are taken in (hypertrophy). The cell may divide into new cells, either with or without enlargement (hyperplasia). Or the cell may be killed (necrosis). The bending of a plant toward light is largely due to enlargement (hypertrophy) of cells away from the light because of preferential migration of auxin into these particular cells. Hormonal rooting of cuttings is the result of cell division (hyperplasia) in the regions affected by the auxin. Some suppose that this response is indirect, that the auxin in turn controls the distribution of a second substance, a hypothetical "caline." Weed control with 2-4-D is due to death (necrosis) of particular tissues and cells.

Cell enlargement and cell division are very important processes in the life of any organism. When properly controlled they are the foundation of all normal growth. When *not* properly controlled they are responsible for teratomas (abnormal growths) in general and for cancerous growths in particular. It is therefore of the utmost importance to know in what ways and to what extent auxins are involved in such responses. Cell division and cell enlargement fall under the general classification of regenerative processes.

Types of Regeneration

Regeneration may be of two sorts. It may involve a relatively prompt, even explosive, development of already formed, fully prepared elements such as cambium, medullary ray cells and pericycle. This takes the form of cell division which may or may not be preceded by cell enlargement. Or it may involve a much slower, progressive change by which a highly differentiated, vacuolated cell, a pith cell for example, gradually builds up its cytoplasm as opposed to the vacuole (dedifferentiation), and then undergoes division with or without enlargement. Now it is noteworthy that this second type of regeneration, in which an actively dividing character is reacquired by a differentiated cell, can usually be shown to have been preceded by a condition of local wounding. The wound may be no more than the slight crushing and stretching of cells resulting from wind action, such as is

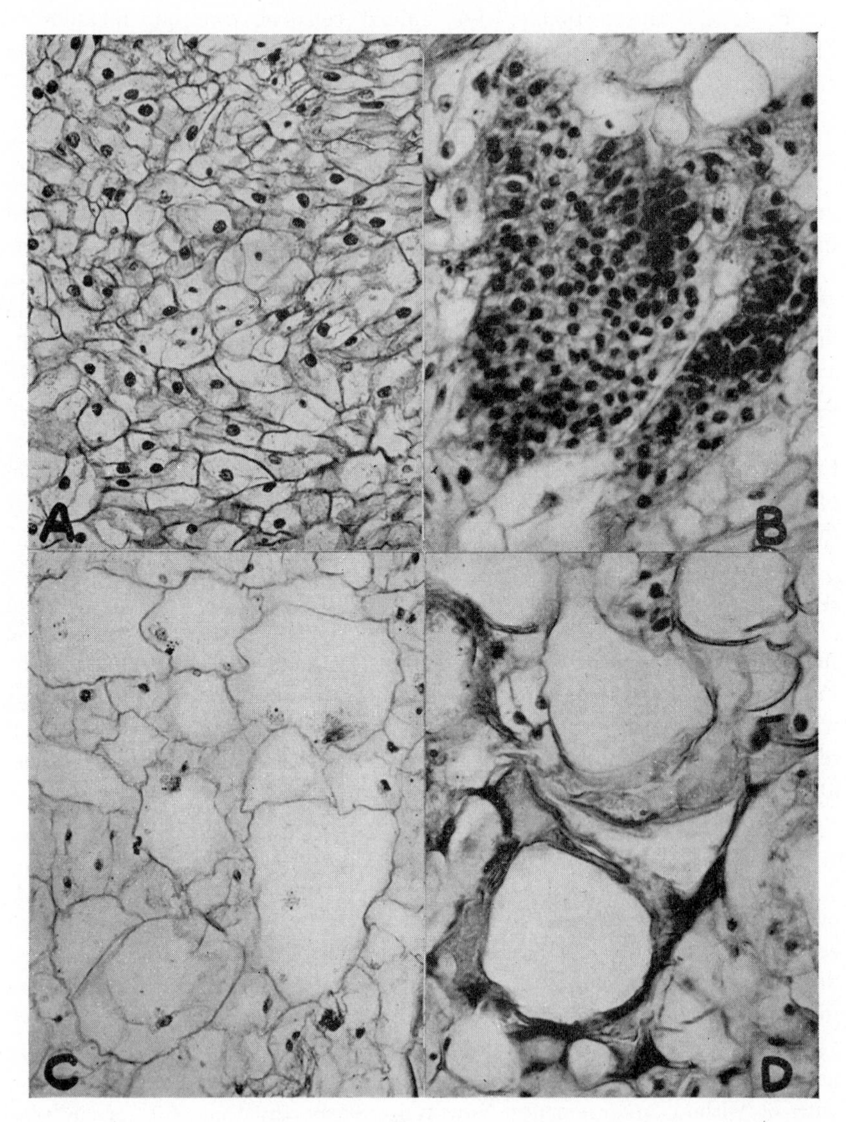

Fig. 1

Different types of behavior in plant tissues. All four figures are of tissues of *Nicotiana* tumor.

A. Section of a young tumor resulting from implantation of a bit of *N. glauca* × *N. Langsdorfii* tumor tissue culture under the bark of a healthy plant of *N. glauca*. Relatively uniform growth. ×230

B. Section of tissue culture showing marked hyperplasia (rapid division of cells) resulting in very small cells with large nuclei, dense cytoplasm, and small vacuoles. ×452 (Note that this figure is magnified twice as much as *A* so that the contrast is even greater than appears.)

C. Another part of the same section as B, showing marked hypertrophy (enlargement of cells without division) resulting in enormous cells with small nuclei, huge vacuoles, and very sparse cytoplasm. ×260 (About the same magnification as *A*.)

D. Another part of the same section as *B* and *C* showing areas of dead and necrotic tissue partly replaced by a gummy deposit. ×275

A is characteristic of the behavior of normal tissues in the absence of external supplies of auxine, *B* of the response to about one part of indoleacetic acid in ten million parts of solution, *C* of the response to one part of indoleacetic acid in one hundred thousand parts of solution, and *D* of the response to one part of indoleacetic acid in ten thousand or less parts of solution. In tumor tissues all types of response may be found in different parts of the same tumor.

responsible for the asymmetrical enlargement of the trunks of cliff-borne trees. But, whether at this or some more intense level, wounding is probably always present. When the tissue is built up to the point where it is no longer wounded by further stresses, cell division ceases and is replaced by consolidation of the area into cork and other differentiated cells. This consolidation can be halted or even reversed by a new wound. Nurserymen recognize this and when a large wound is to be closed, for example where a large branch has been removed, the process is speeded up by repeated shallow incisions around the margin of the healing area, practiced at intervals whenever the formation of callus begins to slow down.

Galls and Tumors

Now there is one place in nature where this rapid consolidation of a traumatized (wounded) area *does not* take place. That is in the development of burls, galls, enations and similar overgrowths in plants. We assume that here there is an internal renewal of the wound which tends to maintain the dividing, growing state. In crown-gall the initial traumatizing agent is a bacterium, in certain enations it is a virus, in insect galls it is the secretions of the insect larvae, and in burls it may be any of a variety of mechanical, chemical or biological agents. In the bacteria-free crown-galls studied in recent years by Braun, White and others, the bacteria disappear yet the regenerative process goes on. If, therefore, the relation between overgrowth and trauma is really an obligatory one, there must reside in the gall some more permanent traumatizing agent independent of the bacteria. The nature of this agent thus becomes of considerable importance.

Tissue Cultures of Tumors and of Normal Tissues

In the experimental laboratory there is also one place in which this matter of consolidation of a traumatized and hence regenerating tissue is of prime importance. That is in the so-called "tissue cultures" of which we have already spoken. In a tissue culture success is dependent on uninterrupted regeneration. Consolidation, with its concomitant cessation of regeneration, is a serious barrier which must be overcome.

This antiphony between regeneration and consolidation and its varied expression in different materials has, in the field of plant tissue cultures, given rise to a curious dichotomy. In the United States the only tissues with which uninterrupted cultures have been successfully initiated and maintained have been tumor tissues (hereditary tumors of *Nicotiana* (White, 1939); bacteria-free crown-gall tumors of sunflower (White and Braun, 1942; Hildebrandt and Riker, 1947; de Ropp, 1947a, b), *Vinca* (White, 1945); virus tumors of *Rumex* (Black, 1947), etc.). Attempts to establish similar uninterrupted cultures from healthy plants of bean (Bonner, 1936), poplar (La Rue, 1936) and a number of others have not succeeded. In France, on the other hand, nontumorous tissues have been successfully grown from a number of plants (carrot (Nobécourt, 1939; Gautheret, 1939a), Jerusalem artichoke (Gautheret, 1947b), grape, blackberry, and hawthorn (Morel, 1947), and many others). Gautheret's cultures now (January, 1948) number 26 distinct and well-established strains. This has been accomplished by the simple expedient of adding one or another of the so-called growth "hormones" to the nutrient.

Gautheret himself looks upon the added hormone as a poison which, by maintaining a constant state of sublethal trauma, continuously stimulates the regenerative response of the tissue, overcomes the tendency to consolidate, organize and stabilize, and thus permits the continuance of hyperplastic growth.

Certain other collateral observations must also be fitted into this picture. The response of a plant to inoculation with certain attenuated (avirulent, non-gall-producing) strains of crown-gall bacteria can be greatly enhanced by simultaneous application of growth hormones (Braun and Laskaris, 1942). This involves no change in the physiology of the bacteria but only of the host plant. The evidence points indirectly to a low auxin content in host tissues and in nonvirulent strains of bacteria, but a high auxin content in virulent bacteria. It has also been shown that tumor tissues grown *in vitro* do not respond to application of growth substances (de Ropp, 1947b) as do normal tissues (Gautheret *et al.,* 1947a). It is believed that this fact depends on a higher level of production of auxin by tumor tissues than by normal ones. This conclusion receives further support from the observation that if bits of cultures of tumor tissue are loosely grafted onto bits of normal tissue the latter undergo hyperplasia in a manner similar to that shown when growth substances are added to the nutrient (de Ropp, 1947a). Direct evidence on this point has unfortunately not yet been obtained.

Auxins as Factors in Tumor Formation

All of these observations lead, directly or indirectly, to the conclusion that the injection of growth substances of one sort or another into the tissue is a major factor in the production of many if not all overgrowths induced by bacteria, molds, insects, worms, etc., yet these responses cannot be induced by mere application of any of the known growth hormones. It is therefore clear either that the growth hormones represent only one of a chain of factors, the others being as yet unidentified, or else that the growth substances involved are not identical with but only similar to the known growth hormones so far tested.

That these other factors may have their origin outside the host is shown by the observation, already cited, that the combined action of growth hormones and attenuated crown-gall bacteria (both "external" factors) will produce typical galls. But it is equally clear that they may sometimes arise within the host. Plants inoculated with crown-galls can be freed of their bacteria after a suitable interval by a number of different means, without diminishing the size or virulence of the galls produced (White and Braun, 1942; Braun, 1947). Here the entire scale of inciting factors has been transferred from external source (the bacteria) to the tissues of the host itself.

It is well known that the plants used in crown-gall experiments—sunflower, tomato, periwinkle, etc.—normally produce growth substances in

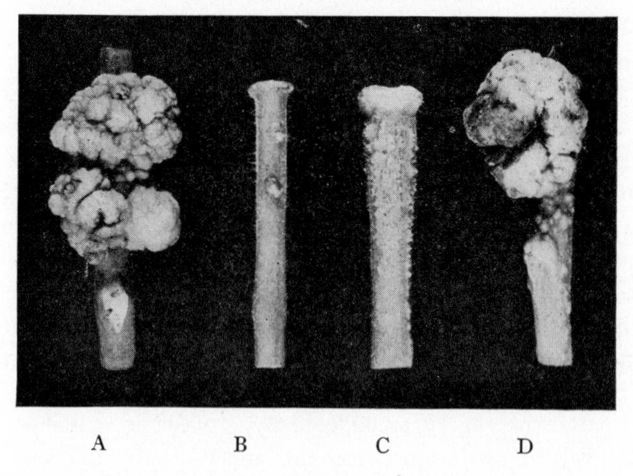

FIG. 2

Enhancing effect of growth hormone on development of tumors on plants inoculated with an attenuated strain of crown-gall bacteria. All are tomato plants.

A. Typical tumor produced by needle prick inoculation with a culture of a virulent strain of bacteria.

B. Result of inoculation with an attenuated strain of bacteria which produces only small tumors.

C. Result of applying a lanolin paste containing 1% of naphthaleneacetic acid without inoculation.

D. Result of combining inoculation with the attenuated bacteria (*B*) and application of hormone (*C*). A large tumor is produced from which sterile tumor-producing tissue can then be isolated.

(Modified from Braun, A. C. and Laskaris, T., *Proc. Nation. Acad. Sci. U. S.* **28**: 470, 1942.)

small quantities at special locations, in buds, probably in leaf blades, etc., but not at the locations where galls are usually inoculated. This low level of *normal* growth hormone production is presumed to be responsible for the need to apply growth substances when avirulent bacteria are used. It nevertheless raises the question whether the change in behavior in bacteria-free crown-galls represents the acquisition of new properties or merely the evocation or enhancement of properties which already existed in the normal tissues but at levels below those critical for gall production.

Cellular Adaptation

This sort of experimental boosting of a subcritical physiological system is not unknown elsewhere in biological materials. Many microorganisms can be "trained" to attack and to survive on certain substrata (nutrient media) on which they would die without previous adaptation (Spiegelman, 1945). It is presumed that the systems required to build up the enzymes suitable to attack these unusual substrata exist in the microorganism but become functional only when actually called upon. The enzymes themselves are present in the unadapted cell but in insufficient quantity to provide, on the new substratum, for the entire metabolic requirement of the cell. They can be gradually built up, however, in the presence of both natural and unnatural substrata to a level capable of eventually taking over the entire requirement. This does not involve the production of any *new* system but only a gradual shift in the relative amounts of pre-existent systems.

"Habituation" in Tissue Cultures

Gautheret has recently found what may prove to be a comparable example in the growth substance metabolism of plant tissues (1947a). If tissues of carrot are planted directly onto a nutrient medium containing all of those salts, carbohydrates and vitamins which we know to be necessary for survival of the tumor tissues grown in this country, the carrot tissue undergoes a limited amount of growth in size but at the same time rapidly consolidates into cork and wood so that it soon ceases to grow. If a growth hormone, indoleacetic acid, is added to the nutrient, the initial increase instead of being followed by cork formation is replaced by a fairly rapid and continued formation of new cells and the culture continues to grow. If, now, at each transfer (cultures must be divided once every month or so and placed on fresh nutrient) half of the cultures are placed on a nutrient containing indoleacetic acid and half on a nutrient which is exactly similar except that it lacks indoleacetic acid, those placed on the hormoneless nutrient will at first regress to the static, corky, consolidated state, whereas

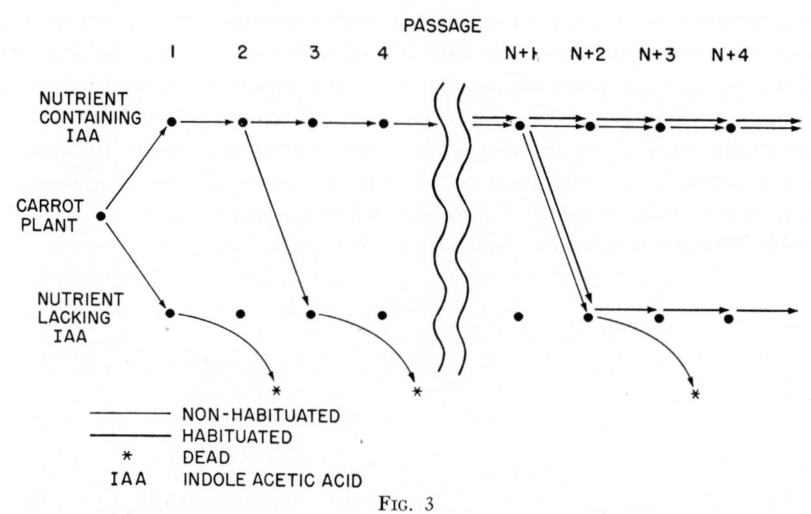

FIG. 3

Diagram showing behavior of carrot cultures on nutrients containing or lacking indoleacetic acid. When first isolated such cultures survive only if provided with indoleacetic acid (or other growth hormone) and any cultures transferred to an indoleacetic acid deficient nutrient soon die. After repeated transfer on an indoleacetic acid nutrient it finally becomes possible to segregate strains capable of surviving on an indoleacetic acid-deficient nutrient (habituated strains) although these continue to be mixed with cells which require an external source of indoleacetic acid. All cells probably require indoleacetic acid, "habituation" merely meaning that they have become capable of supplying their own.

those placed on the hormone nutrient will continue to grow. Eventually there will be a few cultures on the hormoneless nutrient which will not consolidate immediately. These become more and more numerous and persistent, and it eventually becomes possible to establish cultures which will grow indefinitely on the hormone-free nutrient. The cultures have gradually been freed of their dependence on external sources of growth hormones. In this respect they resemble tumor tissues. Apparently this has come about through a gradual enhancement of their capacity to synthesize these substances for themselves. This process, which Gautheret has called "accoutumization," I have translated as "habituation."

In the carrot the release from dependence on external sources of growth substance ("habituation" to absence of indoleacetic acid) is, or appears to be, a slow process. In the tomato stems which were inoculated with attenuated crown-gall bacteria simultaneously with application of a growth substance the process must be fairly rapid, since the change is certainly complete by the time tumors appear—that is within 4 to 6 weeks. In the periwinkle, cured of its bacterial infection without alteration of the gall-forming sequence, it is a very rapid process, since it is completed within 72 hours after inoculation (Braun, 1947). In the carrot tissue habituation we are, of course, dealing with a process brought about by a single substance, indoleacetic acid, under relatively simple *in vitro* conditions, whereas in the periwinkle tumorization we have the result of the response to a complex set of factors emanating from the crown-gall bacteria under the more complicated conditions of the intact plant. These may explain the apparently greater time involved in habituation.

Tissue Autonomy

The end result of these changes, the development of strains of tissue capable of autonomous existence independent of normal formative controls, is evidently something very closely resembling malignancy. Indeed, the resemblance between Gautheret's "habituation" and Gey's spontaneous carcinogenesis in rat tissue cultures,[1] and between Braun's controlled tumorization in *Vinca* and Earle's controlled methylcholanthrene carcinogenesis in mouse tissue cultures,[2] is striking and may be more than coincidental.

Gautheret looks upon the growth substances as mild poisons. In the most clean-cut case studied so far, the Jerusalem artichoke, he recognizes four significantly different effective concentration levels which can be distinguished by their differing effects on the plant. Excised tissues of this plant make no growth whatever in the absence of heteroauxin. If indole acetic acid is added to the nutrient at a concentration of 0.1 mg. per liter (one part in ten million: this is about 5×10^{-7} molar) there results a rapid hyperplasia (division of cells), a cambium is formed, and the tissue continues to grow so long as this hormone is supplied in the nutrient. (Habituation has not been observed in the artichoke.) If the concentration of indoleacetic acid is increased to 1 mg. per liter the relatively uniform enlargement is replaced by a less regular response in which cambial areas are interspersed with root initials. This is the rooting response which is so important in horticulture. If the concentration of indoleacetic acid is again increased, to 10 mg. per liter, both cambial and rooting responses disappear and are replaced by a rapid massive hypertrophy resulting from enlargement of individual cells into callus vesicles (balloonlike cells). These cells are incapable of dividing to form new cells and eventually die. Thus indoleacetic acid (or its equivalent), although evidently toxic at

[1]Cancer cells have appeared spontaneously, without apparent cause, in several of Dr. Gey's cultures of normal rat tissue (Firor and Gey, 1945).

[2]Dr. Earle has produced cancer cells in cultures treated with a chemical, methylcholanthrine (1943).

10 mg. per liter, is nevertheless necessary at a one hundred times smaller concentration (0.1 mg. per liter, 10^{-7}) for continued growth of isolated tissues of the artichoke. It may be presumed that in the intact plant this concentration is being supplied to growing tissues from other parts of the plant, such as the leaves.

The artichoke has not to date been observed to undergo habituation *in vitro*. Except for this fact, the behavior of most plants toward the growth substances is about the same. Freshly harvested kohlrabi is another exception, for tissues of this plant immediately enlarge by excessive absorption of water even on a hormone-free nutrient and fail to grow (response characteristic of artichoke at 10 p.p.m. of indoleacetic acid). They do not respond to any concentration of growth substance and can be shown to form considerable quantities of such substances. This aberrant behavior disappears after the roots have been stored for a few weeks and the excess of hormone depleted. Barring these exceptions the responses of tissues of dicotyledonous plants (monocots have not been extensively studied) toward growth substances is fairly uniform. Habituation has been observed in carrot, grape, *Scorzonera,* Virginia creeper, and some others.

Hypotheses Concerning the Nature of Habituation

Habituation is a very puzzling phenomenon. What happens to a tissue to increase so strikingly its production of a particular substance? Here we come up against the same three evident alternatives which have plagued cancer specialists for generations. Is it a sorting out of cells already present in the fragment which possess, *per se,* a capacity for synthesis differing from that of other cells (the old "embryonic rest" theory)? If this is true under natural conditions and on a hormone-free nutrient, these cells would be encapsulated in consolidating woody or corky tissue and prevented from growing. Indoleacetic acid would cause the differentiated, vacuolated, stroma cells to absorb water, swell and push each other apart. This would serve to decrease the cohesiveness of the mass (which certainly does occur). The embryonic cells, which do in many cases seem to be growth-substance-formers, would thus be permitted to divide, grow and ultimately push aside and overwhelm the consolidating cells. The isolation of strains of tissue of differing growth habit (parenchymatous strains, woody strains, etc.) would seem to favor this interpretation.

Or is "habituation" a case of enzymatic adaptation within the cell in which the presence of a particular substratum, in this case indoleacetic acid, has stimulated the latent cellular mechanisms necessary for the formation of that substratum? Although somewhat similar to the adaptations in microorganisms mentioned earlier this does present some serious differences.

The only really comparable example of which the author is cognizant is the apparent sparing action which insulin seems to exert on insulin-secreting tissues damaged in cases of alloxan poisoning. These tissues, which would degenerate and become completely nonfunctional in the absence of insulin, are in the presence of small amounts of insulin permitted to regenerate and ultimately take over their normal function. This is, in a way, the intracellular counterpart of the "embryonic rest" interpretation.

Or is it, finally, that indoleacetic acid has served to excite the tissues, as so many toxic substances do, to somatic mutations (we know of no other evidence of mutogenic properties in these substances), some of which, being indoleacetic acid formers, are selected out by our subsequent procedures? This seems the least likely of the three possibilities.

Or is the explanation perhaps still a fourth one which we have not as yet envisaged?

Hormones in Biology

In any case it is clear that the concentration levels and specific activities of growth "hormones" are very closely linked with the phenomena of tissue growth and differentiation and that further study of these interrelations can be expected to elucidate many puzzling problems in biology.

References

Black, L. M. 1947. Virus tumors in plants. *Growth (Proc. 6th Growth Symposium)* 79-84.

Bonner, J. 1936. Plant tissue cultures from a hormone point of view. *Proc. Nat. Acad. Sci. U. S.* **22**: 426-430.

Braun, A. C. 1947. Thermal studies on the factors responsible for tumor initiation in crown-gall. *Amer. Jour. Bot.* **34**: 234-240.

Braun, A. C., and Laskaris, T. 1942. Tumor formation by attenuated crown-gall bacteria in the presence of growth-promoting substances. *Proc. Nation. Acad. Sci. U. S.* **28**: 468-477.

Braun, A. C., and White, P. R. 1943. Bacteriological sterility of tissue derived from secondary crown-gall tumors. *Phytopath.* **33**: 85-100.

Earle, W. R. 1943. Production of malignancy *in vitro*. IV. The mouse fibroblast cultures and changes seen in the living cells. *Jour. Nation. Cancer Inst.* **4**: 165-212.

Firor, W. M., and Gey, G. O. 1945. Observations on the conversion of normal into malignant cells. *Ann. Surg.* **121**: 700-703.

Gautheret, R. J. 1939a. Sur la possibilité de réaliser la culture indéfinie des tissus de tubercules de carotte. *Compt. Rend. Acad. Sci. (Paris)* **208**: 118-121.

Gautheret, R. J. 1939b. Action de l'acide indole-acétique sur les tissus du tubercule de carotte. *Compt. Rend. Soc. Biol.* **130**: 7-9.

Gautheret, R. J. 1939c. Remarques relatives à l'action de l'acide indole-β-acétique sur les cultures de tissus de carotte. *Compt. Rend. Soc. Biol.* **131**: 78.

Gautheret, R. J. 1942. Hétéro-auxine et cultures de tissus végétaux. *Bull. Soc. Ch. Biol.* **24**: 13-47.

Gautheret, R. J. 1947a. Plant tissue culture. *Growth* (*Proc. 6th Growth Symposium*) 21-43.

Gautheret, R. J. 1947b. Action de l'acide indole-acétique sur le développement des tissus normaux et des tissus de crown-gall de Topinambour cultivés *in vitro*. *Compt. Rend. Acad. Sci.* (*Paris*) **224**: 1728-1730.

Hildebrandt, A. C., Riker, A. J., and Duggar, B. M. 1946. Influence of crown-gall bacterial products, crown-gall tissue extracts, and yeast extract on growth *in vitro* of excised tobacco and sunflower tissue. *Cancer Res.* **6**: 368-377.

Hildebrandt, A. C., and Riker, A. J. 1947. Influence of some growth-regulating substances on sunflower and tobacco tissue *in vitro*. *Amer. Jour. Bot.* **34**: 421-427.

La Rue, C. D. 1936. Tissue cultures of spermatophytes. *Proc. Nat. Acad. Sci. U. S.* **22**: 201-209.

Morel, G. 1947. Transformations des cultures de tissus de Vigne produites par l'hétéro-auxine. *Compt. Rend. Soc. Biol.* **141**: 280-282.

Nobécourt, P. 1939. Sur la perénnité et l'augmentation de volume des cultures de tissus végétaux. *Compt. Rend. Soc. Biol.* **130**: 1270.

de Ropp, R. S. 1947a. The growth-promoting and tumefacient factors of bacteria-free crown-gall tumor tissue. *Amer. Jour. Bot.* **34**: 248-261.

de Ropp, R. S. 1947b. The response of normal plant tissues and of crown-gall tissues to synthetic growth hormones. *Amer. Jour. Bot.* **34**: 53-62.

Spiegelman, S. 1945. Physiology and genetic significance of enzymatic adaptation. *Ann. Missouri Bot. Gard.* **32**: 139-163.

White, P. R. 1939. Potentially unlimited growth of excised plant callus in an artificial nutrient. *Amer. Jour. Bot.* **26**: 59-64.

White, P. R. 1945. Metastatic (graft) tumors of bacteria-free crown-galls on *Vinca rosea*. *Amer. Jour. Bot.* **32**: 237-241.

White, P. R., and Braun, A. C. 1942. A cancerous neoplasm of plants. Autonomous bacteria-free crown-gall tissue. *Cancer Res.* **2**: 597-617.

Newer Methods in the Rapid Development of Disease-Resistant Vegetables*

BY W. A. FRAZIER

Hawaii Agricultural Experiment Station, University of Hawaii, Honolulu, Hawaii

SYNOPSIS

Diseases take a heavy toll of vegetable crops grown in this country—as the smallest of home gardeners or the largest of commercial growers well know. It would indeed be wonderful if plant breeders could, by developing resistant varieties, defeat all disease-producing organisms. Such shall likely never come to pass, for reasons found in the text of this article. Yet we do know now that heavy vegetable crop losses due to certain diseases can be reduced or in some cases completely eliminated by development of resistant varieties. The protection thus assured the grower is coming to be more and more appreciated, for he has readily recognized the cheap, practical, insurance "wrapped up" in seeds of resistant varieties—seeds which may carry within their embryos perhaps only one tiny gene, far too small to be seen by the best microscope, yet capable of exerting upon the growing plant some known or unknown characteristic which results in resistance to an organism capable of causing disease.

What are some of the problems that must be resolved and some of the manipulations that may be required of the breeder or others in vegetable breeding programs?

The cause of the disease, for which resistance is sought, must, if at all possible, be determined; otherwise the work proceeds in the dark, in which case the correct road in the breeding program may or may not be taken. It is important to know whether there may be several races of the disease, each capable of causing differential reactions in the host plant; if such races exist in the locality the breeder should test his "resistant" plants against all of them.

From whence must come disease-resistant stocks with which to initiate a hybridization program? The breeder may need to contact the U. S. Department of Agriculture, the state experiment stations, seed companies, private individuals, or make contacts with many foreign countries, to secure seed. He may have a good lead on resistant seed stocks from a given source, or he may have to collect seed lots by the thousands, to be tested

*Published by permission of the Director of the Hawaii Agricultural Experiment Station as Technical Paper No. *160*.

without any previous knowledge of their value. He may find resistance only in a different species or even genera from that with which he is working. To secure wide crosses of this type he may need to use a material such as colchicine to double chromosomes, and after the cross is obtained, problems of fertility may be such that extremely large plant numbers may need to be grown, or he may find that seedlings can be secured only by nursing the embryos along in sterilized nutrient media. Such necessities may result in slow progress for a time, but without them there would be *no* progress.

For some vegetable crops, supplemental light, or controlled temperatures or specific nutrient levels may be required to secure flowering and fruit set. Similar exacting conditions may need to be maintained for the pathogen—for its culture perhaps in the laboratory, or for its behavior when in contact with the plant host. The *interrelationship* of host and pathogen is of vital importance.

Plant growth regulators may be used to speed up fruit set, and seed set, thereby increasing rapidity of turnover of generations.

Insects may be called upon to facilitate pollination. In order to secure sufficient numbers they may have to be reared in the laboratory, and pupae perhaps placed under refrigeration, from which they may be removed to higher temperatures for emergence of the adults as required.

Some seeds, such as those of the sweet potato, may remain dormant for months. This delay has been circumvented by use of concentrated sulfuric acid to scarify the seed. Chilling, or treatment with thiourea are effective in breaking dormancy of lettuce seed.

Rapid exchange of the most promising, advanced lines between breeders is of obvious value in regional improvement of a given crop. In the future such exchange will become of greater importance, with the increase in complexity and exactness required in varietal improvement. For example, a few years ago, tomato breeders were content to release a variety with resistance to one disease—today the goal of many programs is resistance to at least five or six diseases. And progress has been relatively speedy because of wholehearted interchange of breeding stocks with which to synthesize new lines for combined resistance. There is also a recognition of the value of climates where rapid year-round turnover of generations may be secured, or where disease epidemics may be commonly expected.

Resistance to several diseases within one variety results, obviously, in killing several birds with one stone, and this combined resistance presents a real challenge to present-day vegetable breeders. In many cases "assembly line" methods are being devised whereby plants are subjected to carefully timed inoculations with a series of different disease-producing organisms. Unless complications with multiple gene inheritance, or troubles with testing sequences arise, the efficiency of selection and speed of attainment of objectives is thereby facilitated. Thus, there may be eliminated, perhaps in seedling stages, large numbers of susceptible plants that need never be taken to the field. If such can be done, there is a great saving in the time and expense involved in the selection program.

Along with progress in disease control by varietal improvement there is increasing demand for attention to such needs as high vitamin content, insect resistance, mineral nutritive value, ability to produce well in poor soils, wide regional adaptation, and improved shipping and keeping quality. To these we may need to add resistance to phytotoxic chemicals used for disease, insect, or weed control, such, for example, as DDT and 2,4-D or materials which may in the future replace them.

Important though new scientific finds and methods may be, there cannot be complete replacement of the art of plant breeding. The breeder, in viewing hundreds, thousands, or tens of thousands of individual plants, may choose a dozen or perhaps a few dozen for seed production or vegetative propagation and in doing so must call upon his experience, his knowledge and his magic, if such he possesses, to put his fingers on the plants which will stand the test of usage by farmer and consumer. The more science in his magic, the better, and so there is good reason why alert breeders are keeping their ears attuned to developments in all fields of biology—for ideas and techniques which may be used in varied ways in more efficient and rapid development of horticulturally desirable disease resistant vegetable plants.

I. Introduction

The vegetable crops, of great importance in the diet of human beings, are subject to disastrous attack by many pathogenic organisms and to myriad types of physiological disorders resulting from climatic or nutritional effects. An increasing amount of attention, dating from approximately the first decade of this century, has been given to control of vegetable pathogens—fungi, bacteria, viruses—by breeding for resistant varieties. The impetus has been due to the realization by pathologists and olericulturists (vegetable crops scientists) that in many cases, such for example, as with the soil-borne fusarium wilts (fungi) of cabbage, tomatoes, watermelons and peas, the most desirable means of practical control is obtained by use of resistant types.

The farmer became interested in disease resistance when he found that with such diseases as bean rust or powdery mildew of cantaloupes, the costly, time-consuming application of sprays or dusts, which at best were only partly effective, could be entirely eliminated. The economic survival of many farmers has rested upon the outcome of projects designed to develop disease-resistant vegetables. But today it is not merely the farmer, the plant pathologist, the olericulturist, the plant breeder, who are interested in disease-resistant vegetables. In nations with starving populations, all of the individuals recognize that plant disease epidemics are calamitous. These peoples realize the importance of surety of crop production—whether it be vegetables, fruits or agronomic crops. Vegetable variety improvement is one means of making food production more sure in the face of four major crop enemies—adverse climate, unproductive soils, insects and diseases.

Even though this country may now be able to feed itself and, in part, the people of some of its fellow nations, we cannot afford to neglect the development of superior varieties of crop plants which will serve as insurance in securing greatly improved production when the need arises—and no one can predict when that need may arise.

Although we may be concerned here primarily with disease resistance in vegetable plants, it should be made clear at the outset that breeding programs must consider not only the question of disease resistance, but yields of vegetables of high nutritional and edible quality which will reach the consumer in a fresh, attractive state. It is one thing to develop a disease-resistant variety; another thing to develop a disease-resistant variety that carries with it horticultural characters equal to or superior to disease susceptible types. Essentially, therefore, breeding for disease resistance differs from any other improvement program only in the disease factor. How this factor may, in varying degrees, complicate the picture will be shown.

II. Basic Relationships

In the initiation of a program of breeding for disease resistance, the following questions arise:

a. What is the disease and its nature? How is it transmitted to the host plant? Are there any physiological races of the disease?

b. Are there known sources of plant resistance to the disease?

c. Can satisfactory progress be made by simple selection within established commercial varieties?

d. If sources of resistance are not known, where can strains, varieties, species be obtained for testing purposes?

e. How will the disease tests be conducted? Can a foolproof method of inoculation for the disease be used?

f. If crosses are necessary and heterozygous (variable) material must be worked with, what are the plant characters that must be sought, along with disease resistance, to insure an acceptable variety?

g. Is it known how the resistance to disease and the desirable horticultural characters are inherited, so that selections may be evaluated as to their chance of remaining true for resistance and type in succeeding generations?

h. What techniques may be used to facilitate the breeding program? If more than one disease is involved, can combined resistance be sought in a sequence of tests designed to carry resistance to all diseases in single lines early in the program?

It is not possible—nor is it necessary—to review in detail the sequential progress in genetics and pathology that has formed the foundation for present developments in breeding disease resistant vegetables. Such reviews have been made (Boswell, 1937; Cook, 1937; Jones, 1937; Magruder, 1937; Poole, 1937; Poole, 1937; Stevenson and Clark, 1937; Thompson, 1937; Wade, 1937; Walker, 1941; Whitaker and Jagger, 1937; Wingard, 1941).

1. The Time Factor

The word "newer" in the title assigned to this article has not been taken by the author to mean a matter of recent months, but a matter of recent years, with emphasis on the past decade and particularly the past 5 years. Nor has it been inferred that "rapid" development of disease-resistant vegetables is nothing more than an overnight task. It is because of the very fact that breeding programs tend to be somewhat slow in their advances that the attempt is made here to discuss briefly, in the light of recent research, those factors concerned with the time required for production of desirable resistant types, for if it is agreed that varietal improvement is for the benefit of the common welfare (Auchter, 1944), then it must follow, logically, that the question of *how soon* the objectives are reached is also of importance.

As indicated in the synopsis, in order to give a rounded picture of questions connected with vegetable improvement, most phases of the problem will be outlined—some of them certainly not new. Major emphasis, however, will be placed on recent techniques involved in efficient elimination of undesirable plants in the process of selection.

2. The Disease Factor

a. The Pathogen. A knowledge of the causal organism involved is highly desirable. Often fungi and bacteria can be cultured artificially and applied to or within seed or plant parts, thereby creating artificial epidemics and providing for the easy elimination of susceptible plants; or if viruses are concerned, plants may perhaps be inoculated mechanically. If mechanical inoculation is difficult, plant-insect vector nurseries may need to be established. In the latter case, obviously, basic information on host plants and vectors must be available before an intelligent program can be outlined. With diseases of this type, the pathologist, the entomologist, the plant breeder meet on common ground. The breeder may find it difficult, for example, to maintain the insect population required to transmit the virus. The insect population may even have to be increased on virus resistant plants, the insects afterward transferred to a diseased host plant, and thence made to move after a few days to the plants to be tested. This latter procedure has been developed recently for breeding tomatoes resistant to the spotted wilt virus (Kikuta and Frazier, 1946).

If the causal organism is not known, or not well understood in its relationship to the host, the question may arise as to whether breeding effort should await the attainment of such knowledge. That such is not in every case an absolute necessity is shown by the practical solution to the brown blight disease of lettuce in the West (Jagger, Whitaker, *et al.*, 1941).

b. Problem of Disease Races. The evidence has become overwhelming that organisms causing plant diseases may through hybridization and/or mutation develop new races (Reed, 1946; Stakman, 1947). These variants of any given organism may produce differential effects on host plants. Although this physiologic specialization has been more thoroughly studied in cereals than in vegetables (Ausemus, 1943), races of vegetable pathogens, such as the rust of beans (Harter and Zaumeyer, 1941; Zaumeyer and Harter, 1941), fusarium wilt of tomato (Alexander and Tucker, 1945), powdery mildew of cantaloupes (Jagger *et al.*, 1938), leaf mold of tomato (Alexander, 1942), and mildew of lettuce (Ogilvie, 1945; Jagger and Chandler, 1933), have been demonstrated. Variants of the nematode causing root knot development in many vegetables in warm areas of the nation, have been demonstrated (Christie and Albin, 1944; Mackie, 1946). Undoubtedly in the future numerous additions will be made to the list.

It is obvious, therefore, that permanency of breeding effort may depend upon the question of disease races, and (1) collections of the disease organism throughout the area for which varieties are to be bred should be tested for their pathogenicity, or (2) tests of the host plant should be run in varying locations to determine whether differential varietal reactions are present. These precautions will uncover variants if present, but cannot take care of the possible appearance of new variants. This latter problem, in order to be taken care of rapidly, should the need arise, must be met by the maintenance of a collection of varieties and wild types from, if possible, endemic sources. An excellent example of this need occurred recently in the appearance of a new race of powdery mildew of cantaloupe in the West. Early uncovering of a source of resistance from stock on hand saved valuable time in the efficient breeding program which resulted within 4 years in the release of a new resistant variety (Whitaker and Pryor, 1942; Pryor, Whitaker and Davis, 1946).

3. *The Plant Factor*

a. Life Cycle. Most vegetable crops have short life cycles, and turnover of generations is rapid, permitting relatively rapid advances providing other factors in the breeding program are favorable. There is a great difference, of course, between a crop such as the tomato requiring three or four months for maturity and asparagus which may require several years before full worth may be evaluated.

Within a given vegetable crop, when the breeding program is of such complexity as to require many generations of selection, serious consideration may well be given to the incorporation of extreme earliness into the breeding material *for the express purpose of saving time.* For instance, in the tomato it is not unusual to find a difference of 30 days in time of maturity between breeding lines. Early lines may mature in 90 days at temperatures of 75-80°F., with others maturing in 120 days. A theoretical turnover of 4 generations per year is possible in 90-day types, and three generations in 120-day types, resulting in a gain of one generation per year through utilization of genes for earliness alone.

b. Resistant Germ Plasm. Since there are many vegetable crops and many diseases capable of attacking each of them, we shall cover later in this article only certain outstanding breeding developments within a limited number of these crops. It is deemed appropriate, however, to present a condensed table which shows the large number of diseases for which resistant germ plasm has been noted (Table 1). References will be found at the end of this article. Although the table is by no means exhaustive, it nevertheless gives a true picture of the fact that a high percentage of present information on disease-resistant vegetables is of very recent origin. It also shows that the question need no longer be asked whether disease resistance can be found in vegetable species, but rather it should be asked whether there are diseases for which resistant germ plasm cannot be found. Admittedly, incorporation of resistance into commercial types has been disappointingly slow in some cases as with western yellow blight of tomato (curly top), but such instances have been rare.

(1) Collection of resistant material. Although plant improvement for local adaptation is now occupying the major attention of many breeders in this country, it is recognized that they must depend heavily on the U. S. Department of Agriculture or workers in other states and in foreign countries for securing types that will insure a wide range of variation in their breeding stocks—thereby increasing the chances of decided improvement

TABLE 1
DISEASE RESISTANCE REPORTED IN VEGETABLE CROPS

Crop	*Diseases for which resistant germ plasm demonstrated in varieties or species*	*Author and Date*
Asparagus	Rust	Norton (1913)
Bean	Anthracnose	Andrus and Wade (1942); McRostie (1921)
	Bacterial blight (Common)	Burkholder (1924); Harter and Zaumeyer (1941)
	Curly top	Murphy (1940)
	Halo blight	Jensen and Goss (1942)
	Mosaic (Virus 1)	Parker (1936); Pierce (1935); Wade and Zaumeyer (1938); Wade and Andrus 1941)
	Mosaic (Virus 4)	Harter and Zaumeyer (1944); Zaumeyer and Harter (1943).
	Lima bean mosaic	Pryor and Wester (1946)
	Powdery mildew	Dundas (1936); Harter and Zaumeyer (1944)
	Rootknot (Bean and cowpea)	Barons (1939, 1940); Isbell (1931); Mackie (1946)
	Rust	Dundas and Scott (1939); Frazier *et al.* (1948); Fromme and Wingard (1921); Harter and Zaumeyer (1944); Parris (1938, 1941); Wingard (1943); Zaumeyer and Harter (1941)
Brussel sprouts	Fusarium (yellows)	Blank and Walker (1933)
Cabbage	Fusarium (yellows)	Jones (1920); Reinking and Gloyer (1940); Walker (1930, 1933); Walker and Blank (1934)
	Combined resistance fusarium and mosaic	Walker (1944)
Celery	Bolting	Jones (1933)
Cucumber	Bacterial wilt	Doolittle *et al.* (1939)
	Downy mildew	Barnes (1946); Cochran (1937); Jenkins (1946); Shifriss *et al.* (1942)
	Mosaic	Wilson and Wilson (1944)
Eggplant	Bacterial wilt	Roque and Adsuar (1939)
Kohlrabi	Fusarium	Blank and Walker (1933)
Lettuce	Mildew	Jagger and Whitaker (1940); Ogilvie (1945); Whitaker and Pryor (1941)
	Brown blight	Jagger *et al.* (1941)
Muskmelon	Alternaria leaf spot	Hartman and Gaylord (1944)
	Downy mildew	Ivanoff (1944)
	Mosaic	Enzie (1943)
	Powdery mildew	Jagger and Scott (1937); Pryor *et al.* (1946); Whitaker and Pryor (1942)
Onion	Bolting	Jones (1933)
	Downy mildew	Jones *et al.* (1939)
	Pink root	Porter and Jones (1933)
	Viruses	Brierley and Smith (1946)
	Smut	Walker, Jones and Clarke (1944)

TABLE 1 (*continued*)

Crop	*Diseases for which resistant germ plasm demonstrated in varieties or species*	*Author and Date*
Peas	Fusarium wilt	Wade (1929)
	Near-wilt	Walker, Delwiche and Hare (1944)
Pepper	Tobacco mosaic	Holmes (1937)
Potato	Bacterial wilt	Thung (1947)
	Early blight	LeClerg (1946)
	Fusarium	Edmundson and Schall (1940)
	Late blight	Becker (1939); Black (1943); Reddick (1940); Stevenson *et al.* (1945); Thung (1947)
	Ring rot	Bonde *et al.* (1947)
	Scab	Clark (1938); Darling *et al.* (1935); Krantz and Eide (1941); Leach *et al.* (1938)
	Virus X (latent mosaic)	Stevenson *et al.* (1939)
	Wart	Black (1935); Salaman and Lesley (1923)
	Yellow dwarf	Larson (1945)
Spinach	Mosaic	Smith (1920)
Squash	Curly top	Dana (1938)
Sweet corn	Bacterial wilt	Ivanoff and Riker (1936); Rand and Cash (1933); Smith (1933); Wellhausen (1937)
Sweet potato	Fusarium	Watanabe (1939)
Tomato	Early blight	Andrus *et al.* (1942); Reynard and Andrus (1945); Locke (1942); Moore and and Reynard (1945)
	Blossom end rot	Young (1942)
	Cracking	Frazier and Bowers (1947)
	Fusarium wilt	Bohn and Tucker (1940); Essary (1912); Porte and Wellman (1941)); Pritchard (1922)
	Leaf mold	Alexander (1942); Bewley (1941); Crane (1945); Guba (1942)
	Tobacco mosaic	Holmes (1943); Kikuta and Frazier (1947); Porte *et al.* (1939)
	Nematodes (root knot)	Bailey (1941); Ellis (1943); McFarlane *et al.* (1946); Romshe (1942)
	Septoria leaf spot	Andrus and Reynard (1945); Locke (1942)
	Spotted wilt	Kikuta *et al.* (1945); Kikuta and Frazier (1946)
	Gray leaf spot	Andrus *et al.* (1942); Hendrix *et al.* (1946)
	Combined resistance to verticilium and fusarium wilts	Shapovalov and Lesley (1940)
	Combined resistance to fusarium wilt, spotted wilt and gray leaf spot	Frazier *et al.* (1946); Frazier *et al.* (1947)
Watermelon	Fusarium wilt	Bennett (1936); Cook (1937); Layton and Wilson (1931); Melhus *et al.* (1931); Orton (1907); Porter (1937); Walker (1936); Wilson (1936)

in varieties for local usage. Without variation, selection for improvement is impossible.

Hesitancy on the part of the plant breeder in asking for all stocks of possible value, wherever they may be located, may mean discouraging delay in attainment of practical objectives. And hesitancy on the part of those who have improved stocks in releasing them only after they have spent years in "purifying" them is a detriment to plant improvement and a policy inimical to the nation's welfare.

There is need for a cataloguing—as completely as possible—of the world's vegetable germplasm based on known desirable characteristics—disease, insect, drought resistance, yielding ability, quality factors and vitamin content. This should include cultivated varieties, as well as all known wild species of possible value. Yearly additions to such a catalogue obviously would be desirable. This is in large part a national and international—not a state—responsibility.

The work of the U. S. Department of Agriculture in collecting and making available a wide range of the world's vegetable seed stocks has been of great value to many breeding programs. This work has been effectively supplemented by genticists and breeders of the U. S. Department of Agriculture—at the Regional Vegetable Breeding laboratory in Charleston, South Carolina, at the Beltsville, Maryland Station and elsewhere. Expansion of this type of work, especially along the lines suggested above, would be of great value in future vegetable breeding projects.

In the past, collections have often been made on a wholesale basis with the hope that one or more introductions would carry the factor being sought. In the future, will there need to be greater objective emphasis made for acquirement of certain specific characters, as for example resistance to a certain disease? This will require a greater degree of specialization on the part of those making the collections, but at the same time it will facilitate and speed up breeding programs, for the breeder will not have to sift through a great mass of material before he discovers the germ plasm required for his work.

As has been shown previously, maintenance of viable seed stocks varying widely for many plant characters is excellent insurance in meeting emergency needs for rapid development of disease resistant lines. Maintenance of such "master" stocks is costly and often not possible in state stations. Stocks of certain vegetables such as tomato can be more easily maintained because of seed longevity, small seed size and number of seed produced per plant than can others, such as beans (bulky, short-lived) and onions (short-lived).

From the practical viewpoint of the plant breeder it is of great value to know not only species and generic characters of economic value but also the genetic relationships of species and genera—their compatibility and behavior in F_1, F_2, and succeeding generations. With such knowledge he is better equipped to size up the possibilities of transference of genes, groups of genes, or chromosomes, as may be necessary for adding new plant characters.

(2) Possible necessity of species crosses. Necessity for transfer of factors for disease resistance from wild species has been established for the Irish potato (Becker, 1939; Reddick, 1940; Thung, 1947) and the tomato (Kikuta and Frazier, 1947; Locke, 1942; McFarlane *et al.,* 1946; Porte and Walker, 1945; Porte, Doolittle and Wellman, 1939). Immunity to late blight of the potato, a disease of great destructiveness, apparently does not occur in *Solanum tuberosum,* but has been demonstrated in *S. demissum.* Active work with the species hybrid has been under way for some time. There is evidence of considerable plasticity in the late blight organism, with apparent ability to assume increased virulence as it passes through potato varieties "resistant" to the common strains of the fungus (Reddick, 1940). The same organism appears to assume extreme virulence on tomatoes after it has passed through the tomato. Such behavior may give some cause for pessimism regarding the long-time effectiveness of varieties resistant to the disease, but such an attitude could, in greater or less degree, apply to most disease-resistance work. Economic proof of the effectiveness of breeding resistant types can be found time and again in research accomplishments cited in Table 1.

With the tomato, resistance to mosaic in *Lycopersicon hirsutum* and to nematodes and mosaic in *L. peruvianum* are factors of great value not found in the common tomato, *L. esculentum.* Thus, it is not surprising that at the present moment major interest in interspecific hybridization of the tomato centers around these two wild species (Kikuta and Frazier, 1947; McFarlane *et al.,* 1946). *L. esculentum* × *L. hirsutum* hybrids are obtained without great difficulty. However, transfer of the gene or gene complex responsible for resistance to tobacco mosaic may be no simple matter (Kikuta and Frazier, 1947). Still greater difficulty has been encountered with hybrids of *L. esculentum* × *L. peruvianum.* Such hybrids have been rare, but recently have been obtained in greater numbers by means of colchicine (Blakeslee, 1938; Bohn, 1947; Nebel and Ruttle, 1938; Thompson and Kosar, 1938) used to double chromosome number of the *L. esculentum* parent (Bohn, 1947; Stair and Showalter, 1942) and by use of embryo culture technique to prevent death of hybrid embryos as a result of collapse of endosperm tissue (McFarlane *et al.,* 1946; Skirm, 1942; Smith, 1944). Sterilities and incompatibilities without doubt will slow down (Anderson, 1939; Anderson, 1939; Stebbins, 1945) progress of breeding programs incorporating desirable genes (Alexander *et al.,* 1942) for disease resistance from these species, but the reports are increasingly optimistic (Holmes, 1943; Kikuta and Frazier, 1947; Watts, 1947). Although progress with certain interspecific crosses will no doubt continue to be slow, it cannot be denied that colchicine and embryo culture have meant *relatively* rapid advances in recent years.

In contrast with *L. hirsutum* and *L. peruvianum,* the species *L. pimpinellifolium* crosses readily with *L. esculentum* and progeny are highly fertile. A high level of resistance to fusarium wilt in improved varieties has been readily obtained from this species. Backcrosses were made to *L. esculentum* to add genes for fruit size (Porte and Wellman, 1941).

As progress is made in improving vegetable crops resulting in combination of the most desirable genes from existing varieties, the need for wider and wider crosses will increase, and the greater will be the problems of genetic incompatibilities. These problems will require cyto-genetic study, and utilization of such tools as colchicine, embryo culture and probably other future discoveries of a fundamental nature.

III. Facilitating Flowering and Fruit Set

1. *Supplemental Light, Temperature, Nutrition*

Environmental conditions conducive to normal growth of the plants are obviously desirable. This is one simple reason why a knowledge of the physiological behavior of plants is advantageous to the breeder. Plants must be grown before they can be hybridized and sufficient seed secured for effective selection work. Light, temperature, humidity, nutrition can all affect flowering and fruit set to a marked degree.

Our two most important vegetable crops, economically, are Irish potatoes and sweet potatoes. Both are propagated vegetatively, but in order to secure a diversity of forms, true seed production is a necessity (although especially in the case of the sweet potato, mutations in vegetative tissues account for occasional improvements). In both crops, production of true seed presents serious problems for the breeder.

Sterility is common in the Irish potato (Stevenson and Clark, 1937). Selection of relatively fruitful types has, in recent years, speeded up rate of breeding progress (Krantz, 1936; Reddick, 1940). Supplemental light has also been useful in securing heavier flowering and fruit set of the Irish potato (Stevenson and Clark, 1933).

Temperature control has been of value in securing flowering and fruit set of the sweet potato (Edmond and Martin, 1946). With this crop, it has been found that girdling of vines or any means of inducing high carbohydrate content in stems and leaves, such as wide spacing and trellising (Miller, 1938) also aids in securing seed. Without these special efforts, the sweet potato rarely blossoms in this country. As with the Irish potato, sterility is common, and a larger number of fertile lines is needed to facilitate the breeding effort with this crop.

In other crops, such as cantaloupes, where cross pollination is common and insect visitation needed for successful pollination, considerable hand pollination is required in the breeding program if pure lines are to be maintained and if unknown crosses are not to jeopardize the value of genetic data.

The use of relatively wide spacing has been found helpful in securing high percentage set of fruit in melons (Frazier, 1940) and as would be expected, pruning of the runners of melon vines on which crosses or selfs have been made often results in a larger number of successful pollinations. Removal of fruit is also helpful (Wolf and Hartman, 1942).

2. *Plant-Growth Regulators*

Can plant-growth regulators be used to aid in fruit set *and seed* production? Numerous investigators have established the effectiveness of chemicals such as indolebutyric acid, beta-naphthoxyacetic acid, and naphthaleneacetic acid in inducing parthenocarpic (seedless) development of fruit. Induction of early flowering is possible with certain of these materials also. Thus, in plants with long life cycles, use of these chemicals may greatly speed up breeding projects (Clark and Kearns, 1942; Cooper, 1942; Van Overbeek, 1946). One compound, 4-chlorophenoxyacetic acid, was found to aid significantly in securing fruit set—*and seed*—from hand pollinated flowers of the cantaloupe (Whitaker and Pryor, 1946). These recent papers indicate that growth-regulating materials may in the future prove widely useful in vegetable as well as other plant breeding projects.

3. *Insect Usage*

It has been known for some time that flies can be used for efficient controlled pollination of onions (Jones and Emsweller, 1934). The maggots, allowed to develop in meat, are allowed to pupate in trays and the pupae removed to cold storage until needed. The cost and the odor involved in use of meat (or fish) for this purpose is an important item. Now it has been demonstrated that, with proper technique, dog biscuits can be used as a simple, cheap, odorless means of rearing blowflies (Frings, 1947).

4. *Clips, Pill Boxes, Soda Straws, Strings*

Such simple equipment as paper clips, pill boxes, soda straws (Edmond and Martin, 1946), and small string or thread (Whitaker and Jagger, 1937) are useful in facilitating controlled pollination of some crops, thereby making possible the collection of larger amounts of hybrid or selfed seed than would otherwise be secured.

5. *Time of Day*

Time of day at which hand pollination is most likely to be successful varies with crops, varieties and environment, so that exploratory work on the problem in early phases of the breeding program may pay big dividends. Certainly a thorough review of the literature on crossing techniques for any given crop should be made.

IV. Seed Germination

Freshly harvested seeds of some vegetables, such as lettuce and sweet potatoes, do not germinate well. Breeders of these crops obviously have not cared to wait for the seed to go through a long rest period. As a result, experiments have shown that new sweet potato seeds can be scarified for 20 to 45 minutes in concentrated sulfuric acid after which germination is excellent (Martin, 1946; Steinbauer, 1937) and lettuce seed, either by means of a chilling treatment (Borthwick, 1932) or treatment with thiourea (Thompson and Kosar, 1938) can be made to germinate satisfactorily.

Although several of the factors discussed under flowering, fruiting and seed germination are not critical time elements in breeding work, it is well to bear in mind that the over-all efficiency of any effort is the sum of all of its components.

V. Seed Storage

With many changes occurring recently in personnel assigned to breeding projects, the question of equipment (refrigeration and low humidity) has become especially important, for vegetable seeds are, in general, short lived, and through negligence years of breeding effort and large expenditures of money can be dissipated simply through loss of seed viability.

VI. Publication

How may rapid publication of results aid in developing new crops? Advances in all sciences are based on research of the past. Rapid publication of results means rapid dissemination of new knowledge—in this case perhaps of new plant forms—which will be sought and utilized by alert breeders at the earliest moment.

VII. Personnel Factor

Some projects move forward rapidly, others slow down for numerous reasons, some of which have been discussed. What of the personnel factor?

Continuity of effort, in which breeders become familiar with behavior of crops under specific conditions—the "art" of plant breeding—is a necessity in rapidly moving plant improvements. Changes in personnel are often, therefore, unusually harmful in breeding projects. In fact, in recent years this has been without question one of the most important factors in retarding progress in synthesis of new vegetable varieties and has been due, of course, to the scarcity of trained personnel.

Who should do vegetable breeding work? Our colleges are turning out graduates who specialize in horticulture, in pathology, in genetics, etc., with the apparent thought that with a background in these sciences, the graduate is equipped for assuming responsibility for breeding work. The value of the basic sciences cannot be questioned. There is room for thought, however, as to whether men who enter the applied field of plant breeding should not be given an additional year or two of training in the *application* and *correlation* of fundamentals to breeding practice. It must be admitted that there is no substitute for experience, and this added training would in part bridge the gap between the fundamental and the applied.

It matters little whether an individual is a graduate in horticulture, in pathology, in genetics, in plant breeding, so long as he uses to the full the known facts in biological science which will contribute to the early, satisfactory solution of the problem. If disease resistance be one objective, then all known facts relative to the disease, as discussed earlier, must be studied and utilized as required. If the facts are inadequate, parallel studies to uncover them may be needed. The administrator in over-all charge of crop improvement may see the need, not only for parallel studies in pathology, but also studies in physiology, chemistry, nutrition, etc., to round out the breeding program. If men in these related fields are brought into the picture, their greatest effectiveness will no doubt result when they are given considerable individual freedom to pursue those lines of work which will mean most to the improvement program.

It is to be questioned whether personnel and funds are being used to best advantage when one finds, within the same research unit, working for the same locality a horticulturist breeding a crop for "horticultural" characters, a pathologist breeding the same crop for resistance to disease, a nutritionist working independently to improve the crop for its nutritive value and so on. Assuredly, society will gain from these research efforts. More would likely be gained by closer coordination. Five years spent on development of a disease-resistant variety that may prove commercially undesirable is not 5 years lost; nor is 5 years spent on a horticultural type that proves worthless because of disease susceptibility necessarily an entire loss. The two may be brought together and after an additional 5 years, perhaps a distinctly superior sort may be developed.

It is likely, nevertheless, that the same result could have been accomplished in 5 or 7 years instead of 10 with earlier combination of the desired characters, permitting more efficient selection (Hazel and Lush, 1942). This brings us, logically, to the question of selection.

VIII. The Selection Program

1. Seedling and Mature Plant Elimination for Disease Susceptibles and for Poor Horticultural Characters

This is the heart of most breeding programs. If often determines the rapidity of their development. Few disease-resistance programs are alike in their exact requirements—techniques and methods employed will vary according to the crop, the disease or diseases, and the environment.

In variable plant material, it is desirable to have as large numbers of mature plants growing under field observation as possible. Therefore, if in the seedling stage disease susceptible plants or other undesirable plant types can be eliminated, relatively larger numbers of field grown plants which may be observed for general horticultural characteristics will be available. Elimination of disease susceptibles in the seedling stage is an outstanding and important development in current vegetable breeding work. As examples may be cited tests for muskmelon mosaic (Enzie, 1943), mildew of lettuce (Whitaker and Pryor, 1941), tobacco mosaic of tomato (Kikuta and Frazier, 1947), downy mildew of muskmelon (Ivanoff, 1944), fusarium wilt of tomato (Wellman, 1939), powdery mildew of muskmelon (Pryor *et al.,* 1946), and gray leaf spot of tomato (Frazier *et al.,* 1946; Hendrix *et al.,* 1946). These techniques are making possible the early, foolproof, elimination of unwanted susceptible plants, although it is widely recognized that seedling resistance does not for all diseases correlate perfectly with mature plant resistance.

If a survey of limiting factors in a crop's production reveals the need for incorporation of resistance to several diseases, the challenge arises whether lines for resistance to each disease should be carried forward *independently* for several generations or whether complex hybrids should be made at the earliest possible moment and a testing system devised that will permit *combined or successive* attacks of the disease organisms involved. Although odds in favor of early development of an acceptable variety resistant to one disease are greater than those in favor of a variety resistant to several diseases, the fact remains that the limiting factor is combined resistance, and as stated previously, *efficiency of selection in such a case should be greater when selection for combined resistance is started at the earliest possible time.* This question is one that should be given more serious study in initiation of vegetable breeding programs.

In 1941 workers at the Hawaii Agricultural Experiment Station were asked to develop a tomato variety resistant to spotted wilt (caused by a virus transmitted by thrips), fusarium wilt (caused by a soil-borne fungus) and gray leaf spot (caused by an air-borne fungus). It was decided to launch a program that would permit the development of lines resistant to spotted wilt only (Kikuta and Frazier, 1946) and lines resistant to gray leaf spot only (Hendrix *et al.*, 1946) while at the same time hybrids were being carried forward for three-way resistance to spotted wilt, gray leaf spot and fusarium wilt (Frazier *et al.*, 1946). Spotted wilt was given early, major attention because of its unpredictable destructiveness under field conditions and difficulties in testing for it under controlled conditions.

Steps taken in testing tomato lines for resistance to the three diseases will be outlined as an example of the varied maneuvers that may be needed to reveal the true value of an individual plant which is being weighed for its possibilities as a disease resistant commercial variety.

Step 1. One hundred seeds (sometimes less) of each line are planted in gallon cans filled with sterilized soil. With fair germination, this provides 60 to 90 seedlings of a given line for subsequent testing. Bottoms of cans are perforated to allow good drainage.

Step 2. Approximately 12 to 15 days after seeds are planted, seedlings have developed their first small, true leaves. A suspension of gray leaf spot spores is sprayed over the seedlings with an atomizer.

Step 3. Plants are left in a humidity chamber for 48 hours, during which time gray leaf spot spores have germinated.

Step 4. Twenty-four to seventy-two hours after plants are removed from the humidity chamber, those showing gray leaf spot lesions on the cotyledons are removed. The test is essentially a cotyledon test, which is highly correlated with mature plant resistance.

Step 5. After gray leaf spot susceptibles are removed, plants are allowed to harden off 4 to 8 days, then are removed from the cans (in which seeds were planted) the roots dipped in fusarium inoculum and seedlings transplanted immediately to gallon cans—usually 5 plants per can.

Step 6. If the weather is dry and hot, cans are kept in the shade 2 to 5 days to reduce losses from transplanting shock, then they are moved to a spotted wilt nursery (in which a host weed, *Emilia sonchifolia,* is grown, and in which a high population of thrips is maintained as a carrier for the virus). Tops of the *Emilia* are cut off to force thrips to move to the tomato plants (Kikuta and Frazier, 1946; Linford, 1932).

Step 7. Plants are left in the spotted wilt nursery for 3 or 4 weeks, during which time fusarium and spotted wilt susceptibles are eliminated. Complete infection of spotted wilt susceptibles is rare, however. Once each week cans are irrigated with a nutrient solution to maintain normal growth. Plants surviving the diseases, but which have weak central stems, leggy growth, and sparse foliage are eliminated. Plants may be left in the nursery long enough for blossom clusters to appear, permitting elimination of seedlings for long styles, small and/or rough fruits, late plants, and if desired, indeterminate plants (Yeager and Meader, 1937).

Step 8. Surviving plants are transplanted to the field or in tile beds where they are given the usual cultural practices.

It is possible that a technique of testing for combined resistance can be worked out that will include not only the above three diseases, but also early blight, septoria leaf spot, mosaic, nematodes (Frazier *et al.*, 1946) and others such as late blight and bacterial wilt.

As fruits mature, selections are made on the basis of a selection sheet which includes observation for: vigor, foliage density (protection from sun), leaf size, leaf color, relative number of fruits above the soil, fruitfulness, yield, fruit size, smoothness, size of stylar scar, size of stem end scar, earliness, number of fruits per cluster, fruit shape, fruit depth, color of mature fruit (outer), inner fruit color, thickness of outer ovary wall of fruit, fleshiness of inner region of fruit and number of locules.

The program outlined has resulted in the release of a variety resistant to spotted wilt (Kikuta *et al.,* 1945), and the availability at present of promising sixth generation lines in farmers' trials resistant to fusarium wilt and gray leaf spot, spotted wilt and gray leaf spot, and fusarium wilt, spotted wilt, and gray leaf spot (Frazier *et al.,* 1947). It may be safely stated that years have been saved by (1) early hybridization for combined resistance, (2) use of methods for testing seedling resistance and (3) careful observation of both seedling and mature plants for desirable horticultural characters. Other circumstances also have contributed materially to rapid forward movement of this work, such as the simple mode of inheritance of resistance to the three diseases (in each case single, dominant genes play a major role), a lack of linkage of disease resistance with undesirable vine or fruit characters, a working knowledge of the fundamental nature of the diseases based on research of others, and a favorable tropical climate.

A northern tropical climate which permits year-round production of large numbers of plants in the field throughout the year can be used to advantage for tomato improvement in (1) rapid turnover of generations, (2) in testing for and in combining resistance to certain diseases such as root knot (nematodes), gray leaf spot, spotted wilt, fusarium wilt, mosaic, and bacterial wilt and (3) in production of seed of wild species or species hybrids which may require many months free of frost to produce appreciable quantities of seed (Frazier *et al.*, 1948). *Choice of favorable climate could well be considered for other vegetable crops in the formation of national and international crop improvement programs.*

Circumstances beyond the control of the breeder may favor or hinder his work; certainly, however, it is wise to take full advantage of the favorable factors that are at hand.

Factors responsible for vine and fruit characters, such as vigor, yielding ability, and fruit size, are likely far more complex in their inheritance than, in general, are factors for disease resistance. Once clear-cut methods of testing for diseases are found, therefore, it is not unusual to find that the great array of genetic factors responsible for yield, quality, etc., will be the most baffling phase of the program (Frankel, 1947; Hayes and Immer, 1942; Hutchinson, 1940; Poole and Grimball, 1945; Smith, 1944; Yarnell, 1942).

In recent years, the research at the U. S. Regional Vegetable Breeding Laboratory, Charleston, South Carolina, and at the U. S. Bureau of Plant Industry Station at Beltsville, Maryland, in uncovering disease resistant tomato material, making initial hybrids, and sending heterozygous lines to workers throughout the nation has been an important factor accounting for the most rapid studies ever made in tomato improvement, especially from the standpoint of disease resistance (Misc. Publ., 1945). Potato breeding has received longer, more intense, and more closely coordinated support. Results obtained in this program show the value of cooperative effort of workers throughout the nation (Stevenson, 1944).

In areas where local problems are acute and complex, the state stations are logically assuming major responsibility for the spade work of early testing, hybridization and selection.

2. *Selection for Disease Resistance Within Common Varieties*

Hybridization of species, or even of horticultural varieties and insertion of the progeny into a breeding program when the necessity is uncalled for is an invitation to long delay in practical results (Anderson, 1939). Some of the outstanding vegetable disease resistance work in this country has been accomplished at the Wisconsin station. Some of their most valuable contributions, as for example, resistance to fusarium (yellows) in cabbage, have been obtained by selection within existing varieties (Walker, 1933; Walker and Blank, 1934).

3. *Short Cuts in Inoculation with Disease*

Improvements in disease inoculation technique are constantly being sought —and found. Some of the virus diseases are easily inoculated into plants by hand, using extracts of plant sap carrying the virus (Kalmus and Kassam, 1945; Rawlins and Tompkins, 1936). It was found that carborundum dusted on leaf surfaces or added to the sap facilitates transfer of certain of the viruses. As an example of "a short cut to a short cut" may be cited recent work in which virus-containing juice plus carborundum powder is sprayed on leaves with a suction-feed glass atomizer at pressures of 30 pounds or above (Richards and Munger, 1944). The method is far faster than that in which leaves on individual plants are rubbed by hand.

4. *Temperature Control*

Favorable temperature for rapid turnover of plant generations is an obvious desirability. Less obvious, but of great importance is the effect of temperature on the disease organism and the interaction between host and pathogen. Unless temperatures used in the testing program are favorable to the pathogen, results of inoculation may be worthless (Walker, 1941; Walker and Jones, 1921; Tompkins and Gardner, 1935). This is likely true of the viruses (Pound, 1945; Pound and Walker, 1945), as well as fungi and bacteria.

5. *Bulking*

The lumping together of closely related disease resistant lines in early generations is a means of saving considerable time in recording data and perhaps of eliminating, with the least effort, large numbers of undesirable lines (Hayes and Immer, 1942).

6. *Backcrossing*

Continued crossing of selected disease-resistant lines back to desirable commercial varieties is a sure and efficient means of adding horticultural characters, many of which may be complex in their inheritance. If resistance to diseases is dominant, and easily tested for, immediate backcrossing with testing of each F_1 for elimination of disease susceptibles should, after four to six backcrosses, result in almost automatic incorporation of desirable plant characters (Knight, 1945; Briggs, 1938). Strong linkage of disease resistance with inferior plant characters would reduce the effectiveness of the method. Efficiency of backcrossing (Knight, 1945) has been clearly shown for such vegetable crops as the Irish potato (Reddick, 1940), tomato (Porte and Wellman, 1941), cantaloupe (Pryor *et al.*, 1946), and the black-eye bean (or pea) (Mackie, 1946).

IX. F_1 Hybrids

Hybrid vigor (heterosis) (Whaley, 1944), in addition to disease resistance, is a possibility in F_1 hybrids. It has been used for some time with sweet corn (1933, 1941) and is possible with such plants as cucumbers (Doolittle *et al.*, 1939), muskmelons (Munger, 1942), onions (Jones and Davis, 1944), and tomatoes (Barrons and Lucas, 1942; Barrons, 1943; Currence *et al.*, 1944; Frazier *et al.*, 1946; Larsen, 1941; Meyer and Peacock, 1941; Pritchard, 1922). In disease resistance studies, F_1 hybrids of disease resistant × commercial types may be commercially acceptable before desirable self-pollinated disease-resistant types can be developed.

Cost of hybrid seed with crops other than corn is a major item. Several studies of this problem have been made with the tomato (Currence *et al.*, 1944; Oba *et al.*, 1945). Male sterility of one of the parents may be utilized in facilitating production of F_1 seed (Currence, 1944, Rick, 1944, 1945). Male sterility is also of economic value in production of high yielding F_1 onion hybrids (Jones and Davis, 1944).

X. Proof of Commercial Value

Premature release of inferior varieties can only be avoided by thorough testing in (1) replicated plots under control of the breeder and (2) widespread trial on farms. If the variety has decided merit, stock seed is usually grown by the breeder and released to seedsmen. Production of seed year after year without occurrence of diseases to eliminate susceptibles may in some cases result in an eventual loss of disease resistance. Fascinating though the development of new varietal forms may be to the plant breeder, therefore, it may be his less interesting job to maintain disease-resistant stocks of varieties he has produced.

XI. The Future

To facilitate breeding operations, it has been shown that the plant breeder of today may need to give thought to problems ranging from rearing of blowflies and maintenance of weed nurseries to physiologic races of pathogenes, cytogenetics of incompatibilities, techniques of vitamin determinations, on to the genetic and biometric problems surrounding inheritance of such important quantitative characters as yield and fruit size.

Although breeders of new vegetable varieties have been giving attention in large degree to disease resistance, high yields, edible quality, and vitamin content, it is likely that, as these requirements are met there will be an even greater search for insect resistance, for types with high mineral content, high absorptive capacity (to more efficiently utilize soil nutrients), regional adaptation (for widely varying regions, where human malnutrition and lack of plant breeding facilities may exist) and keeping and shipping quality (for long storage life and maintenance of high nutritive value when stored or processed) (Auchter, 1944). With the variability present in plant life and advances in research in fields closely allied to plant breeding, there is little reason for skepticism as to possibilities of moulding these new variety forms.

Vegetable breeding, practiced in the past largely as an art, has emerged within the past three decades as a science which looks towards many biological fields to round out its full requirements. As an applied science, it has contributed much to man's welfare in the past—it will contribute more, with greater efficiency, in the years ahead.

Acknowledgment

Helpful suggestions previous to preparation of this manuscript were made by Dr. E. C. Auchter, Mr. H. P. Barss, Dr. H. K. Hayes, Dr. G. H. Rieman, and Dr. E. C. Stakman. Dr. Charles F. Poole and Dr. J. W. Hendrix kindly reviewed the manuscript and made suggestions for improvement. The author, however, assumes full responsibility for the contents.

References

Alexander, L. J., Lincoln, R. E., and Wright, Vedder. 1942. A survey of the genus *Lycopersicon* for resistance to the important tomato diseases occurring in Ohio and Indiana. *Plant Dis. Rptr. Sup.* **136**, 85 pp.

Alexander, L. J., and Tucker, C. M. 1945. Physiologic specialization in the tomato wilt fungus *Fusarium oxysporum, F. lycopersici*. *Jour. Agric. Res.* **70**: 33-313.

Alexander, L. J. 1942. A new strain of the tomato leaf-mold fungus (*Cladosporium fulvum*). *Phytopath.* **32**: 901-904.

Anderson, E. 1939. The hindrance to gene recombination imposed by linkage: an estimate of its total magnitude. *Amer. Nat.* **73**: 185-188.

Anderson, E. 1939. Recombination in species crosses. *Genetics* **24**: 668-698.

Andrus, C. F., and Reynard, G. B. 1945. Resistance to Septoria leaf spot and its inheritance in tomatoes. *Phytopath.* **35**: 16-24.

Andrus, C. F., Reynard, G. B., and Wade, B. L. 1942. Relative resistance of tomato varieties selections and crosses to defoliation by *Alternaria* and *Stemphylium*. *U. S. Dept. Agric. Circ.* 652.

Andrus, C. F., and Wade, B. L. 1942. The factorial interpretation of anthracnose resistance in beans. *U. S. Dept. Agric. Tech. Bull.* 810.

Auchter, E. C. 1944. Agricultural research in the war and after. *Science* **99**: 169-190.

Ausemus, E. R. 1943. Breeding for disease resistance in wheat, oats, barley, and flax. *Bot. Rev.* **9**: 207-260.

Bailey, D. M. 1941. The seedling test method for root-knot-nematode resistance. *Amer. Soc. Hort. Sci.* **38**: 573-575.

Barnes, W. C., Clayton, C. N., and Jenkins, J. M., Jr. 1946. The development of downey mildew-resistant cucumbers. *Proc. Amer. Soc. Hort. Sci.* **47**: 357-360.

Barrons, K. C. 1940. Root-knot resistance in beans. *Jour. Heredity* **31**: 35-38.

Barrons, K. C. 1938. A method of determining root-knot resistance in beans and cowpeas in the seedling stage. *Jour. Agric. Res.* **57**: 363-370.

Barrons, K. C., and Lucas, H. E. 1942. The production of first generation hybrid tomato seed for commercial planting. *Proc. Amer. Soc. Hort. Sci.* **40**: 395-404.

Barrons, K. C. 1943. Spartan hybrid—a first generation hybrid tomato for greenhouse production. *Proc. Amer. Soc. Hort. Sci.* **42**: 524-528.

Becker, C. L. 1939. Inheritance studies in the interspecific cross *Solanum demissum* Lindl. × *S. tuberosum* L. *Jour. Agric. Res.* **59**: 23-39.

Bennett, L. S. 1936. Studies on the inheritance of resistance to wilt (*Fusarium niveum*) in watermelons. *Jour. Agric. Res.* **53**: 295-306.

Bewley, W. F. 1941. New tomato Vetomold leaf mold immune. *Fruit. Grow. Fruiterer, For. and Mark. Gard.* **92**: 430.

Black, W. 1935. Studies on the inheritance of resistance to wart disease (*synchytrium endobioticum* (Schilb.) perc.) in potatoes. *Jour. Genet.* **30**: 127-146.

Black, W. 1943. Inheritance of resistance to two strains of blight (*Phytophthora infestans* de Bary) in potatoes. *Trans. Roy. Soc. Edin.* **61**: 137-147.

Blakeslee, A. F. 1938. Doubling chromosomes by means of colchicine. *Gard. Chron. III,* **103**: 270-271.

Blank, L. M., and Walker, J. C. 1933. Inheritance of fusarium resistance in brussel sprouts and kohlrabi. *Jour. Agric. Res.* **46**: 1015-1022.

Boswell, V. R. 1937. Improvement and genetics of tomatoes, peppers, and eggplant. *U. S. Dept. Agric. Yearbook* pp. 176-206.

Borthwick, H. A. 1932. New method for germinating lettuce seed. *Amer. Fruit Grower* **52** (2): 35.

Bonde, Reiner, Stevenson, F. J., and Akeley, R. B. 1947. Breeding potatoes for resistance to ring rot. *Phytopath.* **37**: 539-555.

Bohn, G. W. 1947. Colchicine treatments for use with tomatoes. *Jour. Heredity.* **38**: 157-160.

Bohn, G. W., and Tucker, C. M. 1940. Studies on fusarium wilt of the tomato. I. Immunity in *Lycopersicon pimpinellifolium* Mill. and its inheritance in hybrids. *Missouri Res. Bull.* **311.**

Briggs, Fred N. 1938. The use of the backcross in crop improvement. *Amer. Nat.* **72** (740): 285-292.

Brierley, P., and Smith, F. F. 1946. Reaction of onion varieties to yellow-dwarf virus and to three similar viruses isolated from shallot, garlic, and narcissus. *Phytopath.* **36**: 292-296.

Burkholder, W. H. 1924. Varietal susceptibility among beans to the bacterial blight. *Phytopath.* **14**: 1-7.

Christie, J. R., and Albin, F. E. 1944. Host-parasite relationships of the root-knot nematode, *Heterodera marieni.* I. The question of races. *Proc. of the Helminthological Society of Washington* **11**: 31-37.

Clark, C. F., Stevenson, F. J., and Schaal, L. A. 1938. The inheritance of scab resistance in certain crosses and selfed lines of potatoes. *Phytopath.* **28**: 878-890.

Clark, H. E., and Kearns, K. R. 1942. Control of flowering with phytohormones. *Science* **95**: 536-537.

Cochran, F. D. 1937. Breeding cucumbers for resistance to downy mildew. *Proc. Amer. Soc. Hort. Sci.* **34**: 541-543.

Cook, Robert. 1937. A chronology of genetics. *U. S. Dept. Agric. Yearbook* pp. 1457-1477.

Cook, H. T. 1937. Watermelon wilt and resistant varieties for its control. *Virginia Truck Sta. Bull.* **97**: 1511-1526.

Cooper, W. C. 1942. Effect of growth substances on flowering of the pineapple under Florida conditions. *Proc. Amer. Soc. Hort. Sci.* **41**: 93-98.

Crane, M. B. 1945. Inheritance of resistance to leaf-mould in tomatoes. *Gard. Chron.* **117**: 123.

Currence, T. M. 1944. A combination of semi-sterility with two simply inherited characters that can be used to reduce the cost of hybrid tomato seed. *Proc. Amer. Soc. Hort. Sci.* **44**: 403-406.

Currence, T. M., Larson, R. E., and Virta, A. A. 1944. A comparison of six tomato varieties as parents of F_1 lines resulting from the fifteen possible crosses. *Proc. Amer. Soc. Hort. Sci.* **45**: 349-352.

Dana, B. F. 1938. Resistance and susceptibility to curly top in varieties of squash, *Cucurbita maxima*. *Phytopath.* **28**: 649-656.

Darling, H. M., Leach, J. G., and Krantz, F. A. 1935. Scab resistance in potato seedlings. (abstract) *Phytopath.* **25**: 13-14.

Doolittle, S. P., Beecher, F. S., and Porte, W. S. 1939. A hybrid cucumber resistant to bacterial wilt. *Phytopath.* **29**: 996-998.

Dundas, B. 1934. Growing powdery mildew on detached bean leaflets and breeding for resistance. (abstract) *Phytopath.* **24**: 1137.

Dundas, B. 1936. Inheritance of resistance to powdery mildew in beans. *Hilgardia* **10**: 241-253.

Dundas, B., and Scott, G. W. 1939. Physiologic strains of bean rust. *Phytopath.* **29**: 820, 821.

Edmond, J. B., and Martin, J. A. 1946. The flowering and fruiting of the sweet potato under greenhouse conditions. *Proc. Amer. Soc. Hort. Sci.* **47**: 391-399.

Edmundson, W. C., and Schaal, L. A. 1940. Potato breeding for fusarium resistance. *Amer. Potato Jour.* **17**: 92-95.

Ellis, D. E. 1943. Root-knot resistance in *L. peruvianum*. U. S. Bur. Plant Indus. Soils and Agric. Engin., *Plant Dis. Rptr.* **27**: 402-404.

Enzie, W. D. 1943. A source of muskmelon mosaic resistance found in the Oriental pickling melon, *Cucumis melo var. conomon*. *Proc. Amer. Soc. Hort. Sci.* **43**: 195-198.

Essary, S. H. 1912. Notes on tomato diseases with results of selection for resistance. *Tenn. Agric. Exp. Sta. Bull.* 95.

Frankel, O. H. 1947. The theory of plant breeding for yield. *Heredity* I, 109-121.

Frazier, W. A. 1940. Fruiting of the powdery mildew resistant No. 45 cantaloupe as affected by spacing. *Proc. Amer. Soc. Hort. Sci.* **37** (1939): 832-835.

Frazier, W. A., and Bowers, John L. 1947. Final report on studies of tomato fruit cracking in Maryland. *Proc. Amer. Soc. Hort. Sci.* **49**: 241-255.

Frazier, W. A., Hendrix, J. W., and Kikuta, K. 1948. Breeding rust resistant pole green beans for Hawaii. *Proc. Amer. Soc. Hort. Sci.* **51**: 468-470.

Frazier, W. A., Kikuta, K., and Hendrix, J. W. 1947. Breeding tomatoes for combined resistance to fusarium wilt, spotted wilt, and gray leaf spot in Hawaii. *Proc. Amer. Soc. Hort. Sci.* **49**: 235-240.

Frazier, W. A., Kikuta, K., and Hendrix, J. W. 1948. Climate and the question of time in tomato improvement. *Proc. Amer. Soc. Hort. Sci.* **52**: 341-342.

Frazier, W. A., Kikuta, K., McFarlane, J. S., and Hendrix, J. W. 1946. Tomato improvement in Hawaii. *Proc. Amer. Soc. Hort. Sci.* **47**: 277-284.

Frings, H. 1947. A simple method for rearing blowflies without meat. *Science* **105**: 482.

Fromme, F. D., and Wingard, S. A. 1921. Varietal susceptibility of beans to rust. *Jour. Agric. Res.* **21**: 385-404.

Guba, E. F. 1942. Bay State, a red forcing tomato bred for resistance to leaf mold. *Mass. Bull.* 393.

Harter, L. L., and Zaumeyer, W. J. 1941. Differentiation of physiologic races of *Uromyces phaseoli typica* on bean. *Jour. Agric. Res.* **62**: 717-731.

Harter, L. L., *et al.* 1935. Studies on bean rust caused by *Uromyces phaseoli typica*. *Jour. Agric. Res.* **50**: 737-759.

Harter, L. L., and Zaumeyer, W. J. 1944. A monographic study of bean diseases and methods for their control. *U. S. Dept. Agric. Tech. Bull.* 868.

Hartman, J. D., and Gaylord, F. C. 1944. The Purdue 44 muskmelon. *Purdue Agric. Exp. Sta. Circular* 295.

Hayes, H. K., and Immer, F. R. 1942. Methods of Plant Breeding. McGraw-Hill, New York, pp. 113-128.

Hazel, L. N., and Lush, J. L. 1942. The efficiency of three methods of selection. *Jour. Heredity* **33**: 393-399.

Hendrix, J. W., Kikuta, K., and Frazier, W. A. 1946. Breeding tomatoes for resistance to gray leaf spot in Hawaii. *Proc. Amer. Soc. Hort. Sci.* **47**: 294-300.

Holmes, F. O. 1937. Inheritance of resistance to tobacco-mosaic disease in the pepper. *Phytopath.* **27**: 637-642.

Holmes, F. O. 1943. A tendency to escape tobacco mosaic disease in derivatives from a hybrid tomato. *Phytopath.* **33**: 691-697.

Howlett, Freeman S., and Marth, Paul. 1946. Aerosal applications of growth regulating substances to the greenhouse tomato. *Proc. Amer. Soc. Hort. Sci.* **48**: 458-474.

Hutchinson, J. B. 1940. The application of genetics to plant breeding. I. The genetic interpretation of plant breeding problems. *Jour. Genet.* **40**: 271-282.

Isbell, C. L. 1931. Nematode-resistance studies with pole snap beans. *Jour. Heredity* **22**: 191-198.

Ivanoff, S. S. 1944. Resistance of cantaloupes to downy mildew and the melon aphid. *Jour. Heredity* **35**: 34-39.

Ivanoff, S. S. 1945. Texas Resistant Cantaloupe No. 1. *Progress Rpt. 933* (mimeo.) Texas Agr. Expt. Sta.

Ivanoff, S. S., and Riker, A. J. 1936. Resistance to bacterial wilt of inbred strains and crosses of sweet corn. *Jour. Agric. Res.* **53**: 927-954.

Jagger, I. C., and Chandler, N. 1933. Physiologic forms of *Bremia lactucae* on lettuce. (abstract) *Phytopath.* **23**: 18-19.

Jagger, I. C., and Scott, G. W. 1937. The development of powdery mildew resistant cantaloupe No. 45. *U. S. Dept. Agric. Circ.* 441.

Jagger, I. C., and Whitaker, T. W. 1940. The inheritance of immunity from mildew (*Bremia lactucae*) in lettuce. *Phytopath.* **30**: 427-433.

Jagger, I. C., Whitaker, T. W., *et al.* 1941. The Imperial strains of lettuce. *U. S. Dept. Agric. Circ.* 596.

Jagger, I. C. *et al.* 1938. A new biologic form of powdery mildew of muskmelons in the Imperial Valley of California. *U. S. Dept. Agric., Pl. Dis. Rep.* **22**: 275, 276.

Jenkins, J. M., Jr. 1946. Studies on the inheritance of downy mildew resistance and of other characters in cucurbits. *Jour. Heredity* 267-271.

Jensen, J. H., and Goss, R. W. 1942. Physiological resistance to halo blight in beans. *Phytopath.* **32**: 246-253.

Johnstone, F. E., Jr. 1939. Chromosome doubling in potatoes induced by colchicine treatment. *Amer. Potato Jour.* **16**: 288-304.

Jones, H. A. 1933. Vegetable breeding at the University of California. *Proc. Amer. Soc. Hort. Sci.* **29** (1932): 572-581.

Jones, H. A. 1937. Onion improvement. *U. S. Dept. Agric. Yearbook* pp. 233-250.

Jones, H. A., and Davis, Glen N. 1944. Inbreeding and heterosis and their relation to the development of new varieties of onions. *U. S. Dept. Agric. Tech. Bull.* 874.

Jones, H. A., and Emsweller, S. L. 1934. The use of flies as onion pollinators. *Proc. Amer. Soc. Hort. Sci.* **31**: 160-164.

Jones, H. A., and Emsweller, S. L. 1936. A male-sterile onion. *Proc. Amer. Soc. Hort. Sci.* **33**: 582-585.

Jones, H. A., Porter, D. R., and Leach, L. D. 1939. Breeding for resistance to onion downy mildew caused by *Peronospora destructor. Hilgardia* **12**: 531-550.

Jones, L. K., Vincent, C. L., and Burke, E. F. 1940. The resistance of progeny of Katahdin potatoes to viruses. *Jour. Agric. Res.* **60**: 631-644.

Jones, L. R., Walker, J. C., and Tisdale, W. B. 1920. Fusarium resistant cabbage. *Wis. Agric. Expt. Sta. Res. Bull.* 48, 34 pp.

Kalmus, H., and Kassanis, B. 1945. The use of abrasives in the transmission of plant viruses. *Ann. Appl. Biol.* **32**: 230-234.

Kikuta, K., and Frazier, W. A. 1946. Breeding tomatoes for resistance to spotted wilt in Hawaii. *Proc. Amer. Soc. Hort. Sci.* **47**: 271-276.

Kikuta, K., and Frazier, W. A. 1947. Preliminary report on breeding tomatoes for resistance to tobacco mosaic virus. *Proc. Amer. Soc. Hort. Sci.* **49**: 256-262.

Kikuta, K., Hendrix, J. W., and Frazier, W. A. 1945. Pearl Harbor: A tomato variety resistant to spotted wilt in Hawaii. *Hawaii Agric. Expt. Sta. Circ.* 24.

Knight, R. L. 1945. The theory and application of the backcross technique in cotton breeding. *Jour. Genet.* **47**: 76-86.

Krantz, F. A. 1936. Potato breeding methods. III. A suggested procedure for potato breeding. *Minn. Agric. Expt. Sta. Tech. B.* 173, 24 pp.

Krantz, F. A., and Eide, C. J. 1941. Inheritance of reaction to common scab in the potato. *Jour. Agric. Res.* **63**: 219-231.

Larsen, R. E. 1941. The F_1 combining ability of certain tomato varieties. *Proc. Amer. Soc. Hort. Sci.* **39**: 313-314.

Larson, R. H. 1945. Resistance in potato varieties to yellow dwarf. *Jour. Agric. Res.* **71**: 441-451.

Layton, D. V., and Wilson, J. J. 1931. Three new wilt-resistant varieties of watermelons. *Phytopath.* **21**: 114.

Leach, J. G., *et al.* 1938. The measurement and inheritance of scab resistance in selfed and hybrid progenies of potatoes. *Jour. Agric. Res.* **56** (11): 843-853.

LeClerg, E. L. 1946. Breeding for resistance to early blight in the Irish potato. *Phytopath.* **36**: 1011-1015.

Linford, M. B. 1932. Transmission of the pineapple yellow-spot virus by *thrips tabaci. Phytopath.* **22**: 301-324.

Locke, S. B. 1942. Resistance in South American *Lycopersicon* species to early blight and Septoria blight. *Phytopath.* **32**: 12. (abst.)

McFarlane, J. S., Hartzler, E., and Frazier, W. A. 1946. Breeding tomatoes for nematode resistance and for high vitamin C. content in Hawaii. *Proc. Amer. Soc. Hort. Sci.* **47**: 262-270.

Mackie, W. W. 1946. Blackeye beans in California. *Calif. Agric. Expt. Sta. Bull.* 696.

McRostie, G. P. 1921. Inheritance of disease resistance in the common bean. *Jour. Amer. Soc. Agron.* **13**: 15-32.

Magruder, R. 1937. Improvement in the leafy cruciferous vegetables. *U. S. Dept. Agric. Yearbook* pp. 283-299.

Martin, J. A., Jr. 1946. Germination of sweet potato seed as affected by different methods of scarification. *Proc. Amer. Soc. Hort. Sci.* **47**: 387-390.

Melhus, J. E., Wilson, J. J., and Layton, D. V. 1931. Three new resistant watermelons. *Iowa Sta. Circ.* 125.

Meyer, A., and Peacock, N. D. 1941. Heterosis in the tomato as determined by yield. *Proc. Amer. Soc. Hort. Sci.* **38**: 576-580.

Miller, J. C. 1938. Further studies and technic in sweet potato breeding in Louisiana. *Proc. Amer. Soc. Hort. Sci.* **36**: 665-667.

Misc. Publ. 1945. Breeding better vegetables for the South at the U. S. Regional Vegetable Breeding Laboratory. *U. S. Dept. Agric. Misc. Publ.* 578, 34 pp.

Moore, W. D., and Reynard, G. B. 1945. Varietal resistance of tomato seedlings to the stem-lesion phase of *Alternaria solani*. *Phytopath.* **35**: 933-935.

Munger, H. M. 1942. The possible utilization of first generation muskmelon hybrids and an improved method of hybridization. *Proc. Amer. Soc. Hort. Sci.* **40**: 405-410.

Murphy, D. M. 1940. A great Northern bean resistant to curly top and common bean mosaic virus. *Phytopath.* **30**: 779-784.

Nebel, B. R., and Ruttle, M. L. 1938. The cytological and genetical significance of colchicine. *Jour. Heredity* **29**: 2-9.

Norton, J. B. 1913. Methods used in breeding asparagus for rust resistance. *U. S. Dept. Agric. Bur. Pl. Ind. Bull.* 263.

Oba, G. I., Riner, M. E., and Scott, D. H. 1945. Experimental production of hybrid tomato seed. *Proc. Amer. Soc. Hort. Sci.* **46**: 269-276.

Ogilvie, L. 1945. Downy mildew of lettuce: further investigations on strains of *Bremia lactucae* occurring in England. *Bristol U. Agric. and Hort. Res. Sta. Ann. Rpt.* 147-150.

Orton, W. A. 1907. A study of disease resistance in watermelons. *Science* **25**: 288.

Parker, M. C. 1936. Inheritance of resistance to the common mosaic virus in the bean. *Jour. Agric. Res.* **52**: 895-915.

Parris, G. K. 1938. The reactions of introduced bean varieties to rust (*Uromyces phaseoli typica*) in Hawaii. *Plant. Dis. Rptr.* **22**: 424-428.

Parris, G. K., and Matsuura, M. 1941. A second strain of bean rust in Hawaii. *U. S. Dept. Agric. Pl. Dis. Rep.* **25**: 311-312.

Pierce, W. H. 1935. The inheritance of resistance to common bean mosaic in field and garden beans. *Phytopath.* **25**: 875-883.

Poole, C. F. 1937. Improving the root vegetables. *U. S. Dept. Agric. Yearbook* pp. 300-325.

Poole, C. F. 1937. Improvement of sweet corn. *U. S. Dept. Agric. Yearbook* pp. 379-394.

Poole, C. F., and Grimball, P. C. 1945. Interaction of sex, shape, and weight genes in watermelon. *Jour. Agric. Res.* **71**: 533-552.

Porte, W. S., Doolittle, S. P., and Wellman, F. L. 1939. Hybridization of a mosaic tolerant, wilt resistant *Lycopersicon hirsutum* with *Lycopersicon esculentum*. *Phytopath.* **29**: 757-759.

Porte, W. S., and Walker, H. B. 1945. A cross between *Lycopersicon esculentum* and disease-resistant *L. peruvianum*. *Phytopath.* **35**: 931-933.

Porte, W. S., and Wellman, F. L. 1941. Development of interspecific tomato hybrids of horticultural value and highly resistant to fusarium wilt. *U. S. Dept. Agric. Circ.* 584.

Porter, D. R. 1928. Infection studies with watermelon wilt caused by *Fusarium niveum* E.F.S. *Iowa Res. Bull.* 112.

Porter, D. R. 1937. Breeding high-quality, wilt-resistant watermelons. *Calif. Bull.* 614.

Porter, D. R., and Jones, H. A. 1933. Resistance of some of the cultivated species of allium to pink root (*Phoma terrestris*). *Phytopath.* **23**: 290-298.

Pound, G. S. 1945. Effect of air temperature on the concentration of certain viruses in cabbage. *Jour. Agric. Res.* **71**: 471-485.

Pound, G. S., and Walker, J. C. 1945. Differentiation of certain crucifer viruses by the use of temperature and host immunity reactions. *Jour. Agric. Res.* **71**: 255-278.

Powers, L. 1945. Relative yields of inbred lines and F_1 hybrids of tomato. *Bot. Gaz.* **106**: 247-268.

Pritchard, F. J. 1922. Development of wilt-resistant tomatoes. *U. S. Dept. Agric. Bull.* 1015.

Pryor, D. E., and Wester, R. 1946. Relative resistance of U. S. 243 and U. S. 343 lima beans to lima bean mosaic. *Phytopath.* **36**: 170.

Pryor, D. E., Whitaker, T. W., and Davis, G. N. 1946. The development of powdery mildew resistant cantaloupes. *Proc. Amer. Soc. Hort. Sci.* **47**: 347-356.

Rand, F. V., and Cash, L. C. 1933. Bacterial wilt of corn. *U. S. Dept. Agric. Tech. Bull.* 362, pp. 1-31.

Rawlins, T. E., and Tompkins, C. M. 1936. Studies on the effect of carborundum as an abrasive in plant virus inoculations. *Phytopath.* **26**: 578-587.

Reddick, D. 1940. Problems in breeding for disease resistance. *Chron. Bot.* **6**: 74-77.

Reed, G. M. 1946. Physiologic specialization of the parasitic fungi II. *Bot. Rev.* **12**: 141-164.

Reinking, O. A., and Gloyer, W. O. 1940. Yellows-resistant varieties of cabbage suitable for New York state. *New York Geneva Bull.* 689.

Reynard, G. B., and Andrus, C. F. 1945. Inheritance of resistance to the collar-rot phase of *Alternaria Solani* on tomato. *Phytopath.* **35**: 25-36.

Richards, B. L., Jr., and Munger, H. M. 1944. A rapid method for mechanically transmitting plant viruses. *Phytopath.* **34**: 1010 (abst.).

Rick, C. M. 1944. A new male-sterile mutant in the tomato. *Science* **99**: 543.

Rick, C. M. 1945. Field identification of genetically male-sterile tomato plants for use in producing F_1 hybrid seed. *Proc. Amer. Soc. Hort. Sci.* **46**: 277-283.

Romshe, F. A. 1942. Nematode resistance test of tomatoes. *Proc. Amer. Soc. Hort. Sci.* **40**: 423.

Roque, A., and Adsuar, J. 1939. The development of new varieties of eggplant resistant to bacterial wilt. *Puerto Rico Agric. Expt. Sta. Ann. Rpt.* 1937-1938, pp. 44-45.

Salaman, R. N., and Lesley, J. W. 1923. Genetic studies in potatoes: the inheritance of immunity to wart disease. *Jour. Genet.* **13**: 177-186.

Seaton, H. L., and Kremer, J. C. 1938. The influence of climatological factors on anthesis and anther dehiscence in the cultivated cucurbits. A preliminary report. *Proc. Amer. Soc. Hort. Sci.* **36**: 627-631.

Shapovalov, M., and Lesley, J. W. 1940. Wilt resistance of the Riverside variety of tomato to both Fusarium and Verticillium wilts. *Phytopath.* **30**: 760-768.

Shifriss, O., *et al.* 1942. Resistance to mosaic virus in the cucumber. *Phytopath.* **32**: 773-784.

Singleton, W. R. 1941. Hybrid vigor and its utilization in sweet corn breeding. *Amer. Nature* **75**: 48-60.

Skirm, G. W. 1942. Embryo culturing as an aid to plant breeding. *Jour. Heredity* **33**: 211-215.

Smith, G. M. 1933. Golden cross bantam sweet corn. *U. S. Dept. Agric. Circ.* 268, pp. 1-12.

Smith, H. H. 1944. Recent studies on inheritance of quantitative characters in plants. *Bot. Rev.* **10**: 349-382.

Smith, L. B. 1920. Breeding mosaic resistant spinach and notes on malnutrition. *Virginia Truck Expt. Sta. Bull.* 135, pp. 31-32.

Smith, P. G. 1944. Embryo culture of a tomato species hybrid. *Proc. Amer. Soc. Hort. Sci.* **44**: 413-416.

Stair, E. C., and Showalter, R. K. 1942. Tetraploidy in tomatoes induced by the use of colchicine. *Proc. Amer. Soc. Hort. Sci.* **40**: 383-386.

Stakman, E. C. 1947. International problems in plant disease control. *Proc. Amer. Phil. Soc.* **91**: 96-111.

Stakman, E. C. 1947. The nature and importance of physiologic specialization in phytopathogenic fungi. *Science* **105**: 627-632.

Stebbins, G. L. 1945. The cytological analysis of species hybrids II. *Bot. Rev.* **11**: 463-486.

Steinbauer, C. E. 1937. Methods of scarifying sweet potato seed. *Proc. Amer. Soc. Hort. Sci.* **35**: 606-608.

Stevenson, F. J. 1944. Potato breeding, whither bound. *Amer. Potato Jour.* **21**: 192-199.

Stevenson, F. J., and Clark, C. F. 1933. Artificial light as an aid in potato breeding. *Amer. Potato Jour.* **10**: 103-107.

Stevenson, F. J., and Clark, C. F. 1937. Breeding and genetics in potato improvement. *U. S. Dept. Agric. Yearbook,* pp. 405-444.

Stevenson, F. J., Schultz, E. S., Akeley, R. V., and Cash, L. C. 1945. Breeding for resistance to late blight in the potato. *New Jersey Historical Soc.* **22**: 203-223.

Stevenson, F. J., Schultz, E. S., and Clark C. F. 1939. Inheritance of immunity from virus X (latent mosaic) in the potato. *Phytopath.* **29**: 362-365.

Thompson, R. C. 1937. Improvement of salad crops. *U. S. Dept. Agric. Yearbook,* pp. 326-339.

Thompson, R. C., and Kosar, W. F. 1938a. Polyploidy in lettuce induced by colchicine. *Proc. Amer. Soc. Hort. Sci.* **35**: 641-644.

Thompson, R. C., and Kosar, W. J. 1938b. The germination of lettuce seed stimulated by chemical treatment. *Science* **87**: 218, 219.

Thung, T. H. 1947. Potato diseases and hybridization. *Phytopath.* 373-381.

Tompkins, C. M., and Gardner, M. W. 1935. Relation of temperature to infection of bean and cowpea seedlings by *rhizoctonia bataticola.* *Hilgardia* **9**: 219-230.

Van Overbeek, J. 1946. Control of flower formation and fruit size in the pineapple. *Bot. Gaz.* **108**: 65-73.

Wade, B. L. 1929. Inheritance of fusarium wilt resistance in canning peas. *Wis. Agr. Expt. Sta. Bull.* 97, 32 pp.

Wade, B. L. 1937. Breeding and improvement of peas and beans. *U. S. Dept. Agric. Yearbook,* pp. 251-282.

Wade, B. L., and Andrus, C. F. 1941. A genetic study of common bean mosaic under conditions of natural field transmission. *Jour. Agric. Res.* **63**: 389-393.

Wade, B. L., and Zaumeyer, W. J. 1938. U. S. No. 5 Refugee, a mosaic resistant Refugee Bean. *U. S. Dept. Agric. Circ. 500.*

Walker, J. C. 1930. Inheritance of fusarium resistance in cabbage. *Jour. Agric. Res.* **40**: 721-745.

Walker, J. C. 1933. Yellows resistant lines of Jersey Wakefield cabbage. *Jour. Agric. Res.* **46**: 639-648.

Walker, J. C. 1941. Disease resistance in the vegetable crops. *Bot. Rev.* **7**: 458-506.

Walker, J. C. 1944. Progress in combination of yellows and mosaic resistance with high ascorbic acid content in cabbage. (abs.) *Phytopath.* **34**: 1012-1013.

Walker, J. C., and Blank, L. M. 1934. Fusarium-resistant Danish ballhead cabbage. *Jour. Agric. Res.* **49**: 983-987.

Walker, J. C., Delwiche, E. J., and Hare, W. W. 1944. A major gene for resistance to near-wilt in pea. (abs.) *Phytopath.* **34**: 1013.

Walker, J. C., and Hooker, W. J. 1945. Plant nutrition in relation to disease development. I. Cabbage yellows. *Amer. Jour. Bot.* **32**: 314-320.

Walker, J. C., Jones, H. A., and Clarke, A. E. 1944. Smut resistance in an Allium species hybrid. *Jour. Agric. Res.* **69**: 1-8.

Walker, J. C., and Jones, L. R. 1921. Relation of soil temperature and other factors to onion smut infection. *Jour. Agric. Res.* **22**: 235-263.

Walker, M. N. 1936. A wilt-resistant watermelon for Florida. *Fla. Bull.* 288.

Watanabe, T. 1939. Studies on the physiologic specialization in *Fusarium sp.* causing the stem rot of sweet potatoes. III. Toxicity of the cultural filtrate. IV. Pathogenecity. V. Morphology and toxonomy of the causal fungus. VI. Conclusion. *Utsunomiya Agric. Col. Bull.* **A2**: 263-321.

Watts, Victor M. 1947. The use of *Lycopersicon peruvianum* as a source of nematode resistance in tomatoes. *Proc. Amer. Soc. Hort. Sci.* (in press).

Wellhausen, E. J. 1937. Genetics of resistance to bacterial wilt in maize. *Iowa State Col. Res. Bull.* 224.

Wellington, R. 1922. Comparison of first generation tomato crosses and their parents. *Minn. Agr. Expt. Sta. Tech. Bull.* 6.

Wellman, F. L. 1939. A technique for studying host resistance and pathogenicity in tomato Fusarium wilt. *Phytopath.* **29**: 945-946.

Whaley, W. G. 1944. Heterosis. *Bot. Rev.* **10**: 461-498.

Whitaker, T. W., and Jagger, I. C. 1937. Breeding and improvement of cucurbits. *U. S. Dept. Agric. Yearbook,* pp. 207-232.

Whitaker, T. W., and Pryor, D. E. 1941. The inheritance of resistance to powdery mildew (*Erysiphe cichoraciarium*) in lettuce. *Phytopath.* **31**: 534-540.

Whitaker, T. W., and Pryor, D. E. 1942. Genes for resistance to powdery mildew in cucumis melo. *Proc. Amer. Soc. Hort. Sci.* **41**: 270-272.

Whitaker, T. W., and Pryor, D. E. 1946. Effect of plant-growth regulators on the set of fruit from hand-pollinated flowers in *Cucumis melo L. Proc. Amer. Soc. Hort. Sci.* **48**: 417-422.

Wilson, J. D., and Wilson, J. J. 1944. A mosaic tolerant pickling-type cucumber. *Ohio Agr. Exp. Sta. Bimo. Bull.* **29**: 110-113.

Wilson, J. J. 1936. The pathological relationship between the host and parasite in varieties and strains of watermelons resistant to *Fusarium Niveum* E.F.S. *Iowa Res. Bull.* 195.

Wingard, S. A. 1941. The nature of disease resistance in plants. I. *Bot. Rev.* **7**: 59-109.

Wingard, S. A. 1943. New rust-resistant pole beans of superior quality. *Virginia Sta. Bull.* 350.

Wolf, E. A., and Hartman, J. D. 1942. Plant- and fruit-pruning as a means of increasing fruit set in muskmelon breeding. *Proc. Amer. Soc. Hort. Sci.* **40**: 415-420.

Yarnell, S. H. 1942. Influence of the environment on the expression of hereditary factors in relation to plant breeding. *Proc. Amer. Soc. Hort. Sci.* **41**: 398-411.

Yeager, A. F., and Meader, E. 1937. Short cuts in tomato breeding. *Proc. Amer. Soc. Hort. Sci.* **35**: 539-540.

Young, P. A. 1942. Varietal resistance to blossom end rot in tomatoes. *Phytopath.* **32**: 214-220.

Zaumeyer, W. J., and Harter, L. L. 1941. Inheritance of resistance to six physiologic races of bean rust. *Jour. Agric. Res.* **63**: 599-622.

Zaumeyer, W. J., and Harter, L. L. 1943. Inheritance of symptom expression of bean mosaic virus 4. *Jour. Agric. Res.* **67**: 287-292.

Influence of Environmental Factors on the Vitamin Content of Food Plants

BY KARL C. HAMNER

Director, U. S. Plant, Soil, and Nutrition Laboratory, U. S. Department of Agriculture, Agricultural Research Administration, Tower Road, Ithaca, New York

An understanding of the influence of environment variables on the vitamin content of plants is of importance to scientists for two reasons. (1) The knowledge may have practical value. In the production of food crops, it is possible to exercise a limited control of some of the environmental factors, and the knowledge of the relationship between environment and vitamin content may enable us to produce food crops with the highest possible vitamin values. A knowledge of the influence of the environmental factors is desirable in any attempt to produce, through a breeding program, varieties higher in vitamin content than those available at present. (2) An understanding of the specific influence of the particular environmental variables should contribute to our basic scientific knowledge concerning the particular vitamins. It should provide clues as to their physiological function and the possible mechanisms of their synthesis.

In this discussion no attempt will be made to give a comprehensive review of the literature in this field. A list of general references is appended giving detailed information concerning the research in this field. Certain research results will be used for illustrative purposes. These have been chosen in an arbitrary manner without any attempt to establish priority or to acknowledge the most significant contributions.

Because of the ease with which ascorbic acid analyses may be made, a great deal of information is available concerning the occurrence of this substance in plants. Since our knowledge concerning variations in the other vitamins is so fragmentary, this discussion will deal chiefly with ascorbic acid. The findings with respect to this constituent illustrate the kind of experimentation needed with the other vitamins. The marked effects of variations in illumination on ascorbic acid content and the minor effects of many other environmental variables leads one to hope that known differences in amounts of the other vitamins may be found to be associated primarily with variations in only one or a few of the environmental factors.

Research on the influence of environment on plant composition nearly always involves a large number of samples and a large number of analyses, and because of the many environmental variables involved, evaluation of the results usually comes from a statistical analysis of the experiment. In designing the experiment, consideration must be given to the influence of the age of the plant, variations from one plant part to another, variations in environmental condition between locations only a few feet apart, the handling of the samples in order to prevent losses of vitamins during the taking of samples, etc. Very often thousands of analyses are involved in a very simple experiment, and even so, variations of less than 15 per cent due to treatment are often not significant. Perhaps the greatest need for research in this field is for the development of new methods of vitamin assay which can be used in a routine way for the rapid analysis of very large numbers of plant samples.

I. Ascorbic Acid (Vitamin C)

The ascorbic acid content of plants varies greatly. Some plant parts (green walnut hulls, green persimmons and rose hips) may contain as high as 2 or 3 per cent of ascorbic acid on a fresh weight basis. Other plant parts (dry seeds) may contain so little ascorbic acid that the amount cannot be measured by most methods available. Variations from one part of a single plant to another part may be quite great, and variations from one plant to another of the same species or variety show considerable magnitude. Just why some plants should contain extremely large amounts of ascorbic acid whereas other plants contain very little is, of course, not known. So far, we have been unable to ascribe a special physiological role to the ascorbic acid which is present in the plant, although there has been considerable speculation as to the possible significance of this substance. The fact that ascorbic acid seems always to be present in living cells that exhibit rapid metabolic activity strongly suggests that it may have some function in the metabolism of the living cells. Although the ascorbic acid content of dry seeds is extremely low, during germination it increases rapidly. There is some evidence that an external supply of ascorbic acid during early growth of the seedlings may actually stimulate the rate of growth, further indicating a possible function of the substance. On the other hand, the extremely high values obtained for the ascorbic acid content in certain plants—more particularly in specific plant parts, such as rose hips, green walnut hulls and pine needles—has not been correlated with any particular metabolic acticity of these tissues, and this might be taken to indicate that ascorbic acid is merely a by-product of metabolism.

Ascorbic acid occurs in tissues in two forms, the reduced and oxidized, ascorbic and dehydroascorbic acid, respectively. In living plant tissues, the reduced form predominates, and only a small percentage is in the oxidized form. Both forms of ascorbic acid possess vitamin C activity. Practically all of the research dealing with the ascorbic acid content of plants involves determinations of the reduced ascorbic acid. Conclusions drawn from such analyses are probably valid in terms of the entire vitamin C activity of the plant, since the percentage of dehydroascorbic acid in living plant tissues has never been shown to be very high nor to vary greatly. Some of the ascorbic acid seems to be found with other materials in the cell or is otherwise modified so that it may not react with the usual reagents used for its determination. This might be expected if ascorbic acid functions in conjunction with a protein to form an oxidizing-reducing enzyme system.

II. The Influence of Climatic Factors on Ascorbic Acid Content

It has long been recognized that the vitamin C content of a given plant varies with the season and locality at which the plant is grown. The magnitude of the variations may be quite large—up to 100 per cent are quite common. These variations have claimed the interest of research workers from the standpoint of the possible practical application of an understanding of the cause. Control of these variations, of course, might make it possible to produce more crops with the high values, thus increasing the average vitamin content of the crop reaching the consumer.

1. *Illumination*

Illumination is an important factor in determining the ascorbic acid level of the growing plant. In turnip greens, variations in illumination, such as might occur under natural conditions, can result in an eightfold variation in ascorbic acid content within a few days. Individual fruits from the outer portion of the tree (where they are brightly illuminated) may be much higher in ascorbic acid content than fruit more centrally located in the tree where they are shaded by leaves. The side of a fruit which is exposed directly to sunlight during the day may be much higher in ascorbic acid content than the shaded side. Plants grown in the shade contain less ascorbic acid than those grown in the sun. Plants produced in the greenhouse during the winter period when light intensity is relatively low are usually lower in ascorbic acid content than summer-grown plants. The magnitude of the variations which may be induced by variations in illumination are of sufficient extent to account for the variations which occur from one locality to another and from one season to another. However, it has not yet been shown that such variations are actually always correlated with variations in illumination, particularly under field conditions. The effect of illumination on ascorbic acid synthesis has been shown in so many experiments that there may be a tendency to conclude that the synthesis of ascorbic acid is dependent directly upon illumination. For example, the ascorbic acid content of young seedlings is greatly increased if the seedlings are illuminated. In discs of green turnip leaves floating on nutrient solution, the ascorbic acid content may increase if the discs are illuminated and decrease if the discs are placed in darkness. In cultures of isolated roots, the ascorbic acid content of the roots is greatly increased if the roots are illuminated (and consequently develop chloroplasts). The synthesis of ascorbic acid in illuminated green tissues seems to be dependent upon the presence of CO_2. All of these facts indicate that ascorbic acid synthesis may have some connection with the process of photosynthesis. On the other hand, it has been shown that illumination is not essential for the synthesis of ascorbic acid. Some ascorbic acid is synthesized in seedlings germinated in complete darkness.

The ascorbic acid content of an individual plant organ or tissue seems to be dependent upon the environmental conditions prevailing around that particular tissue. Thus, there is little evidence that ascorbic acid synthesized in one plant part is translocated in any great amount to other plant parts. It was indicated above that the amount of illumination of individual fruits on a tree may determine the ascorbic acid level of the fruits. By experimentally varying the illumination of tomato plants, it has been shown that the amount of illumination reaching the leaves is not necessarily correlated with ascorbic acid content of the fruits but rather a correlation exists between the direct illumination of the fruits and the ascorbic acid content. The outer leaves of cabbage and of lettuce are much richer in ascorbic acid than the inner leaves, presumably because the outer leaves are more brightly illuminated. A striking experiment further illustrating the probable lack of translocation of any great amounts of ascorbic acid is indicated in grafting experiments with potatoes. When the scions of varieties naturally high in ascorbic acid content are grafted to stocks of varieties usually low in ascorbic acid, the tubers developed remain low; and vice versa, the grafting of scions from varieties naturally low in ascorbic acid has no effect on the ascorbic acid content of the high ascorbic acid stock.

Thus, the evidence to date indicates that the most important environmental variable influencing ascorbic acid content is light. From a practical standpoint, this is of considerable interest. Although illumination is not ordinarily under control, our knowledge of the influence of light is a great aid in understanding the variations which do occur. Contradictory reports in the literature as to the influence of particular environmental variables may be explained in some cases by lack of control of light variations. For example, the effect of nitrogen fertilization in decreasing ascorbic acid values may possibly be explained by the influence of nitrogen in increasing the amount of foliage on a plant and thus increasing the shading of one plant part by another. The possible influence of other fertilizer treatments might be correlated with the effect of improved growth on the amount of illumination reaching individual plant parts. Variations in the ascorbic acid content of fruits might be expected in association with defoliation diseases or cultural treatments which affect the amount of illumination reaching the fruits, such as the practice of growing tomatoes on stakes or rather heavy thinning out of the branches of fruit trees. A correlation between the amount of rainfall and ascorbic acid values could be associated with the correlation between rainfall and illumination. Any other cultural practice which affects the amount of illumination of the plant part to be harvested might be expected to affect the ascorbic acid values.

2. *Temperature*

The influence of temperature on ascorbic acid content of plants has been studied much less extensively than has the influence of light. In studies wherein plants have been grown continuously at various temperatures, the final ascorbic acid content of the plants has not varied to any great extent. Some reports have indicated a slight increase in ascorbic acid content with increasing temperatures, and other reports have shown a decrease. One might expect that different plants would vary in their response to temperature but the results indicate that temperature effects are minor. On the other hand, studies of isolated plant tissues have shown temperature to affect the rate of accumulation of ascorbic acid during exposure to light and the rate of destruction during darkness. In the latter case, the temperature coefficient is of a magnitude characteristic of ordinary chemical reactions. In general, studies of the influence of temperature on the rates of synthesis and breakdown of ascorbic acid, and on the final ascorbic acid content after an extended period of growth at a given temperature, have not been sufficiently detailed to warrant any conclusion concerning the mechanism of synthesis or utilization of ascorbic acid by the plant.

3. *Relative Humidity and Wind Movement*

Little research has been reported with respect to the influence of variations in other climatic factors on ascorbic acid values. Experimental work on the influence of relative humidity, wind movement, etc., requires the use of chambers wherein all of the climatic factors may be under control. The little work that has been done has indicated that these variables produce relatively little effect, and it seems probable that they play a minor role in determining the variations which occur under natural conditions.

III. The Influence of Soil Variables on Ascorbic Acid Content

Many experiments have indicated that the locality where plants are grown has an effect on the ascorbic acid content. Attempts have been made to correlate these influences of locality with differences in soil conditions at the different locations. However, since climatic variations nearly always occur between locations, it has been difficult to determine just which of the variations are due to climate and which to soil. A few controlled experiments that have been conducted have given negative results; i.e., they have indicated no influence of soil type on ascorbic acid content.

1. *Fertilization*

There have been numerous reports that different types of fertilization affect ascorbic acid values. Reports that any particular fertilization regime which has influenced ascorbic acid content are matched in nearly every case by others that indicate such a regime would produce no effect. Reports on the influence of fertilization with nitrogen and with manganese are perhaps worthy of discussion here. Data regarding fertilization with other elements are so contradictory that they are of little help in a general understanding of the problem.

The reports that nitrogenous fertilization results in a decrease of ascorbic acid content are of sufficient number to indicate a real relationship. This seems true in spite of the fact that there are almost an equal number of reports that such fertilization has no effect upon ascorbic acid content. It seems possible as pointed out earlier, that the effect of nitrogenous fertilization is an indirect one and that the application of nitrogen may result in increased vegetative growth by the plant with resultant increased foliage and increased shading of one plant part by another, thus resulting in a decrease in the average illumination of the organs which are analyzed. Such an explanation could account for the variability in the reports, which, in general indicates either no effect of nitrogenous fertilization or a resultant decrease in ascorbic acid values. Evidence is available that differing ascorbic acid values may be correlated closely with *p*H changes, and that with germinating seedlings certain nitrogen sources affect ascorbic acid content because of associated effects on *p*H. There seems insufficient evidence to justify the speculation that ascorbic acid is involved in the processes of nitrogen assimilation simply because ascorbic acid content tends to decrease with increasing nitrogen supply.

The reports that manganese fertilization results in an increase in ascorbic acid content are persistent. In general, these reports of a positive effect of manganese are based upon experiments with soil fertilization. Experiments under controlled conditions with plants growing in pure cultures have not supported the view that ascorbic acid content is dependent upon manganese supply. Such experiments have resulted in little or no effect of the rate of manganese supply on ascorbic acid values.

There has been very little experimental work dealing with the effects of other soil variables on the ascorbic acid content of plants. There is need for studies on the effect of soil moisture supply, temperature, soil organic material, etc. There has been a great deal of speculation, for example, as to the possible effect of organic materials in the soil on the nutritive value of crops. Certain individuals have put forward radical claims as to the possible beneficial effects of organic materials. Unfortunately, there are few data which can be used to justify or refute these claims.

2. *Carotene*

Results reported in the literature do not justify any general conclusions with respect to the effects of specific environmental variables on the carotene content of food plants. Indications that climatic factors are influential in affecting carotene content are found in several observations, however. Greenhouse-ripened tomatoes contain less carotene than sun-ripened tomatoes (perhaps indicating an influence of quality or quantity of lights). It has also been found that turnip greens vary greatly in carotene content from one season to another and from one location to another. Winter-grown carrots are reported to be lower in carotene content than those maturing during summer and fall. The influence of seasonal factors has been indicated in work with Nebraska grasses and with corn. Marked differences in carotene content or plants grown throughout the year in Palestine were found related to season (values were high during the winter rainy season). All of these results indicate an influence of climatic variables, but they are not very helpful in indicating which factors are of the most importance.

That soil factors influence carotene content especially in the leafy organs cannot be questioned. In general, any mineral deficiency which results in visible chlorosis of the crops also results in decreased carotene values. Similarly, toxic amounts of minerals which result in the development of chlorosis also bring about decreases in carotene content. There is very little evidence of the influence of soil factors and fertilizer practices on the carotene content over the range of variations which will result in a normal green crop. There is also very little evidence that mineral nutrient supply and other soil variables affect the carotene content of storage organs, such as carrots, corn grains and various fruits. With respect to the storage organs, the state of maturity has such a marked influence on carotene values that the influence of other factors is hard to evaluate. Any variable which affects the rate of maturity is likely to affect carotene content.

In conclusion, it may be said that there is need for additional research concerning the influence of climatic factors on the carotene content of storage organs as well as the green leafy organs. It seems probable that one or more of the climatic factors, such as light intensity, quality or duration, temperature, or moisture supply may have a marked effect on the carotene content. In spite of the almost invariable decrease in carotene values which are associated with marked decreases in chlorophyll content, it seems possible that the carotene values may, under certain circustances, decrease without an associated decrease in chlorophyll. If marked changes in carotene values can be shown to be independent of variations in chlorophyll and if these fluctuations can be correlated with variations in specific environmental factors, the results may have considerable practical and theoretical significance.

3. *Other Vitamins*

Research on the effect of environmental factors on the other vitamins has been so limited that detailed consideration of the results to date are scarcely worth while. Most of the work has been done with cereal grains, particularly wheat. There are adequate data available to indicate that the season and locality at which wheat is grown markedly affects the thiamine and nicotinic acid content. Very meager results indicate that riboflavin, pantothenic acid, and vitamin B_6 are influenced but little by the season or locality.

The marked variations in thiamine content associated with season and locality have not been correlated with variations in any specific environmental factor. There have been several studies of the influence of fertilization of the soil on the thiamine content of cereals and some other crops. In general, the results have been negative, indicating a lack of influence of soil fertility. It seems probable that climatic factors have the dominating influence, and it is unfortunate that there is insufficient research to indicate just which of the individual environmental variables are of primary importance. That the amount of illumination may be one of the important factors is indicated by work on the influence of day length on the thiamine content of cabbage, tomatoes and cocklebur. With these plants the thiamine content was higher when grown under long-day conditions as compared with short days. It has been reported also that wheat grown in the greenhouse during the winter is much higher in thiamine content than the same varieties grown in the field during the summer.

IV. The Influence of Storage, Handling, Processing and Cooking

1. *Effect of Storage*

This discussion is concerned primarily with the influence of growing conditions on the vitamin content of the living plant up until harvest time. The changes in vitamin content subsequent to harvest represent special problems beyond the scope of this discussion. Brief mention may be made of some of the special information known.

Very often the vitamin content of the plants or plant parts decreases during storage. Vitamin C especially may decrease rapidly. Potatoes during a few months storage may lose more than one-half or two-thirds of their vitamin C content. On the other hand, thiamine in stored wheat remains fairly constant. The influence of storage must be studied with respect to each plant and each vitamin. One might naturally assume that storage at low temperatures would decrease the rate of vitamin loss. In potatoes such does not seem to be the case; the rate of loss of vitamin C seems to increase with decreases in storage temperature, and the losses at 32° and 40° F. are much greater than at 50° and 60° F. In general, the more food plants are handled, the greater is the vitamin loss. Most plant foods remain alive until processed or cooked for consumption. If during the process of handing, the cells are crushed or killed, there may be rapid vitamin loss presumably due to the action of various oxidizing enzymes. During processing, an attempt is usually made to treat the material so as to inactivate these enzymes at the same time that the cells are killed. The effectiveness of any processing methods depends to a certain extent upon the rapidity with which the inactivation of the enzymes follows the killing of the cells. Exposure of the dead tissue to oxygen may also result in rapid oxidation of some of the vitamins. Certain metals such as copper may act as catalysts in the destruction of the vitamins, and exposure of the material to these metals during processing may be deleterious. Exposure of some of the vitamins, e.g., riboflavin, to light may result in relatively rapid destruction after the cells have been killed. Special processing methods may determine the amount of the vitamin reaching the consumer. For example, in the milling of wheat much of the thiamine may be lost, not because it is destroyed during the milling process, but because it is discarded with the bran which is not used in making flour.

2. *Effect of Cooking*

Many studies have been made of the influence of cooking on vitamin loss. Perhaps the most important factor here is the loss of vitamins in the cooking water. Many of the vitamins are water soluble, and if a large amount of water is used during the cooking, and this water is then discarded, much of the vitamin content may be discarded with it. If food is cooked too long or if it stands for a long time after cooking, its vitamin content may be greatly reduced.

It seems likely that methods will be devised which will preserve a large part of the vitamin actually present in the crop at the time of harvest so that they will reach the consumer. No amount of care or efficiency, however, can result in more than a simple preservation of vitamins. Recommendations have been made that canned tomatoes and tomato juice should contain 25 milligrams of ascorbic acid per 100 cc. of product. Very often fresh tomatoes contain less than this amount of ascorbic acid and no amount of care in handling or processing can increase the amount of ascorbic acid in the final product over and above the amount present in the fresh material unless some artificial means of adding ascorbic acid to the product is introduced. It is during the production of the food crop that the opportunities are available for really increasing the vitamin content.

V. Discussion

Biologists unfamiliar with the problems of the plant scientists are often astounded at the paucity of the information concerning the influence of specific environmental variables on plant composition. There have been a tremendous number of experiments with plants in which analyses have been made for a large number of plant constituents. Very often it is necessary for the experimenter to report that such and such a result was obtained *under the conditions of his experiment.* Another experimenter, attempting to repeat the work, often obtains entirely different results, and these discrepancies are usually ascribed to differences in the environmental conditions between the two experiments. So many factors of the environment are known to influence plant growth and composition that, even though an attempt is made to measure precisely the environmental conditions prevailing during an experiment, it is usually impossible to ascribe differences between experiments to any one variable or set of variables.

Environmental variables that influence plant growth and composition are very numerous. They include the climatic factors, such as temperature, wind movement, atmospheric humidity, and the quality, duration and intensity of light. They also include soil variables, such as soil temperature, moisture, aeration, physical texture, organic material and mineral content. The various environmental variables are often closely related to one another, and a variation of one factor often influences another. For example, variations in atmospheric temperature are intimately correlated with variations in atmospheric humidity. Variations in light intensity are often associated with variations in temperature. The occurrence of rainfall is likely to be associated with decreases in light intensity and temperature, increases in atmospheric humidity and increases in soil moisture. Increases in soil moisture, in turn, are associated with decreases in soil temperature and aeration. So many variables are involved that it is usually impossible to ascribe a particular experimental result solely to the action of variations in a single environmental factor.

Recently there have been some reports of research with plants growing under so-called controlled conditions. Plants are produced in chambers illuminated with artificial light and provided with temperature, wind movement and humidity controls. By using culture solutions for maintaining a standard root environment in such chambers, the experimenter has fair control over most of the environmental factors which are known to influence plant growth and is able experimentally to vary one environmental factor at a time. Results of such experimentation give a far more precise measure of the influence of a specific environmental factor than do field experiments.

In general, the problem may be summarized as follows. It is impossible at the present time for an experimenter to reproduce under controlled conditions or even to measure accurately variations in climate which are known to occur from one location to another and from one season to another. In order to study the effects of climatic variations, therefore, the experimenter is forced to grow his plants at different locations or during different seasons of the year. In order to study the effects of soil differences, he must also grow his plants at different locations. It is usually impossible to ascribe the results obtained either to variations in soil or to variations in climate, and it is even more impossible to ascribe the results to a specific variable.

It seems to the author that there are two approaches to this problem and that both approaches must be made before there is any real progress. First, plants may be grown with all of the environmental variables as much as possible under experimental control. By decreasing to a minimum the variations in all environmental factors, except the one under study, one may correlate accumulated data concerning the specific influence of variations of a single factor. Each factor in turn may be studied in this way. This gives some measure of the relative importance of the various factors in influencing specific constituents. The second approach involves the production of crops at different locations under the natural variations which occur in the field. Briefly, this method consists of growing the same crop at many different locations, making detailed records of the environmental conditions prevailing during the production of the crop and analyzing the crop at the same stage of maturity at each location for specific constituents. Statistical methods should be used in the interpretation of the results.

In conclusion, mention should be made of the marked differences in the vitamin content of different varieties of plants. With respect to every vitamin that has been studied, there have been indications that some varieties contain much more than other varieties. This leads to the hope that real improvement in the nutritive value of many of our food crops may be accomplished through a careful breeding program. Such a program may be the most practical way of increasing the vitamin content of our national diet. For such a program to be successful, it is essential that we obtain more information than we now have concerning the influence of environmental variables. It is to be hoped that future understanding of these problems may bring about a marked improvement in the nutritive value of our food crops as they are produced with a consequent improvement in the quality of the national diet.

References*

Fellers, C. R. 1940. Effect of processing on the vitamin A (carotene) content of foods. *Proc. Institute of Food Technologists* 97-107.

Fenton, F. 1945. Retention of vitamin values in large-scale food service. *Proc. Institute of Food Technologist* 35-48.

Giroud, A. 1938. L'acide ascorbique dans la cellule et les tissus. *Protoplasma Monographien* **16**: 1-187.

Hamner, K. C. 1944. A chamber for growing plants under controlled conditions. *Bot. Gaz.* **105**: 437-441.

Hamner, K. C. 1945. Minor elements and vitamin content of plants. *Soil. Sci.* **60**: 165-171.

Hamner, K. C., and Maynard, L. A. 1942. Factors influencing the nutritive value of the tomato. A review of the literature. *U. S. Dept. Agric. Misc. Publ.* **502**: 23 pp.

Harris, R. S., and Procter, B. E. 1940. Effect of processing on the vitamin B_1 content of foods. *Proc. Institute of Food Technologists* 109-121.

King, C. G., and Tressler, D. K. 1940. Effect of processing on the vitamin C content of foods. *Proc. Institute of Food Technologists* 123-132.

Maynard, L. A., and Beeson, K. C. 1943-44. Some causes of variation in the vitamin content of plants grown for food. *Nutrition Abstracts and Reviews* **13**: 155-164.

Somers, G. F. The role of ascorbic acid in plants. *U. S. Plant, Soil and Nutrition Lab.*, unpublished review of literature.

Somers, G. F., and Beeson, K. C. The influence of climate and fertilizer practices upon the vitamin and mineral content of vegetables. *Advances in Food Research* **1**.

*No attempt has been made to list all of the publications pertinent to this paper. The few references are to review articles or to papers covering some particular point.

Ecological Studies on Populations

BY G. E. HUTCHINSON AND E. S. DEEVEY, JR.
Osborn Zoological Laboratory, Yale University, New Haven, Connecticut

SYNOPSIS

Literally, ecology means a discourse on houses; it is the usual term expressing the study of the relationships of organisms and their environments. The houses may be of various sizes, ranging from the universe as a whole (of which certain chemical properties that evidently date from the remote and largely unknown processes of creation, may be of considerable importance to all organisms) down to the ionic atmosphere of a clay particle, which may constitute the environment of a soil bacterium. Moreover the environmental influences vary greatly in complexity. The two examples just given concern relatively simple physicochemical properties of the environment. In contrast to them may be set all those cases where other organisms form a significant part of the environment of the organism under consideration. The biotic factors involved in such a case may be extremely complex, owing to the inherent complexity of the living beings that constitute the interacting system. Any apparent simplicity in such cases is likely to prove illusionary; physicochemical considerations are seldom of value in the elucidation of the interaction of organisms and the problems of such interaction must be treated at a purely biological level.

The science of ecology has frequently been regarded as divisible into *autecology* and *synecology*. Autecology is the study of the environmental relationships of a single individual, or of any member of a class of relatively homogeneous individuals, such a class being usually a species. It deals largely with the range of environmental variables that permit a species to survive or allow it to reach its maximum development. Synecology has for the objects of its study, not individual organisms but biological communities, which are groups of organisms living in a given space, the properties of which space select a certain assemblage of organisms of definite autecological characteristics. Such communities are moreover not merely collections of organisms of restricted autecology, but tend to become organized by the biotic relationships that exist between the various individuals comprising the community. Some authors have preferred the term *biocoenology* to designate this aspect of ecological science, as synecology has come to have a largely botanical connotation. One special group of cases, where all the organisms are of one species, and all the organizing relations are intraspecific, can be abstracted from the community. These cases have proved to be of particular importance. The study of this group of cases is often referred to as population ecology, the term *biodemography* may be used if a more formal word be desired. Other methods of approach to the biological community make other kinds of abstraction. It is possible for instance to consider whole biological communities as metabolic machines, transforming the matter and energy available to them into forms that differ from those that would be present if the community did not exist. The study of the community by such an extreme form of abstraction becomes *biogeochemistry*. All these branches of investigation, autecology, biocoenology, biodemography, biogeochemistry, may conveniently be regarded as branches of ecology, though they deal with different levels of integration or employ different degrees and kinds of abstraction.

At the present time we have a vast amount of autecological information, which is the basis of applied biology and which is of theoretical interest either because of the physiology that underlies it, or because it provides explanations of biocoenological observations. By itself, such autecological information permits few significant generalizations. Descriptive biocoenology is also well developed, and some of its dynamic aspects are understood, though they perhaps tend to be those the statement of which is a painful elaboration of the obvious. The most striking general propositions of ecology, the results that are not obvious, have mainly been obtained from the remoter and more abstract aspects of the science, where by omitting much, though in a known and systematic way, we can at last reduce the complexity of nature to a degree of simplicity that our minds can grasp. It is one of these more abstract aspects, namely biodemography or the ecology of homogeneous populations, and its extension to very simple cases of interaction of two species, with which this contribution is concerned.

To present a review of all significant advances in ecology in a single article, produced in collaboration by a finite number of writers, is obviously impossible. It has therefore seemed best to plan a series of articles to appear over a number of years that will finally cover the significant modern advances in those sciences that consider organisms in relation to their environments and to one another. When the whole field has thus been surveyed the present article will be sufficiently out of date to justify returning to its subject matter. This subject matter has been chosen for several reasons. Firstly, it occupies a central place in modern ecological thought, and has a considerable bearing on other aspects of biology, notably evolution theory. Secondly, though demographic concepts have primarily been evolved in the study of animal ecology, there is no reason why they should not be applicable to plant ecology and might indeed play a part in the current rejuvenation of that science, which has in the past shown an arthritic tendency. Thirdly, the kind of matter that is presented below is the only part of biology other than genetics to have developed an autonomous quantitative theory independent of the physico-chemical sciences. Fourthly, though the heroic period in the development of that theory reached its peak rather more than a decade before the publication of most of the material to be considered, the years since 1934 have shown an interesting and significant cooperation involving the field naturalist, taxonomist, experimentalist and mathematician, which has of course also affected genetics and evolutionary studies. The attitude is an extraordinary and healthy reaction from the time when the field naturalist was a rank amateur, the taxonomist a mere stamp collector, the experimentalist out of touch with nature and the theoretical worker incomprehensible and over-speculative. In choosing to initiate a survey of ecological progress with a summary of the present position of ecological studies on populations we believe that we are attacking the problem in a way that is both topical and of considerable enduring interest.

I. The Growth of a Population

The first significant development of the fundamental idea of Malthus was made by Verhulst in 1838 and rediscovered by Pearl and Reed in 1920. Verhulst's logistic equation, most easily handled in differential form

$$\frac{dN}{dt} = bN \cdot \frac{(K-N)}{K} \qquad (1)$$

may be regarded as a modification of Malthus' proposition that populations increase geometrically. The constant b is in fact the Malthusian coefficient or net birth rate in an unrestricted universe in which the population can expand indefinitely. The term $(K-N)/K$ may be regarded as a term continually modifying b; when N is very small the modification is negligible and the net rate of growth is practically Malthusian, when N approaches K the net rate of increase approaches zero, every individual born replacing one that dies.

In any particular case it may be possible to produce other deductive mathematical models which are more appropriate. A good example is given by Crombie (1946) in his consideration of the growth of populations of graminivorous insects (cf. also Stanley, 1941). Neglecting a very small larval death rate independent of density which may occur in some cases, the major control of the population is by (1) m, the death rate of adults, (2) the fecundity and (3) cannibalism. Fecundity is a function $f(N)$ of adult density N, the exact form of the function requiring empirical investigation. The rate of destruction by cannibalism depends on the number of prey stages (eggs and pupae), the number of predator stages (larvae and adults) per unit mass of medium and on the length of oval and pupal life.

It is found that the *proportion* of eggs and pupae eaten per day is, at low densities (less than 20 predator stage individuals per gram of flour), practically a linear function of the density (n) of predators. If $(1-qn)$ be the proportion of eggs left each day by a population of density n and $(1-pn)$ the proportion of pupae, the reduction of the population by cannibalism will be given by the factor $(1-qn)^h(1-pn)^j$ where h and j are the lengths of oval and pupal life respectively. The rate of increase of the adult population (N) will therefore be

$$\frac{dN}{dt} = N[bf(N) \cdot (1-qn)^h(1-pn)^j - m] \qquad (2)$$

This equation, in which the effective rate of increase depends not on the rate of utilization of the potential of the resources of K but on cannibalism, is obviously of a different form from the logistic. Yet when it is developed for application to the competition of two species, the coefficients of competition turn out to have practically the same significance as they do in the elaboration of the logistic to fit interspecific competition, and the rest of Crombie's paper is developed the same way as it would have been if the logistic had been the appropriate form.

In field studies of populations we practically never have the entire cycle of development available. The changes that are normally observed represent changes towards the steady-state condition appropriate at the time of observation, from some previous population determined by previous conditions. From the standpoint of the field ecologist the forces determining the population at any moment, the *natality* and the *mortality*, on the relationship of which the value of dN/dt depends, may often be more interesting when analyzed empirically than by means of a deductive model. The latter will prove its immense usefulness in considering competition, but first it is desirable to consider natality and mortality separately.

II. Natality

Although it is easy to see qualitatively that natality is a function $f(N)$ of density, it is not yet possible to define this function in such a way as to include it in a general theory of population growth; this is one of the defects of the deductive mathematical models like that underlying the logistic equation. Empirical investigations of the relationship between crowding and birth rate have been prosecuted actively for many years, and much of the information is summarized in such accessible sources as Allee

(1931). In this section we shall indicate briefly the form of relationship to be expected, with emphasis on contributions since 1931.

1. *Natality and Density. Simple Cases*

The simplest relationship, established experimentally in the classical work of Pearl and collaborators, is represented by *Drosophila*. The fecundity falls exponentially with densities above the minimum (1 pair per culture bottle), the curve taking the form

$$y = ae^{-zx}x^{-w} \tag{3}$$

where y = offspring per mated female per day and x = mean population density. Additional experiments showed that it is egg production, not fertility or larval survival, which is affected by density, and that the effect is related to the surface area of the medium on which the flies feed and oviposit rather than to the volume of air space above the medium. The mechanism seems to have a psychological basis; the flies dislike being jostled while ovipositing, and the fecundity suffers accordingly. As Allee points out, where contact stimulation is harmful, exponential relationships with density are likely to result. A similar curve has been found for *Daphnia* by Pratt (1943).

2. *Natality and Density. Complex Cases*

A rather different result is obtained with the flour beetle, *Tribolium confusum,* when fecundity is studied in relation to density. Here there is a clear-cut *optimum density* for fecundity, and the curve rises before it falls; the fall is again exponential at densities above the optimum. Experiments by T. Park and others (summarized in Park, 1941) have led to the formal explanation of this sort of complex curve: fecundity is increased by recopulation; recopulation increases with the density; but at higher densities accidental cannibalism (eating of eggs and pupae by adult beetles and larvae) supervenes to counteract the effect of recopulation on fecundity.

3. *Allelocatalysis*

The complex type of relationship, involving an optimum density for natality, though it has attracted a good deal of interest, is apparently rather rare. A great controversy has raged over whether protozoan populations show it or not. Early experiments, such as the original ones of Robertson (1921), purporting to show that division rates of certain ciliates are enhanced by increasing population densities, suffered from inadequate control of the food supply. With advances in technique of pure culture it has become possible to state that optimum density effects are occasionally shown (Kidder, 1941a; Reich, 1938; Mast and Pace, 1938), i.e., that the reproductive rate sometimes varies positively with the size of the inoculum. It is often assumed that such an effect must be due to a substance (*allelocatalytic* in nature) released into the medium by the protozoans for their mutual benefit. Such substances have not yet been isolated, though in a few cases the evidence is strong that they exist; they may be vitamins. The assumption that all such allelocatalytic effects must inevitably be due to a specific substance is, however, misleading.

Analysis of population growth among ciliates (Kidder) and amoebae (Reich) in terms of the logistic equation shows that when optimum density effects are found what really happens is that the length of the *lag period* is reduced. Mathematically a *lag period* may be regarded as demonstrated when the *specific rate of population growth*[1] increases. Biologically it is the period before logistic (customarily called the *logarithmic phase* by workers in this field) growth begins. It is perhaps to be understood as a period of acclimation on the part of the inoculated organisms to the new culture conditions, and in this sense it is a phase in which *mass protective effects* of the sort demonstrated by Allee and others are likely to be observed. Thus if there is some substance already in the fresh culture medium which is somewhat inimical, members of a larger initial population will absorb less of the substance per individual. The reasonableness of this hypothesis (Kidder, 1941b) suggests that many supposed allelocatalytic substances will prove to be chimaeras.

4. *Optimum Density in Natural Populations*

The period under review has been characterized by an immense growth of interest in population biology as observed in the field. Typical of this interest is the attention attracted by the hypothesis of F. Fraser Darling (1938), according to which the percentage of nesting success in birds increases with the size of the colony. Such social breeders as the herring gull apparently stimulate each other to breeding activity by sexual displays which are in part public and thus subject to mutual reinforcement by larger numbers. Darling maintains that such species are likely to have a threshold of numbers, below which the stimulating effect is too slight for successful breeding. At densities great enough to permit the laying of eggs and the hatching of young it is still possible to picture the reproductive success

[1]This is formulated as $\frac{1}{N} \cdot \frac{dN}{dt}$: in practice it is approximated by

$$\frac{\text{increase of population in time interval}}{\text{population size at the beginning of time interval}}$$

as enhanced through the synchronization of nesting activity. At least on those small islands where Darling made his observations, predator pressure being relatively slight, synchronization of egg-laying, incubation, and care of the young among all members of the colony should reduce the relative toll by predators at critical stages in the life history.

The evidence in Darling's own observations was extremely slender, and it is probably fair to say that although his thesis remains a distinct possibility and an ingenious synthesis of laboratory and field ecology, it still rests almost entirely on inference. Fisher and Waterston (1941) pointed to the fulmar petrel, which is extending its range around the British coasts, as a possible case in point, since the pioneers at any new breeding site are few in number and do not ordinarily breed until their numbers are augmented by further immigration. But it is more likely in this instance that the first colonists are immature birds, "playing" at nesting as do many other sea birds. Again, in a study of the Arctic tern, Bullough (1942) found some evidence for synchronization of breeding activity, and thus of an earlier mean date of nesting, in a larger colony, but there was no indication that the reproductive success was thereby improved. Vogt (1942) believes that there is a critical lower limit for successful breeding in the colonies of the guanay *Phalacrocorax bougainvillei* Lesson. In this case large colonies appear to have an advantage in that the ratio of circumference to population size is smaller than in small colonies; loss of chicks at the edge of the colonies is thus reduced in large aggregates. Other factors are doubtless also involved, but there is no synchronization in reproductive behavior. Data on the red-winged blackbird (H. S. Smith, 1943) did not reveal any differences between large and small colonies, though in this case it could be argued that Darling's thesis need not hold; the redwing is a communal nester, but is not given to mutual sexual display. A discussion of the Darling principle is given by von Haartman (1945), who accepts the possibility of its existence while denying that there is any incontrovertible evidence for it.

Another possible case of an optimum density for breeding has been reported by Errington (1945) for the muskrat. Populations smaller than about one pair per linear mile of stream or per 15 acres of marshland appear not to breed successfully, but as is shown below in the discussion of cyclical fluctuations of numbers, this example is not likely to have any simple explanation.

Several other instances of an optimum effect of density are known both from the field and the laboratory, but as these have to do with longevity rather than natality they are best deferred until mortality is considered in the next section. It appears that in general the effect of crowding is to reduce the reproductive rate of the members of populations, and this is one aspect of the "environmental control" which is ultimately imposed on the Malthusian increase. The effect is not linear, however, but tends to have an exponential form in thoroughly studied cases. Under special circumstances and particularly at very low densities effects of a different sort may appear, establishing the reality of "undercrowding." This phenomenon is of immense interest to general sociology, but its importance in a general theory of population growth must, in the nature of things, be quantitatively insignificant.

III. Mortality

The other aspect of the equilibrium between births and deaths, which, like natality, must be handled empirically at present, is mortality. In this field attention has chiefly been focused on the form of the age distribution of mortality and the physiological factors controlling it. Some of this material must be presented first, before considering the relation between mortality and population growth.

Mortality statistics are most easily embodied in life tables, or presented in graphical form as survivorship curves, and such tables or curves can very advantageously be constructed for laboratory populations. When the members of a cohort (such as the offspring of a single pair of *Drosophila*) are born at the same time and followed throughout their life spans until the last member is dead, age at death (d_x) is directly observed, survivorship (l_x) is obtained by successive subtraction, and mortality rate (q_x) is given for any age interval (such as 1 day) as d_x/l_x. Survivorship curves plotted on semi-logarithmic graph paper decline toward zero with slopes which correspond to mortality rate.

1. *Laboratory Observations*

Pearl and Miner (1935) published a review of the comparative mortality of lower organisms which adequately summarizes the information up to the beginning of the period covered by this review and which indeed requires little modification today. Data are given by Pearl and Miner for *Hydra,* the rotifer *Proales decipiens,* the slug *Agriolimax agrestis,* the roach, two moths, *Drosophila,* the domestic fowl and the laboratory mouse. Additional data are now available for several other rotifers (Edmondson, 1945 and references cited therein), *Daphnia magna* (MacArthur and Baillie, 1929; Pratt, 1943), *D. longispina* (Ingle, Wood and Banta, 1937), the flour beetles *Tribolium confusum* (Pearl, Park and Miner, 1941), *T. madens* (Park, 1945), and *Trogoderma versicolor* (Davis, 1945), the blowfly *Calliphora erythrocephala* and the Palestinian housefly *Musca vicina*

(Feldman-Muhsam and Muhsam, 1946), the black widow spider (Deevey and Deevey, 1945), the white rat (Wiesner and Sheard, 1934) and the vole *Microtus agrestis* (Leslie and Ranson, 1940).

The origin of the data has had to be taken at various biologically different ages, e.g., birth for a rodent, emergence for an insect, the antepenultimate instar for the black widow spider, and comparisons are perforce tentative. Three different sorts of life table are apparent, with various intermediate conditions: the negatively skew rectangular survivorship curve, implying nearly perfect survival until the end of the life span, with all deaths concentrated at old age, is approached by certain rotifers (Edmondson, 1945), namely *Epiphanes senta* (Ferris, 1932) and *Lecane inermis* (Miller, 1931). The positively skew rectangular type, with deaths heavily concentrated in early ages, still remains to be found in a laboratory species. Most life tables are variations of the diagonal type, showing constant mortality rate with respect to age but departing from diagonality at the beginning or at the end of the life span or both.

The published tables were obtained with laboratory animals under rigidly specified conditions of temperature, humidity, food supply, etc., and do not necessarily apply to the same species under different conditions. In particular, the well-known effect of population density on longevity makes it necessary to accept a given life table with considerable reserve. In most cases the density was allowed to decrease systematically with the death of the members of the cohort. This objection does not apply, however, to the longevity data obtained for *Daphnia magna* by Pratt (1943), and when Pratt's survivorship curves for densities of 1, 5, 10, 25, etc. per 50 cc. culture jar are compared on the same basis (by expressing age as a percentage of the mean life span of the cohort and regraduating the age scale accordingly) it is evident that the *form* of the survival distribution is not appreciably affected by density, though the absolute longevity differs widely with the density.

Complete life tables are relatively rare, and are not customarily available even for man. Feldman-Muhsam and Muhsam (1946) have recently taken the trouble to incorporate oval, larval, and pupal mortality in the life table for *Musca vicina,* a Palestinian species which can be reared in cow dung. The survivorship curve (Fig. 1) proves to be closely similar to that of man with fetal mortality included, with an initial dip, a steady mortality rate during middle life, and an increased mortality rate in old age. Probably all ordinary laboratory animals will eventually be found to have survival curves like these, but the resemblance between the curves for man and the flour beetle *Tribolium confusum* (Pearl *et al.,* 1941) is fictitious, the published curves starting at different biological ages.

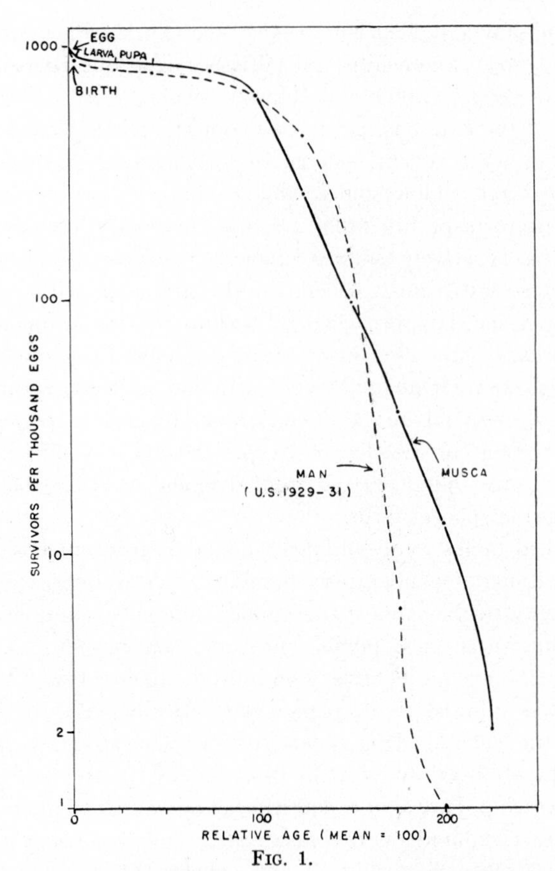

Fig. 1.

Survivorship curve for the Palestinian housefly *Musca vicina*, beginning at oviposition, and compared with the survivorship curve for a modern human population beginning at conception. Redrawn from Feldman-Muhsam and Muhsam, 1946.

It is apparent that organisms differ rather widely in their order of dying, and mortality rate cannot be assumed to be constant with respect to age, even among well-protected laboratory species.

2. *Mortality in Natural Populations*

Ecological information bearing on the age-distribution of mortality in nature is very scanty. A few examples of ecological life tables have been collected in a recent review (Deevey, 1947) but comparisons between them are made difficult by the incompleteness of the data and the different biological ages at which the available observations begin. In the few cases in which the ages of members of natural populations can be determined, three kinds of computation can lead to the construction of a life table. In the first, which is comparable to the prosecution of a laboratory study, survival (l_x) is observed by repeated censuses of a population all of whose members were born at approximately the same time. In the second, animals are found dead and their age at death can be determined, thus providing a d_x distribution for the sample but as a rule the number living at any age is not known. In order to use such data, it is necessary to make the dangerous assumptions (1) that the population is not growing or declining, and (2) that the probability of finding a dead animal is not influenced by the age of the animal. In the third situation the age distribution of the living members of the population can be observed by sampling methods, and the mortality rate inferred from the shrinkage between successive age-classes. This method, widely used in fisheries research, also requires the acceptance of assumption (1).

The most nearly unobjectionable life tables so far available for natural populations are those calculated (Deevey, 1947) from the data of Hatton (1938) on the barnacle *Balanus balanoides* at St. Malo. These populations were allowed to settle on cleaned areas on rocks in the intertidal zone and followed for more than three years. The superiority of these data to others, such as those for the song sparrow (Nice, 1937), the pheasant (Leopold *et al.*, 1943) and the sessile rotifer *Floscularia* (Edmondson, 1945) which are also based on direct observation of l_x, lies primarily in the greater accuracy of the census figures. They are not complete, however, as the larval segment of the life span is left out of account. The survivorship curves from attachment (adult stage) onward are remarkably sinuous, but do not fall in the J-shaped or positively skew rectangular type of Pearl and Miner. Variations in mean longevity and in the form of the survivorship lines among the nine populations studied are due in a general way to variations in their situation with respect to tidal levels. But a calculation based on the geometry of crowding by barnacles growing radially on a plane surface shows that population density is an important determinant of life expectancy, and may have a more direct effect than the physical ecology of the intertidal zone.

As to ecological life tables calculated by other, statistically less respectable methods, it need only be said that wide variations in mortality rate with respect to age are strongly suggested by the data. To judge by the data on the age at death of banded individuals, several species of birds, including song birds and water birds, seem to have exceedingly constant mortality rates from the adult stage onward. Considerably higher rates in pre-adult life, leading to a somewhat J-shaped survivorship curve for the whole life span, are to be considered likely, though not yet proved. The data for fish are less satisfactory, but it seems certain that complete data will show Pearl to have been right in his suggestion that pelagic fish have positively skew survivorship curves in nature; Sette (1943) calculates that the mackerel suffers 99.9996% mortality in its first 70 days of life. On the other hand, not all ecological life tables are of this sort: the Dall mountain sheep, for example (Murie, 1941), after an initial dip in survivorship during infancy (a dip which is probably somewhat more prominent than shown by the actual data, which are based on age determinations of skulls), maintains a high survival ratio until near the end of the life span. Apparently this species, which is subject to depredations by a single important predator, the timber wolf, has evolved mechanisms, perhaps mainly psychological, for stretching its survivorship curve toward the maximum, somewhat as man has through the ages.

Data on survival of species in nature are just beginning to be collected, and the advantage of the life table notation has not yet been widely appreciated by ecologists. But such preliminary comparisons as can be made imply that species can eventually be classified in terms of the three fundamental types of Pearl and Miner. Thus, if the maximum life span in nature is only 2 or 3 times the mean, the survivorship curve is negatively skew and the species may be called "thrifty"; a species with a diagonal life curve is "indifferent," and one whose maximum life span is 10 or 15 times the mean might well be called "prodigal." But although the ecological information, when ultimately it is summarized in this form, can contribute to a general theory of mortality, it can never serve as a substitute for such a theory. For even if all environmental causes of death were dissected out of the life table, we would still be left with the thorny problem of the nature of physiological senescence. On this matter the reader's attention is drawn to the interesting contribution of Lansing (1942, 1947), which demonstrates that aging in the rotifer *Philodina citrina* is a function of the accumulation of calcium, which can be removed by appropriate treatment. The eggs of aged individuals are laid in an aged condition and are infertile.

3. *Human Survival*

Population problems as seen by the demographer are beyond the scope of this review, but a certain amount of extremely interesting material, recently collected by the physical anthropologists, deserves notice here lest it escape the attention of the general biologist. The age at death of a human individual can be determined (within rather wide limits) by osteological characters. Hence, subject to the limitations implied in assumption (1) above, survivorship curves can be constructed for various peoples known

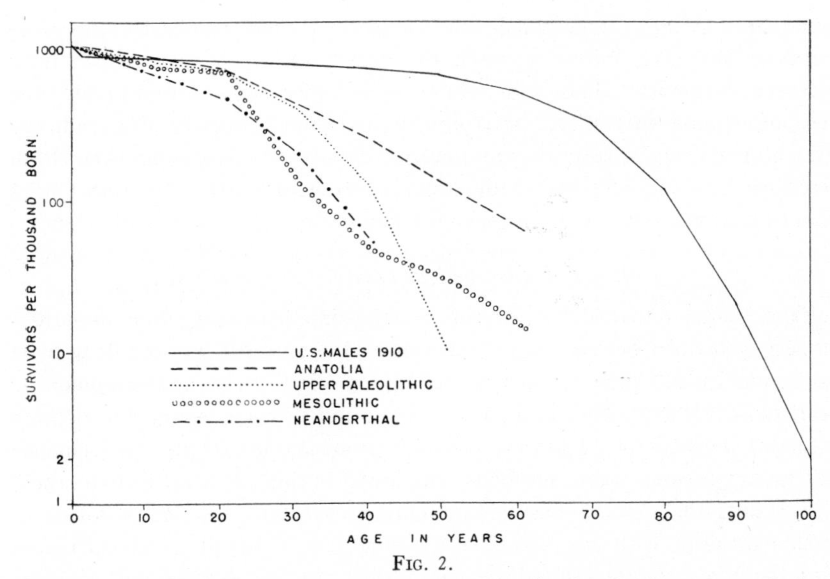

FIG. 2.

Rough survivorship curves for several "populations" of primitive man, calculated from the age at death as determined from skeletal material. Data from Vallois (1937) and Senyürek (1947).

only to archaeology. A few such crude curves are presented in Fig. 2, based on the review by Vallois (1937) and the important recent paper by Senyürek (1947) on the duration of life in ancient Anatolia. The samples are of course small, and the reliability of the data can be seriously questioned, but the curves suggest a principle of great interest: that the survival of mankind increases, not in proportion to the age of man as a species, but according to his cultural stability. Thus the environmental vicissitudes suffered by the Mesolithic forest peoples of northern Europe during early post-glacial times evidently are reflected in higher mortality rates and a lower mean life span as compared with the Upper Paleolithic peoples who preceded them in time. The curve for the Anatolians is a composite curve, as the skeletons come from all levels from the Chalcolithic-Copper age through Roman-Byzantine times; within this span the mean length of life probably increased with the progress of civilization. Although the data are inadequate to establish this conclusion firmly, the same impression was obtained by Angel (1947) from a study of Greek skulls covering a long cultural span. All the archaeological survivorship curves are of course distinctly inferior to those for modern civilized man, as would have been expected since the work of Macdonell (1913) on Roman demography. Data recently collected by Cook (1947) for primitive American peoples, living and extinct, show much the same thing, but emphasize the wide variation among primitive races in the degree to which they realize their potential longevity. This wide variation includes some astonishingly low rates of juvenile mortality.[2] It is obvious that the human race is gradually stretching its survivorship curve toward the perfect negatively skew form described by Pearl and Miner, but there is no evidence that the upper limit of extreme longevity has been extended in the process.

4. Mortality and Population Density

Experiments designed to test this relationship have not often been performed, probably because most experimental organisms are too long-lived for convenience. Such an experiment was performed with *Drosophila* by Pearl *et al.* (1927). The result was a broad and rather irregular but definite optimum density for longevity, densities from 35 to 55 flies per 1-ounce vial giving greater mean survival than lower or higher densities. In these experiments the density was not maintained constant, but was allowed to decline steadily with the death of the flies; mean density was calculated over the life span by laborious computation. In the experiments of Pratt (1943) with *Daphnia magna* this objection does not apply, since "charter members" of the populations were replaced as they died with marked *Daphnia* of the same age. Pratt also found an optimum density for mean longevity in this species.

Human population data do not readily yield any valid conclusions as to the effect of density on longevity. Statistics for England and Wales, analyzed by Farr (1875) and later by Brownlee (1915) gave an exponential relationship, but this cannot be confirmed for U. S. populations. The difficulty here is probably a technical one, that in a culturally homogeneous civilization political density (population per square mile, per county, etc.) is not necessarily a biologically meaningful measure of economic density. The suggestion (above) that man's mean length of life increases with his cultural stability implies that data could be manipulated to reveal a direct relationship between density and longevity, and this, combined with confirmation of "Farr's Law" would mean that an optimum density for survival actually exists. But at present the procedure would have to be so arbitrary as not to be worth the trouble.

A series of particularly interesting cases involving natural populations has recently been studied by Lack (1946a, 1947a, b; Lack and Arn, 1947). Here the population to be considered consists of the eggs or nestlings in

[2]A verbal suggestion by Dr. Margaret Mead, that the infant mortality of primitive peoples may be a function of lactation time and of tabu on coitus during lactation, deserves careful statistical study.

a nest; it is, in fact, a direct expression of natality. In the best studied case of a nidicolous bird, namely that of *Apus melpa,* the Alpine swift, breeding at Solothurn in Switzerland, clutches of three eggs are normal, occurring in 66% of the cases recorded; clutches of two eggs constitute about 30% of the cases, of one egg about 3% and of 4 eggs about 0.6%. The clutches of two are probably in part produced by young birds; in general it seems probable that about 10% of the laying birds have an hereditary tendency towards two egg clutches and about 1% towards four egg clutches. The hatching success is almost 100% for all clutch sizes. The mortality of hatched chicks, however, is markedly density dependent so that the nests with four eggs produce no more chicks that survive to leave the nest than do nests with three eggs (Fig. 3). Post-fledging mortality appears to be about the same for all groups. It is supposed that, if five eggs were laid and hatched, the nest mortality would be so great that such higher natality would be markedly disadvantageous and would prevent the parents of such broods from leaving adequate descendants. Assuming that a genetic factor is involved in determining brood size, as seems probable

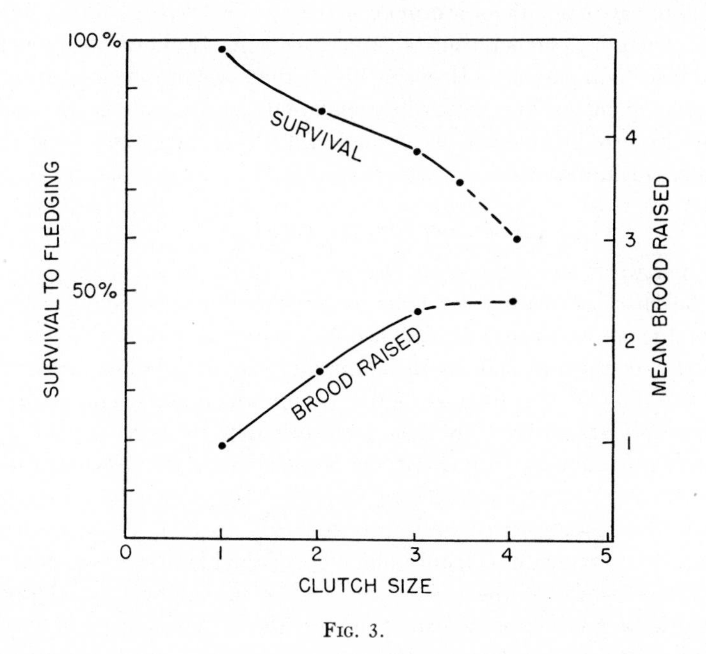

FIG. 3.

Percentage of hatched chicks that survive to fledging and mean size of resulting brood in *Apus melpa* plotted against clutch size. Data from Lack and Arn (1947).

from other data, birds producing the smallest clutch sizes would be at an evolutionary disadvantage because, although the survival of their offspring through fledgling is likely to be nearly 100%, there are too few individuals involved; whereas the birds producing the largest clutches would be at a disadvantage because, in spite of high initial numbers of offspring, the survival rate is too poor. Lack believes that the food supply available to the parents is the critical factor involved in determining optimal clutch size, and he has shown how geographical variation in this character can be interpreted in terms of abundance of food or length of feeding time.

One remarkable case showing a positive effect of crowding on survival has come to light in a *natural* population. Edmondson (1945) found that the mean length of life of the sessile rotifer, *Floscularia,* is practically doubled if the young rotifer, instead of living a solitary existence on a water plant, attaches to the tube of an older *Floscularia,* thus establishing a small colony. The meaning of this discovery is completely obscure. Indeed the explanation of the optimum density for longevity in *Drosophila* and *Daphnia* is far from apparent, though it has been suggested that small, supra-minimal populations are more successful in keeping "wild" organisms (molds, bacteria?) under control. Under completely different circumstances it has been pointed out (Deevey, 1947) that certain species of intertidal barnacles might survive better in population densities above the minimum if they live so high above mean high tide level that their own shade is mutually advantageous.

5. *Time Lags in the Effect of Density*

In their work on longevity of *Drosophila,* Pearl, Miner and Parker found that the effect of density need not be expressed immediately. Flies which started life at a density of 200 per 1-ounce vial and were then brought back to a density of 200 on their 16th day of life showed a significantly lower duration of life than a control group which started at a density of 35 and were transferred on their sixteenth day to a density of 200. So the life expectancy at 16 days of age is affected by the previous experience of crowding.

Analogous results with natality are not easy to find, but it is clear from the data of Pratt with *Daphnia* and implied in his discussion, that such a lag is responsible for the oscillations set up in *Daphnia* populations: the natality at a given intermediate point on the sigmoid curve of population growth is determined, not by the current density, but by some previous lower density; the population overshoots its equilibrium value. Then mortality, the dominant process at high densities, begins to exceed natality, but again there is a time lag between the attainment of a given density and the effect of that density on the mortality, and the population falls below its equilibrium. The implications of this mechanism for a theory of cyclical fluctuations are discussed in another section.

IV. Competition Between Two Species

Perhaps the most important theoretical development in general ecology has been the application of the logistic by Volterra, Lotka, Gause and others to cases where two species occupy the same universe.

If we suppose that the second species inhibits the first by an amount which depends on its number, and the first the second likewise, we may write

$$\frac{dN_1}{dt} = \frac{b_1 N_1 [K_1 - N_1 - f_2(N_2)]}{K_1}$$
$$\frac{dN_2}{dt} = \frac{b_2 N_2 [K_2 - N_2 - f_1(N_1)]}{K_2} \qquad (4)$$

It is obvious that the functions $f_1(N_1)$ and $f_2(N_2)$ contain no absolute terms, and most authors have assumed that they may be suitably expressed as linear. The equations thus become

$$\frac{dN_1}{dt} = \frac{b_1 N_1 (K_1 - N_1 - \alpha N_2)}{K_1}$$
$$\frac{dN_2}{dt} = \frac{b_2 N_2 (K_2 - N_2 - \beta N_1)}{K_2} \qquad (5)$$

where α and β are *coefficients of competition.* Where α and β are positive four cases must be considered

(1) $$\alpha < \frac{K_1}{K_2}, \ \beta < \frac{K_2}{K_1}$$

(2) $$\alpha < \frac{K_1}{K_2}, \ \beta > \frac{K_2}{K_1}$$

(3) $$\alpha > \frac{K_1}{K_2}, \ \beta < \frac{K_2}{K_1}$$

(4) $$\alpha > \frac{K_1}{K_2}, \ \beta > \frac{K_2}{K_1}$$

The first case corresponds to the situation in which each species limits the rate of increase of the other less than its own rate of increase. *This implies that the ecological niches of the two species do not overlap com-*

pletely. The populations can form a stable mixture of the two species, the saturation values for N_1 being $\frac{K_1 - \alpha K_2}{1 - \alpha\beta}$ and for N_2, $\frac{K_2 - \beta K_1}{1 - \alpha\beta}$.

The second and third cases correspond to complete replacement of one species by the other irrespective of the initial numbers. In the fourth case, in which the effect of each species on the other is more inhibitory than on itself, the nature of the final population consisting of a single species is determined by the relative initial concentrations. By the use of negative values of the coefficients, commensalism and symbiosis can be described. For a fuller discussion, with description of experimental verification, the writer is referred to the contributions of Gause (1934, 1935; Gause and Witt, 1935).

The generalization implicit in cases (2) and (3), that two species with the same niche requirements cannot form mixed steady-state populations in the same region has become one of the chief foundations of modern ecology.

The whole problem has recently been reviewed by Crombie (1947) and its evolutionary significance in terms of the replacement of one form by a new, better adapted mutant is, of course, implicit in the whole of modern mathematical evolutionary theory. Lack (1944, 1945, 1946a, b) has given particular attention to the ecological and evolutionary aspects of competition found among related species of birds, and finds that in all well analyzed cases the niches of sympatric species are not identical. In some cases, however, the differentiation of the niches is manifest only when some abundant food eaten by several species is temporarily reduced in availability. Certain special aspects of competition theory are of particular ecological interest and are at present being actively investigated.

1. *Experiments on the Diversification of Niches*

In every case in which adequate experimental studies have been made, it has been demonstrated that in rigidly single niche systems only one species survives. In the earlier work, Gause indicated that it was possible to set up conditions in which two species could live singly, but which consisted of a single niche in which mixed populations always ended with a single species surviving, and that by modification of the environment two niches could be made, which permitted both species to survive. The following experiments of Crombie (1945, 1946) beautifully illustrate these generalizations. In constantly renewed cracked wheat the beetle *Rhizopertha dominica* always displaced the moth *Sitotroga cerealella* whatever the initial numbers. This is fundamentally due to fighting on the part of larvae within the wheat grain, for in such encounters the ratio of survivors is as 1.3/1 in favor of *Rhizopertha* (Crombie, 1944a). Either species can be cultured permanently with the beetle *Oryzaephilus surinamensis* which lives outside the grain and so occupies a slightly different niche.

Competition between *Tribolium confusum* and *O. surinamensis* in flour always led to displacement of the latter. Both species eat each other's resting stages and the more voracious species wins. If the culture contains fine glass tubes which exclude the larger larvae and the adults of *Tribolium,* but permit entrance of the smaller *Oryzaephilus,* a second niche is present and both species survive. When the two species are reared in cracked wheat, both survive, because of the pupation of *Oryzaephilus* inside hollowed-out wheat grains. The population of *Oryzaephilus* at equilibrium was, however, much depressed whereas that of *Tribolium* was little depressed.

Competition between *Tribolium* and *Rhizopertha,* one living inside and one outside the cracked wheat grains, permitted a mixed population to survive, but *Rhizopertha* was very depressed by *Tribolium* destroying its eggs. When *Tribolium* competes with both *Rhizopertha* and *Oryzaephilus* its population is more depressed than when competing with either one. The depression of *Rhizopertha* and *Oryzaephilus* was no greater than when they competed with *Tribolium* alone.

2. *The Modification of Direction of Competition*

In the earlier work by Gause and his coworkers (Gause, 1935) it was shown that the direction of competition between *Paramecium aurelia* and *P. caudatum* depended on the nature of the medium, *P. aurelia* displacing *P. caudatum* in old biologically conditioned media, *P. caudatum* displacing *P. aurelia* in fresh media.

A similar condition has evidently been observed in the extensive series of experiments conducted by Park and his associates, though at the time of writing the results are published only as a note appended to Crombie's (1947) review. Park's case relates to two species of *Tribolium.* When *T. castaneum* is cultured with *T. confusum* it normally displaces the latter. When, however, the cultures are infected with the protozoan parasite *Adelina tribolii* competition leads normally to the elimination of *T. castaneum* by *T. confusum.* The field data of Beauchamp and Ullyott (1932) indicate clearly the same sort of control of direction of competition by ecological variables. Moore (see Moore and Kitching, 1939; Moore and Sproston, 1940) has suggested that this is an aspect of a principle of wide application in field ecology: when conditions are not optimal for a species with respect to one ecological factor (such as salinity or exposure in a marine organism), the range of tolerance is reduced with respect to other ecological factors (such as competition).

In any case in which the length of a generation is short compared to the length of the annual cycle of seasons there is a possibility for continual changes in competitive direction by some such mechanism. At any point in the illuminated zone of the ocean or a lake the phytoplankton is normally quite diversified. There is no opportunity for niche specialization and the fundamental trophic requirements of all forms will cause them to draw on the same food supply. Such populations cannot therefore represent equilibria, but since in general the plankton, though continually changing, remains in a highly diversified state, one can only suppose that the direction of competition is continually undergoing change with the progress of the seasons and concomitant thermal and chemical changes in the water and that no opportunity for the establishment of a single species equilibrium condition ever occurs (Hutchinson, 1941, 1944).

3. *The Possibility of Nonlinear Competition Functions*

The replacement of the competition functions $f_2(N_2)$ and $f_1(N_1)$ by αN_2 and βN_1 may appear arbitrary, but is apparently justified by the regularity with which the expected end results are obtained experimentally. One experimental case has been described in which there is a suggestion of some other phenomenon. Park, Gregg and Lutherman found that in competition between two granary beetles, *Tribolium confusum* and *Gnathocerus cornutus*, the end result depended on the relative sizes of the initial populations. Accepting the linear relationship implied by the constant coefficients this could be an example of case (4), in which each species inhibits the other more than itself. Models of such a situation could doubtless be made in cultures of microorganisms each producing an antibiotic against the other. It has, however, been pointed out (Hutchinson, 1947) that if the competitive effect exerted by one individual was in part a social one, depending on the number of the individuals present, the competition functions would take quadratic forms

$$\begin{aligned} f_2(N_2) &= \alpha N_2 + \gamma N_2^2 \\ f_1(N_1) &= \beta N_1 + \delta N_1^2 \end{aligned} \qquad (6)$$

and this will lead to the same end results as in case (4) if γ and δ are large and α and β small. It appears quite probable that phenomena of this sort are of importance in the establishment of bird colonies, for Vesey-Fitzgerald (1941) found that in competition between noddy and sooty terns either species is at a disadvantage when present in small numbers in contact with a large population of the other species.

4. The Effect of Competition on Community Structure

In general the most closely allied species are allopatric and occupy similar niches in different regions. Competition will usually prevent entry of such species into each other's territories. It might therefore be thought that when any single habitat is examined the proportion of genera with few species would be higher than when the whole region in which the habitat occurred is examined. Elton (1946) found that when a series of communities was studied the percentage of genera with single species was 84% for plants and 86% for animals, whereas for large regions much lower figures were obtained.

Williams (1947) has, however, pointed out that a better measure can be obtained by supposing that the number of genera with n species be represented by $\frac{\alpha x^n}{n}$, so forming a logarithmic series in which α is a constant, independent of the size of the sample, called the *index of generic diversity*. Using this method he shows quite clearly that in seven plant surveys and seven animal surveys in Britain the index is never greater and is usually much less than that derived for Britain as a whole. This suggests that although increasing the area may decrease the generic diversity by introducing representative or allopatric species, it increases the generic diversity as much or more by increasing the environmental diversity. Further work along these lines using α either as an index of specific (Fisher *et al.*, 1943) or generic diversity should provide a method for the solution of a great number of ecological problems. In particular the belief that the diversity of a community, after having increased early in succession, may decrease as the climax is approached, can be submitted to a more rigorous test than is provided by floral or faunal lists.

V. Periodic Fluctuations in Population Density

It has long been known that certain species of animals undergo rather regular variations in population density. The exact nature of these regular variations has proved very difficult to elucidate.

It is desirable first to exclude from consideration what may be called *statistical pseudoperiodicities* (Fig. 4). Such are to be expected whenever the rapid increase or decrease of a population depends not only on the size of the breeding stock, but on the occurrence of a certain critical meteorological condition which has a definite probability in the region in question. In cases of this sort the period between maxima might in one part of a time span have a mean value that closely approximated the value in another part of the time span. No true periodic fluctuation would, how-

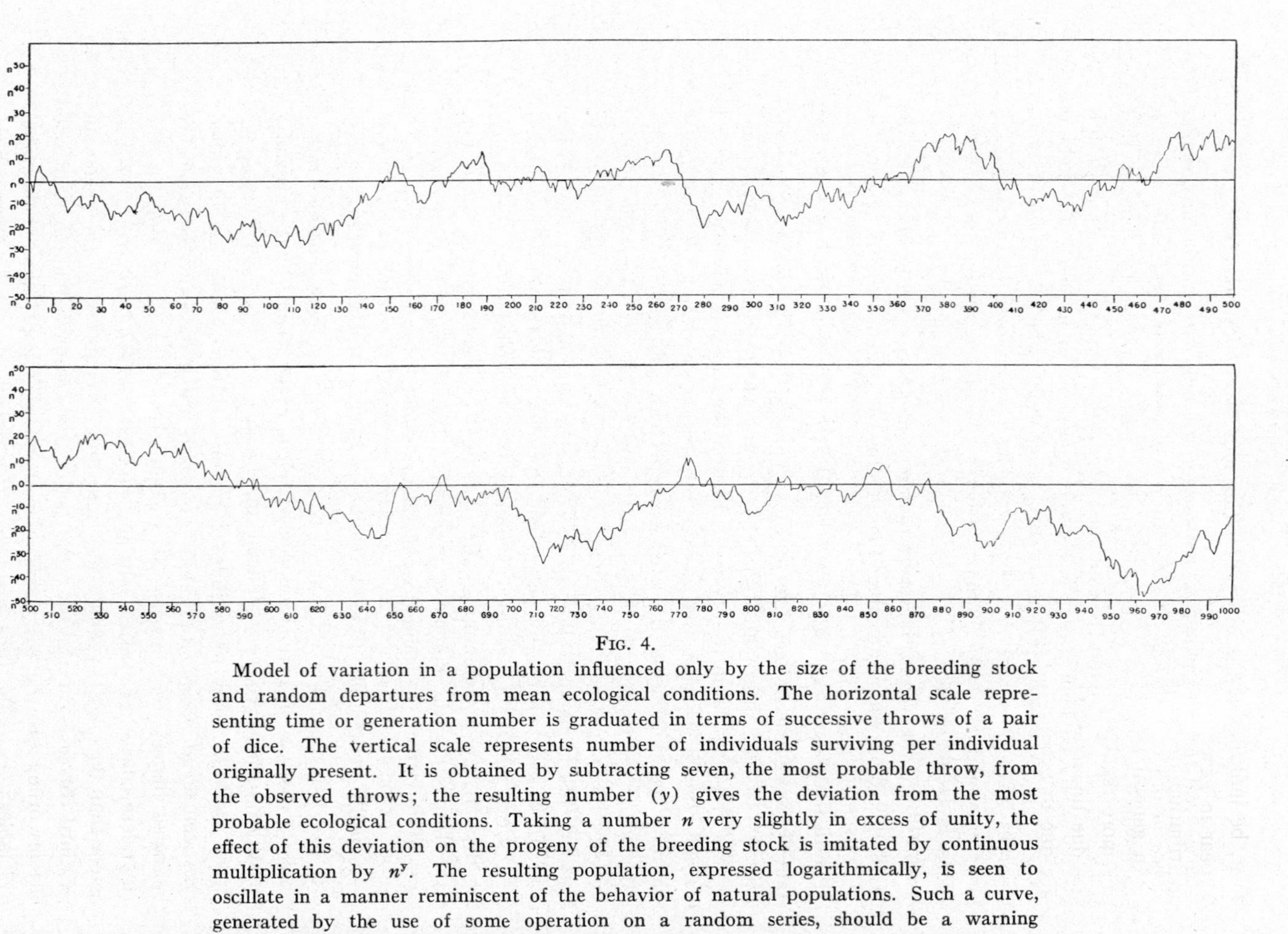

FIG. 4.

Model of variation in a population influenced only by the size of the breeding stock and random departures from mean ecological conditions. The horizontal scale representing time or generation number is graduated in terms of successive throws of a pair of dice. The vertical scale represents number of individuals surviving per individual originally present. It is obtained by subtracting seven, the most probable throw, from the observed throws; the resulting number (y) gives the deviation from the most probable ecological conditions. Taking a number n very slightly in excess of unity, the effect of this deviation on the progeny of the breeding stock is imitated by continuous multiplication by n^y. The resulting population, expressed logarithmically, is seen to oscillate in a manner reminiscent of the behavior of natural populations. Such a curve, generated by the use of some operation on a random series, should be a warning against over-enthusiastic search for hidden periodicities. (Data obtained in class ever, be indicated by such an agreement. The cases to be analyzed below appear in general to depend on more definite mechanisms than the random distribution of certain meteorological coincidences.

In general two groups of hypotheses have been put forward to explain the more regular cases. Some investigators have favored the idea that they are due to *intrinsic* properties of the biological community, others that they are due to *extrinsic* fluctuations in the inorganic environment.

1. *Intrinsic Cycles*

As is indicated below it is possible for a species to possess properties that will produce a fluctuation in population with a period of several generations due solely to the properties of its own life history in an environment that is maintained entirely constant, and one good case of this has been investigated experimentally. More usually the interaction of more than one species is necessary. The interaction of two species can take two forms; it may be either a continuous process in time, as in the prey-predator relationship investigated by Volterra, Lotka, Nicholson, Nicholson and Bailey and others, or it can be discontinuous in time as in the case of the spread of an epidemic dependent on the achievement of a critical density of the populations through which it is spreading. The evidence of continuous interactions causing cycles in nature is not extensive. Gause has treated the matter at length in two well-known works (1934, 1935) that appeared before the period to be covered in detail by the present review. The existence of catastrophic declines in a population caused by the spread of epidemics has appeared to many workers to be a reasonable explanation of observed cycles. It is therefore most remarkable that so little field evidence has been obtained supporting this view. There seems to be a widespread belief at present that intrinsic is more probable than extrinsic control, but practically every case, however well studied, has remained mysterious.

2. *Extrinsic Cycles*

Any organism with a life span that is short in comparison with the seasonal cycle is liable to undergo great changes in population size during the course of a year, particularly in extra-tropical regions of marked seasonal change. The proponents of extrinsic control of periodicities consider that less conspicuous cyclical changes in the environment, with periods of more than one year, are responsible for the observed periodic changes. Such cyclical changes have generally been supposed to be imposed either by tidal cycles or by the sunspot cycle, acting through a variety of meteorological variables.

3. *Possible Importance of Resonance*

It is important to realize that in a dynamic system of the kind constituting a biological community it is by no means unlikely that the system may be inherently subject to oscillations of certain periods, which might appear in a feeble form in a constant environment, but which could become very violent in a changing environment because of the resonance of the biological system to rather obscure periodicities in the organic environment. The distinction between intrinsic and extrinsic control may therefore not be so great as at first would appear.

4. *Intrinsic Cycles in Single Species*

In the differential form of the logistic, the expression $(K—N)/K$ may be regarded as a sort of corrective to the potential net rate of increase or Malthusian parameter b. It usually is assumed that this corrective operates instantaneously, producing the ordinary sigmoid curve of population growth. If, however, it were to operate with a finite time lag, oscillations could be set up in the system. When the time lag is short, these oscillations die out, when long, they persist, causing the population to oscillate violently between finite limits.[3]

It is quite likely that oscillations introduced through the biological properties of a single species may be introduced in this way into the biological community. One such case has been described by Pratt (1943). In *Daphnia magna* the fecundity of a parthenogenetic female depends on the size of the population in which it has developed, so that the rate of increase of the population is dependent in part on its history prior to the time of observation. As is to be expected, oscillations are set up by this mechanism.

A situation which has some formal similarity to that encountered by Pratt is believed by Errington (1946), in part following Elton, to be a possible mechanism of periodic fluctuation in rodents in temperate regions where reproduction is markedly seasonal. In such regions the breeding stock of the smaller rodents, at the beginning of spring, consists of overwintered animals that will not survive another winter. Fighting occurs in such species and it is reasonable to suppose that the number of encounters is a function of density. In a population not showing seasonal reproductive rhythms and with a constant age structure the mortality from such fighting could be regarded as an expression of the operation of the corrective factor $(K—N)/K$. If, however, there is a seasonal breeding cycle, and a tendency for young animals to be killed more frequently than old, as seems probable,

[3]These conclusions emerge from an examination of the rather formidable mathematical presentation of the problem kindly given us by Professor Lars Onsager.

the effect of the corrective factor, by the end of the season, is to produce a population which, although it may be appropriate to the available space and food, or in other words has practically reached the asymptotic value K, is of an age structure that will lead to a catastrophic decline, for most of the survivors will be old animals that have passed one winter and will die before the end of a second winter. The size of the breeding stock and so the rate of increase in the next spring will be in effect a nonlinear function of the density of the previous summer. Errington's data strongly suggest that something of this kind operates in producing fluctuations in the muskrat *Ondatra zibethica*.

5. *Cycles Caused by Interaction*

The Lotka-Volterra type of cycle involves the continuous interaction of two species, one preying on the other. The theoretical derivation of the cycle assumed that the incidence of predation was a linear function of the number of prey and of predators. It has been shown by Gause (1934, 1935) that in practice predation in limited universes is usually so intense that at the time of minimum the populations become very small and random statistical variation can completely destroy the system. Moreover in some cases mechanisms exist increasing the rate of predation per unit biomass of predator as the prey decreases so that the linear relationship postulated breaks down. Nicholson and Bailey (1935) have attempted a more general formulation. Various experiments by Gause and others, summarized in the works already quoted, have shown that under some, usually very artificial, circumstances the cycles can be set up. This has been confirmed by De Bach and Smith (1941) in an artificial system in which *Musca domestica L.* was parasitized by *Mormoniella vitripennis* (Walk.). So far none of the natural systems that are known to show regular fluctuations have been susceptible of analysis in terms of interaction of this sort. Gause's suggestion of a series of discontinuous catastrophic relaxations caused by epidemics, that might decimate a population when it reaches a certain critical density, also gives a very plausible explanation of cyclical fluctuations. This explanation is simply a formalization of the ideas that must have been in the minds of all the early observers of the mammalian cycles. It is, however, rather doubtful whether the mechanism would work out as smoothly in nature as the observed variations demand. The summary by Topley (1942) of recent British work on experimental epidemiology gives interesting examples of the effect of the sudden incidence of aggregation on the initiation of epidemics but it is by no means clear that the same effect would be produced by a continuous increase in population. Topley's work in fact seems to indicate that steady-state conditions may then be expected.

The analyses of such cases of marked periodic fluctuation as are given below certainly do not indicate any clear cases of the phenomenon postulated by Gause.

6. *The Three- to Four-Year Murid Cycle*

Elton (1942) has summarized in a monumental work the entire literature, up to about 1940, of the 3- to 4-year variation in the populations of murid rodents, notably species of *Microtus, Lemmus* and *Dicrostonyx,* in the northern hemisphere. This cycle is reflected in variations in abundance and changes in behavior of a large number of other species.

The biological changes brought about by an excess of rodents have been described by travelers who have visited arctic Canada during the years of maxima, and Elton has enriched his book with many of their graphic accounts. The entire community structure is changed and even fishes feed on mice. The incidence of the snowy owl (*Nyctea nyctea*) as far south as New England would seem to be related to the periodic rise and fall of its main food in the far north (Gross, 1947), the owls increasing as the rodent population increases, and dispersing in search of food as the rodents fail.

Elton comes to no conclusion as to mechanism. Hidden in his text there are essentially three suggestions. One of these is based on the great modification of vegetation by abundant rodents, and implies in fact a Volterra-Lotka cycle between the animal population and the plant community. One is the suggestion developed further by Errington relating to the life cycle and survivorship curve, and the effect of fighting. The third suggestion relates to a periodicity in atmospheric pressure, of three to four years, observable in Scottish meteorological data. If any extrinsic control by such a meteorological cycle operates on murid populations it presumably would have to act by resonating with some inherent mechanism.

Shelford (1943), working in the Canadian tundra near Churchill, concluded that the growth of high populations of *Dicrostonyx groenlandicus richardsoni* Mer. was determined by the occurrence of two successive years of relatively favorable meteorological conditions. The favorable conditions for high winter survival and reproduction are in general average or more than average snowfall combined with average or more than average temperature. Cold winters with little snow to afford protection lead to a decline. The variation in the population seems to be much more regular than that of the meteorological elements involved. It is conceivable that a pseudo-periodicity based on the probability of occurrence of the correct conditions is involved, but in view of the widespread occurrence of murid cycles of similar periods this seems unlikely.

Hamilton (1937, 1940) has made a detailed study of the reproductive cycle in *Microtus pennsylvanicus* in central New York state. He found that during the low part of a cycle the breeding season was curtailed and the number of young per litter was reduced. Elton, Ford, Baker and Gardner (1937) had previously published data that appear to indicate similar variations in the length of the breeding season and consequently in the size of the population in *Apodemus*. Hamilton found that at the time of the decline from the maximum in 1936 many mice were suffering from an unidentified disease, the causative agent of which could not be isolated in spite of much research. In the spring of 1939 after the next maximum no such disease heralded the decline. Elton's school likewise failed to find any consistent pathological condition responsible for the fall in numbers after the maximum. It appears therefore unlikely that an epidemiological cycle is involved. An interesting study of *Clethrionomys* by Evans (1942) suggests that during minima the population is least reduced on territories that have not supported excessive populations during maxima. Such less favorable ground may be essential as a reservoir from which is derived the stock that will build up the new maximal population. There is evidence (R. C. Clement in Gross, 1947) that a similar phenomenon occurs in the lemming population of northern Quebec.

7. The Nine- to Ten-Year Lepus canadensis *Cycle*

The most remarkable biological cycle yet described is that in the population of the snowshoe rabbit, *Lepus canadensis,* and in the carnivores, notably *Lynx canadensis,* which prey upon it. The data for the lynx extend back to 1735. The problem of this cycle has been treated by MacLulich (1937), Elton and Nicholson (1942b) and from a different point of view by Green and Evans (1940a, b, c; also Green, Larson and Bell, 1939).

MacLulich's work should have disposed, once and for all, of the idea that this cycle is connected with the 11.4 year periodicity in sun-spot numbers. Since the period of the snowshoe rabbit cycle is about 9.6 years, for several decades a high positive correlation with sun-spot numbers is apparent, for other decades a high negative correlation. Unfortunately a causal connection is still suggested in popular writings. Elton and Nicholson (1942a) have assembled evidence that there is a similar though less regular periodicity in Canadian muskrat populations, and (1942b) point out that in some rivers the salmon fluctuate in the same way. They also draw attention to the general synchrony, within certain limits, over the whole of Canada, an area including more than one subspecies of *L. americanus*. Of even greater interest is their statement indicating that they have data that snowshoe rabbits introduced onto Anticosti Island fluctuate with the mainland population. These facts suggest an extrinsic control. Huntington (1945) who was one of the most enthusiastic proponents of extrinsic control, and whose work has rightly been both praised as imaginative and depreciated as uncritical, suggested that the 9.6 year cycle which is also apparently shown by populations of the tent caterpillar *Malacosoma americana* in eastern North America be correlated with a cycle that he discovered in the old data for the ozone content of the air in western Europe It is very doubtful what these data mean in terms of the chemistry of the atmosphere, but they evidently indicate fluctuations of some sort. The crudity of the method used led to its abandonment. When the mean data, evidently far from concordant, from London and Paris (1877 to 1910) are treated to eliminate seasonal effects and secular trends and minor variations are removed by taking appropriate moving averages, a curve results with maxima close to the *Lynx* maxima in 1887, 1896 and 1904. The error involved in the comparison of but three cycles, the arbitrary nature of the smoothing and the uncertainty of the meaning of the ozone curve make this result at best a suggestive lead for future work.

Although Huntington's conclusions can hardly be accepted as they stand, it is of importance to note that cycles of about 9½ to 10 years are certainly recognizable in the tree ring records studied by Douglass (1936), and in some series are actually more prominent than the sun-spot cycle of just over 11 years.

If the cycle of the snowshoe rabbit were confined to regions in which *Lynx* populations were naturally developed it would be tempting, though probably incorrect (Hutchinson, 1942) to regard the oscillation as a Lotka-Volterra prey-predator interaction. Since it is certain that the cycle can occur in the absence of significant predation, this explanation must be excluded. Other kinds of intrinsic cycle are, however, perhaps suggested by the work of Green and his associates.

Green and Evans (1940a, b, c) in an important contribution to the population dynamics of *Lepus americanus* in Minnesota have shown that the decline in the population after the maximum in 1933 primarily affected young animals. The fertility of the female does not appear to vary throughout the cycle. The cause of the mortality in the epidemic decline is referred to by Green and his coworkers (Green and Evans; Green, Larson and Bell, 1939; Green, Larson and Mather, 1938; Green, Mather and Larson, 1938) as shock disease. The disease is characterized by a degeneration of the liver, a failure to store glycogen and finally hypoglycemia which terminates in death from shock when any slight strain is put on the animals.[4]

---

[4]Mr. R. B. Henson tells us that it is well known to the Indians of Northern Canada that in some years, but not in others, rabbits die on the run.

Green and his associates were entirely unable to transmit an infective agent to healthy animals and no microscopic evidence of such an agent was ever found. The disease is apparently simulated by certain disturbances of mineral nutrition. It can be induced by keeping animals at high densities in fenced areas of their normal range. If an infective causal agent may really be excluded, it is evident that the animals either exhaust something from their environment which is slowly regenerated after the decline, or contaminate their environment with something that slowly decomposes. The most reasonable alternative would be the former; conceivably the vegetation constantly being eaten and regrowing declines in sodium content, the latter element being washed off slowly from the excreta of the animals. This suggestion is obviously very hypothetical, though easily tested; it seems unlikely that it could account for declines over wide areas, exhibiting diverse soil conditions.[5]

8. A Supposed Extrinsic Eleven-Year Murid Cycle in Australia

Crombie (1944b) in a brief note, suggests with some degree of plausibility, a control of a mammal population by the 11-year solar cycle. He points out that in western Queensland the four known plagues of the long-haired rat *Rattus villosissimus* Waite have occurred 1 or 2 years after each sun-spot maximum. The cycle therefore is much longer than in the case of the well-known murid fluctuations in the northern hemisphere. The behavior of the animals during the maxima is characteristic. Males swarm out from certain localities eating everything edible that they find: the exhaustion of the food supply leads to cannibalism among the females and young. A population at the time of the plague evidently represents over-saturation; presumably after the plague a very considerable reduction below normal occurs. There is a marked increase in predators at the time of the plague. Though internal mechanisms may be involved, a climatic factor which may be dependent on the solar cycle, permitting the supersaturation, does indeed seem possible, though it will require many decades of observation to establish or refute the hypothesis.

[5]Since this review went to press, a very important contribution by Lauri Siivonen (Structure of short cycle fluctuations in numbers of mammals and birds in the northern parts of the northern hemisphere. *Finnish Foundation Game Res., Papers on Game Research* **1**, 166 pp., 1948) has appeared. Siivonen interprets the 3- to 4-year murid cycle as a cycle of 3.33 years which tend to be expressed by maxima 3, 3, and 4 years apart. The maximum after the longer, 4 year, interval appears to be greater than the other two. By suppression of the two smaller maxima in the southern part of the regions involved a 10-year cycle results. Siivonen makes no suggestion as to the controlling mechanism but seems to regard it as extrinsic. His paper reviews a great deal of otherwise inaccessible data.

9. Possible Control of Insect Populations by the Solar Cycle

A good deal of early work has suggested that excessive outbreaks of insects were controlled through climate by the solar cycle. MacLagan (1941) has collected all the cases of serious outbreak in Britain recorded in the literature and has shown that such outbreaks are considerably more probable in the early part of the rise in sun-spot number than at any other time. This is supposed to be due to the incidence of warm wet years during such periods. It is improbable that the scattered data from many species over a period of more than a century would introduce errors owing to the confusion of independent solar and biological cycles differing little in wavelength. None of the species involved, however, are markedly periodic and the results if valid merely indicate a higher probability of outbreak at certain times in the solar cycle, without indicating that at any time the probability approaches unity as would be the case in a truly solar-periodic species.

Shelford and Flint (1943) have studied the variations in the population of the chinch bug, *Blissus leucopterus,* in the upper Mississippi valley. Their data cover an extended period from 1823 to 1940. During the present century there has been a marked tendency for the population to vary inversely with the sun-spot number, and between 1925 and 1940 a good inverse correlation with ultra-violet intensity during the summer is observed. During the nineteenth century the correlation with sun-spot number is very imperfect and the authors evidently do not consider the species to be truly periodic. The mean period between major outbreaks is 9.6 years, but there is great variation, individual periods varying from 7 to 13 years. Even for the rather regular periodicity in the twentieth century it is impossible to discriminate between a cycle of the same length as that found in the snowshoe rabbit, which may also be exhibited by the tent caterpillar, and a solar cycle; comparison of all the available data strongly suggests that no significant correlations would be found. Shelford and Flint believe that meteorological factors, notably rainfall in early summer, are probably involved; unexplained variations of the general vigor of laboratory cultures derived from over-wintered adults apparently reflect the conditions of the previous autumn, but the variations do not run parallel with those of natural populations.

10. A Possible Seven-Year Cycle Controlled by Meteorological and Oceanographic Factors

Vogt (1940) has given a detailed account of the apparently cyclical changes in the populations of guano-producing sea-birds, notably *Phalacrocorax bougainvillei,* off the coast of Peru. These populations have undergone catastrophic reduction on a number of occasions. During the twentieth century the catastrophes have occurred at about 7-year intervals. It seems, however, that the cycle is now tending to disintegrate (Anon., 1947). The evidence for the nineteenth century is imperfect, though it is not unlikely that the cycle continued back for some time prior to 1891. There is evidence that the abundance of available food fishes is involved in the periodicity (cf. Fiedler, Jarvis and Lobell, 1943), but whatever the immediate biological causes of the decline there is no doubt that it is determined by meteorological and oceanographic factors which lead to a movement of warm water from the northeast into the region of the cold productive waters of the Peru current during the critical months when the young birds are being fed. This movement of water, usually miscalled *El Niño* (Schweigger, 1943) has long been known and is discussed by all oceanographers and most travelers who have written on the region. Although to the present writers it appears to be a rather regular but essentially nonpersistent cycle, it is perhaps the most definite known example of an extrinsic periodic event causing marked fluctuations in a biological system. The relation of the apparent seven-year cycle to the cycles that have been detected in meteorological and solar data is obscure.

References

Allee, W. C. 1931. Animal aggregations. A study in general sociology. Univ. of Chicago Press, Chicago, ix+431 pp.

Angel, J. L. 1947. The length of life in ancient Greece. *Jour. Gerontol.* **2**: 18-24.

Anonymous. 1947. Twenty million pets. In Science Section, *Time Mag.* **50**, No. 11 (Sept. 15) p. 67.

Beauchamp, R. S. A., and Ullyott, P. 1932. Competitive relationships between certain species of freshwater triclads. *Jour. Ecol.* **20**: 200-208.

Brownlee, J. 1915. Studies in the meaning and relationships of birth and death rates. *Jour. Hyg.* **15**: 11-35.

Bullough, W. S. 1942. Observations on the colonies of the Arctic Tern (*Sterna macrura* Naumann) on the Farne Islands. *Proc. Zool. Soc. Lond.* **112A**: 1-12, pl. 1.

Cook, S. F. 1947. Survivorship in aboriginal populations. *Human Biol.* **19**: 83-89.

Crombie, A. C. 1944a. On intraspecific and interspecific competition in larvae of graminivorous insects. *Jour. Exptl. Biol.* **20**: 135-151.

Crombie, A. C. 1944b. Rat plagues in western Queensland. *Nature* **154**: 803-804.

Crombie, A. C. 1945. On competition between different species of graminivorous insects. *Proc. Roy. Soc. Lond.* **132B**: 362-395.

Crombie, A. C. 1946. Further experiments on insect competition. *Proc. Roy. Soc. Lond.* **133B**: 76-109.

Crombie, A. C. 1947. Interspecific competition. *Jour. Anim. Ecol.* **16**: 44-73.

Darling, F. F. 1938. Bird Flocks and the Breeding Cycle. A contribution to the study of avian sociality. Cambridge Univ. Press, Cambridge, England, x+124 pp.

Davis, M. B. 1945. The effect of population density on longevity in *Trogoderma versicolor* Creutz. (=*T. inclusa* Lec.). *Ecology* **26**: 353-362.

De Bach, P., and Smith, H. S. 1941. Are population oscillations inherent in the host-parasite relation? *Ecology* **22**: 363-369.

Deevey, E. S. 1947. Life tables for natural populations of animals. *Quart. Rev. Biol.* **22**: 283-314.

Deevey, G. B., and Deevey, E. S. 1945. A life table for the black widow. *Trans. Conn. Acad. Arts and Sci.* **36**: 115-134.

Douglass, A. E. 1936. Climatic cycles and tree growth. Vol. III. A study of cycles. *Carnegie Inst. Washington Publ.* 289, **3**, 171 pp.

Edmondson, W. T. 1945. Ecological studies of sessile Rotatoria, Part II. Dynamics of populations and social structures. *Ecol. Monogr.* **15**: 141-172.

Elton, C. 1942. Voles, mice and lemmings. Problems in population dynamics. Oxford, Clarendon Press, London, 496 pp.

Elton, C. 1946. Competition and the structure of ecological communities. *Jour. Anim. Ecol.* **15**: 54-68.

Elton, C., Ford, E. B., Baker, J. R., and Gardner, R. D. 1931. The health and parasites of a wild mouse population. *Proc. Zool. Soc. Lond.* **1931**: 657-721.

Elton, C., and Nicholson, M. 1942a. Fluctuations in numbers of the muskrat (*Ondatra zibethica*) in Canada. *Jour. Anim. Ecol.* **11**: 96-126.

Elton, C., and Nicholson, M. 1942b. The ten-year cycle in numbers of the lynx in Canada. *Jour. Anim. Ecol.* **11**: 215-244.

Errington, P. L. 1945. Some contributions of a fifteen-year local study of the northern bobwhite to a knowledge of population phenomena. *Ecol. Monogr.* **15**: 1-34.

Errington, P. L. 1946. Predation and vertebrate populations. *Quart. Rev. Biol.* **21**: 144-177.

Evans, F. C. 1942. Studies of a small mammal population in Bagley Wood, Berkshire. *Jour. Anim. Ecol.* **11**: 182-197.

Farr, W. 1875. Effects of density of population on health. Reg. General of Births, Deaths, and Marriages in England, 35th Ann. Rep., Supplement, pp. xxiii-xxv.

Feldman-Muhsam, B., and Muhsam, H. V. 1946. Life tables for *Musca vicina* and *Calliphora erythrocephala*. *Proc. Zool. Soc. Lond.* **115**: 296-305.

Ferris, J. C. 1932. A comparison of the life histories of mictic and amictic females in the rotifer, *Hydatina senta*. *Biol. Bull.* **63**: 442-455.

Fiedler, R. H., Jarvis, N. D., and Lobell, M. J. 1943. La pesca y las industrias pesqueras en el Perú. Lima (Comp. Admin. Guano). 371 pp.

Fisher, J., and Waterston, G. 1941. The breeding distribution, history and population of the Fulmar (*Fulmarus glacialis*) in the British Isles. *Jour. Anim. Ecol.* **10**: 204-272, pls. 4-8.

Fisher, R. A., Corbet, A. S., and Williams, C. B. 1943. The relation between the number of species and the number of individuals in a random sample of an animal population. *Jour. Anim. Ecol.* **12**: 42-58.

Gause, G. F. 1934. The Struggle for Existence. Williams and Wilkins, Baltimore. 163 pp.

Gause, G. F. 1935. Vérifications expérimentales de la théorie mathématique de la lutte pour la vie. Paris, Actualités Scientifiques. Hermann et Cie, Paris. 63 pp.

Gause, G. F., and Witt, A. A. 1935. Behavior of mixed populations and the problem of natural selection. *Amer. Nat.* **69**: 596-609.

Green, R. G., and Evans, C. A. 1940a. Studies on a population cycle of snowshoe hares on the Lake Alexander area. I. Gross annual censuses, 1932-1939. *Jour. Wildlife Management* **4**: 220-238.

Green, R. G., and Evans, C. A. 1940b. Studies on a population cycle of snowshoe hares on the Lake Alexander area. II. Mortality according to age groups and seasons. *Jour. Wildlife Management* **4**: 267-278.

Green, R. G., and Evans, C. A. 1940c. Studies on a population cycle of snowshoe hares on the Lake Alexander area. III. Effect of reproduction and mortality of young hares on the cycle. *Jour. Wildlife Management* **4**: 347-358.

Green, R. G., Larson, C. L., and Bell, J. F. 1939. Shock disease as the cause of the periodic decimation of the snowshoe hare. *Amer. Jour. Hyg.* **30**, Sect. B: 83-102.

Green, R. G., Larson, C. L., and Mather, D. W. 1938. Occurrence of shock disease among young snowshoe hares. *Proc. Soc. Exptl. Biol. and Med.* **38**: 816-817.

Green, R. G., Mather, D. W., and Larson, C. L. 1938. The natural occurrence of shock disease in hares. *Trans. Third North Amer. Wildlife Conf.* 877-881.

Gross, A. O. 1947. Cyclic invasions of the snowy owl and the migrations of 1945-1946. *Auk* **64**: 584-601.

Hamilton, W. J. 1937. The biology of microtine cycles. *Jour. Agric. Res.* **54**: 779-790.

Hamilton, W. J. 1940. Life and habits of field mice. *Sci. Month.* **50**: 425-434.

Hatton, H. 1938. Essais de bionomie explicative sur quelques espèces intercotidales d'algues et d'animaux. *Ann. de l'Inst. Océanogr.* **17**: 241-348.

Huntington, E. 1945. Mainsprings of Civilization. Wiley, New York, Chapman and Hall, London, xii+660 pp. (*vide* Ch. 25).

Hutchinson, G. E. 1941. Ecological aspects of succession in natural populations. *Amer. Nat.* **75**: 406-418.

Hutchinson, G. E. 1942. Nati sunt mures, et facta est confusio. A review of "Voles, mice, and lemmings" (Elton). *Quart. Rev. Biol.* **17**: 354-357.

Hutchinson, G. E. 1944. Limnological studies in Connecticut. VII. A critical examination of the supposed relationship between phytoplankton periodicity and chemical changes in lake waters. *Ecology* **25**: 3-26.

Hutchinson, G. E. 1947. A note on the theory of competition between two social species. *Ecology* **28**: 319-321.

Ingle, L., Wood, T. R., and Banta, A. M. 1937. A study of longevity, growth, reproduction, and heart rate in *Daphnia longispina* as influenced by limitations in quantity of food. *Jour. Exptl. Zool.* **76**: 325-352.

Kidder, G. W. 1941a. Growth studies on ciliates. V. The acceleration and inhibition of ciliate growth in biologically conditioned medium. *Physiol. Zool.* **14**: 209-226.

Kidder, G. W. 1941b. Growth studies on ciliates. VII. Comparative growth characteristics of four species of sterile ciliates. *Biol. Bull.* **80**: 50-68.

Lack, D. 1944. Ecological aspects of species-formation in passerine birds. *Ibis* **86**: 260-286.

Lack, D. 1945. The ecology of closely related species with special reference to cormorant (*Phalacrocorax carbo*) and shag (*P. aristotelis*). *Jour. Anim. Ecol.* **14**: 12-16.

Lack, D. 1946a. Darwin's Finches. Cambridge Univ. Press, Cambridge, England, x+208 pp.

Lack, D. 1946b. Competition for food by birds of prey. *Jour. Anim. Ecol.* **15**: 123-129.

Lack, D. 1947a. The significance of clutch-size. *Ibis* **89**: 302-352.

Lack, D. 1947b. The significance of clutch-size in the partridge (*Perdix perdix*). *Jour. Anim. Ecol.* **16**: 19-25.

Lack, D., and Arn, H. 1947. Die Bedeutung der Gelegegrösse beim Alpensegler. *Ornith. Beobachter* **44**: 188-210.

Lansing, A. I. 1942. Some effects of hydrogen ion concentration, total salt concentration, calcium, and citrate on longevity and fecundity of the rotifer. *Jour. Exptl. Zool.* **91**: 195-211.

Lansing, A. I. 1947. A transmissible cumulative and reversible factor in aging. *Jour. Gerontol.* **2**: 228-239.

Leopold, A., Sperry, T. M., Feeney, W. S., and Catenhusen, J. A. 1943. Population turnover on a Wisconsin pheasant refuge. *Jour. Wildlife Management* **7**: 383-394.

Leslie, P. H., and Ranson, R. M. 1940. The mortality, fertility, and rate of natural increase of the vole (*Microtus agrestis*) as observed in the laboratory. *Jour. Anim. Ecol.* **9**: 27-52.

MacArthur, J. W., and Baillie, W. H. T. 1929. Metabolic activity and duration of life. I. Influence of temperature on longevity in *Daphnia magna*. *Jour. Exptl. Zool.* **53**: 221-242.

Macdonell, W. R. 1913. On the expectation of life in ancient Rome, and in the provinces of Hispania and Lusitania, and Africa. *Biometrika* **9**: 366-380.

MacLagan, D. S. 1940. Sunspots and insect outbreaks: an epidemiological study. *Proc. Univ. Durham Philos. Soc.* **10**: 173-199.

MacLagan, D. S. 1941. Recent animal-population studies; and their significance in relation to socio-biological philosophy (Part I). *Proc. Univ. Durham Philos. Soc.* **10**: 310-331.

MacLulich, D. A. 1937. Fluctuations in numbers of the varying hare (*Lepus americanus*) Univ. Toronto Studies, Biol. Ser. No. 43, 136 pp.

Mast, S. O., and Pace, D. M. 1938. The effect of substances produced by *Chilomonas paramecium* on rate of reproduction. *Physiol. Zool.* **11**: 359-382.

Miller, H. M. 1931. Alternation of generations in the rotifer *Lecane inermis* Bryce. *Biol. Bull.* **60**: 345-381.

Moore, H. B., and Kitching, J. A. 1939. The biology of *Chthamalus stellatus* Poli. *Jour. Marine Biol. Assoc. United Kingdom* **23**: 521-541.

Moore, H. B., and Sproston, N. G. 1940. Further observations on the colonization of a new rocky shore at Plymouth. *Jour. Anim. Ecol.* **9**: 319-327.

Murie, A. 1944. The wolves of Mount McKinley. U. S. Dept. Int., Nat. Park Serv.; *Fauna of the Natl. Parks of the U. S., Fauna Series No. 5,* xix+238 pp.

Nice, M. M. 1937. Studies in the life history of the song sparrow. Vol. I. A population study of the song sparrow. *Trans. Linn. Soc. N. Y.* **4**: vi+247 pp.

Nicholson, A. J., and Bailey, V. A. 1935. The balance of animal populations. I. *Proc. Zool. Soc. Lond.* **1935**: 551-598.

Park, T. 1941. The laboratory population as a test of a comprehensive ecological system. *Quart. Rev. Biol.* **16**: 274-293, 440-461.

Park, T. 1945. Life tables for the black flour beetle *Tribolium madens* Charp. *Amer. Nat.* **79**: 436-444.

Pearl, R., and Miner, J. R. 1935. Experimental studies on the duration of life. XIV. The comparative mortality of certain lower organisms. *Quart. Rev. Biol.* **10**: 60-79.

Pearl, R., Miner, J. R., and Parker, S. L. 1927. Experimental studies on the duration of life. XI. Density of population and life duration in *Drosophila*. *Amer. Nat.* **61**: 289-318.

Pearl, R., Park, T., and Miner, J. R. 1941. Experimental studies on the duration of life. XVI. Life tables for the flour beetle *Tribolium confusum* Duval. *Amer. Nat.* **75**: 5-19.

Pratt, D. M. 1943. Analysis of population development in *Daphnia* at different temperatures. *Biol. Bull.* **85**: 116-140.

Reich, K. 1938. Studies on the physiology of amoeba. II. The allelocatalytic effect in amoeba cultures free of bacteria. *Physiol. Zool.* **11**: 347-358.

Robertson, T. B. 1921. Experimental studies on cellular reproduction. II. The influence of mutual contiguity upon reproductive rate in *Infusoria*. *Biochem. Jour.* **15**: 612-619.

Schweigger, E. H. 1943. Pesquería y oceanografía del Perú y proposiciones para su desarollo futuro. (Spanish with English summary). Lima, Gil, S. A. 356 pp.

Şenyürek, M. S. 1947. A note on the duration of life of the ancient inhabitants of Anatolia. *Amer. Jour. Phys. Anthropol.* n.s. **5**: 55-66.

Sette, O. E. 1943. Biology of the Atlantic mackerel (*Scomber scombrus*) of North America. Part I: Early life history, including the growth, drift, and mortality of the egg and larval populations. *U. S. Fish and Wildlife Serv., Fish Bull.* 50 (38): 147-237.

Shelford, V. E. 1943. The abundance of the Collared Lemming (*Discrostonyx groenlandicus* (Tr.) var. *Richardsoni* Mer.) in the Churchill area, 1929 to 1940. *Ecology* **24**: 472-484.

Shelford, V. E., and Flint, W. P. 1943. Populations of the chinch bug in the Upper Mississippi Valley from 1823 to 1940. *Ecology* **24**: 435-455.

Smith, H. M. 1943. Size of breeding populations in relation to egg-laying and reproductive success in the eastern Red-wing (*Agelaius p. phoeniceus*). *Ecology* **24**: 183-207.

Stanley, J. 1941. A mathematical theory of the growth of populations of the flour beetle *Tribolium confusum* Duv. IV. *Ecology* **22**: 23-37.

Topley, W. W. C. 1942. The biology of epidemics (The Croonian Lecture). *Proc. Roy. Soc. Lond.* **130B**: 337-359.

Vallois, H. V. 1937. La durée de la vie chez l'homme fossile. *L'Anthropol.* **47**: 499-532.

Vesey-Fitzgerald, D. 1941. Further contributions to the ornithology of the Seychelles Islands. *Ibis* (ser. 14) **5**: 518-531.

Vogt, W. 1942. Informe sobre las Aves guaneras elevado a la Compañia Administradora del Guano. *Bol. Comp. Admin. Guano* **18** (3): 3-132.

Von Haartman, L. 1945. Zur Biologie der Wasser und Ufervögel im Schärenmeer Südwest-finnlands. *Acta Zool. Fenn.* **44**, 129 pp., 8 pls., map.

Wiesner, B. P., and Sheard, N. M. 1934. The duration of life in an albino rat population. *Proc. Roy. Soc. Edin.* **55**: 1-22.

Williams, C. B. 1947. The generic relations of species in small ecological communities. *Jour. Anim. Ecol.* **16**: 11-18.

Author Index*

*Names in parentheses indicate senior authors and are included to assist in locating references where a particular name is not on a given page, or where the reference is alphabetized under the senior author's name. The numbers in italics refer to the pages on which references are listed at the end of each chapter.

H

I

J

M

N

S

T

Y

Z

Subject Index

F

G

S

T